SAGEBRUSH TRILOGY

VINTAGE WEST REPRINTS

Sagebrush Trilogy

IDAH MEACHAM STROBRIDGE AND HER WORKS

Introduction by Richard A. Dwyer and
Richard E. Lingenfelter

University of Nevada Press
Reno and Las Vegas

Vintage West Series Editor: Robert E. Blesse

The three collections in the present volume were originally published by the author in limited editions: *In Miners' Mirage-Land,* 1904; *The Loom of the Desert,* 1907; and *The Land of Purple Shadows,* 1909. All were copyrighted by the author. Some of the copies were published with and some without a brief advertising section at the back of the book, describing the author's own Artemisia Bindery and its output. Some copies were bound as paperbacks, others bore hand-crafted leather covers or hand-tinted chapter openings. The present volume reproduces the original editions except that the front matter of each has been modified to reflect the new publisher. Richard A. Dwyer and Richard E. Lingenfelter have provided illustrations, a foreword, and an introduction for the new edition.

The paper used in this book meets the requirements of American National Standard for Information Services—Permanence of Paper for Printed Library Materials, ANSI Z39.48-1984.

Library of Congress Cataloging-in-Publication Data
Strobridge, Idah M. (Idah Meacham), 1855–1932.
Sagebrush trilogy: Idah Meacham Strobridge and her works / introduction by Richard A. Dwyer and Richard E. Lingenfelter.
p. cm. —(Vintage West series)
Reprint (1st work). Originally published: Los Angeles: Baumgardt Pub., 1904.
Reprint (2nd work). Originally published: Los Angeles: Artemisia Bindery, 1907.
Reprint (3rd work). Originally published: Los Angeles: Artemisia Bindery, 1909.
Includes bibliographical references.
Contents: In miners' mirage-land—The loom of the desert—The land of purple shadows.
ISBN 0-87417-164-4 (pbk.: alk. paper)
1. Nevada—History—Fiction. I. Title. II. Series.
PS3537.T8534A6   1990
813'.52—dc20   90-39026
                                CIP

University of Nevada Press, Reno, Nevada 89557 USA
Copyright © 1990 University of Nevada Press
All rights reserved
Cover design by Kaelin Chappell
Printed in the United States of America

2   4   6   8   9   7   5   3   1

CONTENTS

FOREWORD

For their inherent quality and interest as well as for being the work of "the first woman of Nevada letters," the writings of Idah Meacham Strobridge (1855–1932) are thoroughly worthy of revival from their original limited editions, printed in the first decade of this century. In presenting the best of her evocations of the Nevada desert and its people, we here reprint complete *In Miners' Mirage-Land* (1904), *The Loom of the Desert* (1907), and *The Land of Purple Shadows* (1909), while respecting her judgment not to present in book form a few items that appeared only in magazines. We introduce her work with as full a biographical sketch as the available documents allow. In pursuing these, we much thank the staff of the Humboldt County, Nevada, recorder's office; Dr. Edwin H. Carpenter of the Huntington Library; Mary S. Pratt of the Los Angeles Public Library; Ruth-Ann Rohman of the Southwest Museum; Lee Mortensen and Phillip Earl of the Nevada Historical Society, Reno; and the California Room staff of the California State Library, Sacramento, for their help. Our introduction concludes with a checklist of Strobridge's writings and previous commentary on them.

INTRODUCTION

The Woman and Her Works

In the bottom of a small prospect hole, dug into a sulfur bed far out on a sagebrush flat of Nevada's Great Basin, an eighteen-year-old woman made some discoveries:

> At that time it attracted my attention by reason of the very great number of freshly-shed snake-skins that lay about in the crevices of the gypsum and lava, the sulphur and ash. Dozens of them! Hundreds of them! And, paying heed to the fact, I observed thereafter that each spring they were replaced by others, while the old ones were blown away by the whirlwinds. Evidently it was a famous place for reptiles; yet it was a puzzle to me, always, that in such a quarry of snake-skins, I should never chance to see the snakes themselves.

> Back in those years when I first knew sagebrushland as home, I was an omnivorous—if not always a discriminating—reader; and, on summer days when the desert sun shone hot and a particularly fascinating book fell into my hands, I at once sought some spot that offered both cool shade and quiet. What better place than just within the deserted incline of the old sulphur mine? There, surrounded by the white and yellow of gypsum and sulphur walls festooned with the silvery-white skins, I had a retreat all my own, and quite as full of charm to me as any rose-hung bower could have been to another girl—a girl not of the gray wastes and solitudes of the Desert. There, with eyes and heart deep buried in my books, I spent many and many a delightful hour, retreating farther and farther down the incline, as the afternoon sun found and followed me there. . . .

Then—by and by—I left the Desert for a home at tide-water; and straightaway forgot all about the sulphur beds. [*In Miners' Mirage-Land,* pp. 105–6]

How that self-styled girl came to be Nevada's first woman of letters, and what riches she gleaned from its land, both at first-hand and in later recollection from her tidewater home, will be the subject of this book.

George Washington Meacham was just 22 when he reluctantly parted from his sweetheart, Phebe Amelia Craiger, to seek his fortunes in the West. He came around the Horn on the ship *Orpheus* in the company of James H. Strobridge, headed for the California Gold Rush of 1849. After three years of indifferent luck in the placer diggings of the Sierra, he returned to his native New Jersey where he married Phebe in Newark on 2 June 1852. At first she declined to return west with him, perhaps expecting him to make that quick fortune and get home again. But on arriving back in the West, George learned that his partner had sold their claim in his absence. At the news of this misfortune, Phebe promptly set out for California and remained with her husband from then on. Their only child, the daughter named Laura Idah, was born 9 June 1855 at a ranch they were working in Moraga Valley.

The new family moved from California to Humboldt County, Nevada, in the mid-1860s and homesteaded ranchlands in Lassen Meadows, about halfway between the present Winnemucca and Lovelock, where the old Applegate Route split off from the California Trail and headed northwest into the Black Rock Desert.

After the Central Pacific railroad drove east along the Humboldt River in 1868, Meacham built a popular hotel and eatery known as Humboldt House. The situation of the place, so important in forming Idah's outlook, is described in Crofutt's *New Overland Tourist* (1878):

About seven miles to the northeast may be seen Star Peak, the highest point in the Humboldt Range, on which the snow continues to hold its icy sway the whole year round. Two and one half miles southeast are the Humboldt mines—five in number—rich in gold and silver. The discovery of a borax mine near the station has recently been reported. Five miles to the north-west are the Lassen Meadows, on which are cut immense quantities of as good grass as can be found in the country. Thirty miles north are the new sulphur mines. [p. 166]

(The old sulfur mine to which Idah frequently retreated was just a mile southwest of the hotel.)

Idah Meacham was thus raised on an isolated cattle range in north-central Nevada and witnessed the passing of wagon trains on the nearby overland trails and their replacement by locomotives on the transcontinental iron rails. The region was also part of the range of the Paiute and Bannock Indians, and later, Mexican vaqueros and Chinese placer miners added to the ethnic mix. All of these caught her attention and reemerged in her writing.

For her higher education, Idah was sent to Mills Seminary in Oakland, California, in 1878. She excelled in "elocution" and was graduated in 1883. During this time she met Samuel Hooker (Whitmarsh) Strobridge of Auburn, California, the son adopted by James H. Strobridge, who had become a construction manager for the Southern Pacific. Sam was 21 and Idah was 29 when they married in San Francisco on 3 September 1884. They took up ranching on land given them by her father near his own ranges in Humboldt County. Over the next four years, Idah bore three sons: Earl, Gerald, and Kenneth. But tragedy gripped the family from the start. Her first child died the day after he was born in December of 1885. Then the infamous fall and winter of 1888–89 descended, pneumonia killed her husband and other children, and the blizzard wiped out much of the family's herds. The youngest son died in October of 1888 at the age of five months. A month later his father, who was then only 25, fell gravely ill and was accompanied by Idah to the West Coast where he died just a week later. She buried him in Oakland. Her middle son barely survived the winter, only to die the following year.

Thus stricken, Idah stayed for a while in California. But by the end of 1890 she was back in Nevada. She seems to have thrown herself heartily into ranching and even mining. A correspondent of the *Mining and Scientific Press* reported in 1895:

Idah Meacham Strobridge in
1884 at 29, married one week.
(Courtesy of Nevada
Historical Society)

Samuel H. Strobridge at 23 in
1886. (Courtesy of Nevada
Historical Society)

I have spent the month of June in the Humboldt Mountains, looking over gold prospects. The main claim is called the "Lost Mine." . . . During the past four years persistent searches were made for the mine, but each time were abandoned, until this spring when a cultured woman of the new age appeared in the person of Mrs. Ida M. Strobridge, in company with a young man lately employed on her father's ranch near Humboldt. She is a most remarkably bright woman, and will climb a precipitous cliff where the average man would not dare to venture. In addition to mining she looks after the business of her father's cattle ranch, and is quite a sportswoman and would probably carry off the first prize in a shooting tournament, as she brings down her game every time. She wears a handsome brown denim costume, which she dons in climbing the very steep and rugged cliffs of the Humboldt Mountains. She has located five claims on the lode, laid out a new camp and named it after her father, "Meacham," and reorganized the district anew as the "Humboldt"; she has four men to work and is superintending operations herself. She has also located the water and springs flowing over her claims, which are nine miles east of the Central Pacific Railroad, at the Humboldt House. She is the New Woman. . . . Mrs. Strobridge is now engaged running a tunnel under the shaft where the vein is showing up finely, and if the present appearance is maintained the New Woman will in due time be reckoned a millionairess, and all by her indomitable will and perseverance. She is now sacking ores for shipment. [13 July 1895, p. 24]

Those millions failing to materialize, the New Woman took up another avocation—serious bookbinding, as later described in this item from the *Los Angeles Times:*

She ran across an amateur who knew a few rudiments of the art and got her start. The start was all wrong, as she laughingly says, but the things she found were wrong she set about to right by applying her fertile brain to the problem. For a while it was

hard to find where to write for simple instructions and materials. Bookbinders to whom she appealed through the mails did
not care to give out information to amateurs—they were too
stingy.

At last she found a scrap of an envelope which bore the name
and address of an eastern firm that furnished bookbinder's supplies. She procured some material from them and a hand press.
When she got it she did not know how to use it. Her father came
to her aid and devised a stand for it—the same one she now
uses. . . .

So it was with almost all the other large pieces of furniture
necessary to the little shop—they were devised and built by Mr.
Meacham, her father, and are possessed of little improvements
not to be found in the stores. "The first thing you must have, if
you want to learn bookbinding for a living, is a father," says Mrs.
Strobridge. [Reprinted in the Reno *Evening Gazette,* 21 March
1902]

Her bindings would go on to win the highest medals at the California State Fair in 1908 and the Seattle Exposition in 1909, but Idah
next turned her energy to making something to bind. In 1895 at the
age of forty she began to write, at first under the composite pseudo-
nym of "George W. Craiger," about her father's voyage to the gold-
fields. She soon tried her hand at short stories and sketches which
she sent to the San Francisco and Los Angeles papers and to peri-
odicals like the short-lived *Nevada Magazine,* published in Winnemucca. The seriousness with which she took up writing can be
seen in the series of items she placed in a magazine called *The Editor,* "A Journal of Information for Literary Workers," published in
Franklin, Ohio. The September 1896 issue contains a piece called
"Why Typewritten Manuscripts?" in which she proclaims her conver-
sion: "So I say, all hail to the Hammond, the Franklin, and the Bar-
Lock! Honor to the Smith-Premier, the Remington, the Densmore,
and the Yost! Glory to the Caligraph, the National and all those help-
ers of busy fingers and brains!" [p. 99] In the May 1897 number, she

"Idah Meacham Strobridge (taken by herself 250 miles from
a photograph gallery—otherwise you should have a more
conventionally arranged picture). Yours—without apology—The
Bookbinder." (Courtesy of Nevada Historical Society)

has a letter to the editor about an apparent plagiarism of a magazine story, and the following issue runs another letter on how to address ladies in correspondence.

Idah also struck up a correspondence with Jack London, then in Oakland. Her letters to him do not survive, but there are three relevant notes of his in the Hoffman collection of the Huntington Library. In one of these, dated 17 June 1900, London says: "I see you have a cosmopolitan nature akin to mine. And that's the only kind of a nature to have in this good old world. The rut—the well-greased groove—bah! Have breadth and thickness, as well as length to one's life."

But Idah found her most appreciative reader in the flamboyant Charles Fletcher Lummis who, in the mid-1880s, had hiked from Cincinnati to Los Angeles. His weekly letters to the *Times* en route had earned him the post of city editor by the time he arrived. Now, after a six-year sojourn in the New Mexican desert spent overcoming paralysis and divorce, he issued *Land of Sunshine* from Los Angeles, lyrically promoting the glories of the West. In the January 1901 number, Lummis wrote an appreciation of Idah Strobridge under the heading "A Sage-Brush Oasis":

> For several years a pretty sure welcome has been standing in this office for MSS in blue covers in a firm, round fist and with the postmark "Humboldt, Nev."—if you chance to know where that dot of the map is on "yan" slope of the Sierra. These stories and sketches are of the literary merit which inheres in directness, sincerity and impulse. It is not too much to call them well-written—but even more, they are well felt. They are earnest and honest work and of an excellent sympathy and strength. A harassed editor often wishes he had to read no MS less like dried cod than the alive contributions signed Idah M. Strobridge.
>
> Up on that remote and beautiful mountain ranch, a long way out of the world—as the world wobbles now—this ranchwoman of the sage-brush is turning her own competent hands to sev-

eral good uses. Aside from the big ranch on the Humboldt, she has a gold mine up in the canyon—and there is no tenderfoot overseer.

Lummis then discusses Idah's new avocation.

And as housekeeping and mining and ranching are not enough for a really active spirit, and as writing is only half enough recreation, Mrs. Strobridge has plunged as heartily into bookbinding. Not as a fad, nor yet commercially; but, so far as can be seen, for pure love of work worth while. And though this sagebrush artisan has been studying out this exigent trade by herself, off there in the wilderness, her work is emphatically worth while. A commercial-bound book looks cheap beside her staunch and honest and tasteful bindings; and when I have a book that merits to endure longer than the commercial binds can make it, off it goes to Humboldt, and never in vain. The old tomes on my shelves will last as well—the books bound from one to four centuries ago—but practically none of the modern ones will keep their jackets so long.

The "Artemisia Bindery" (for so Mrs. Strobridge merrily calls her home work-and-play shop) is not open for business. If it were, it would have its hands full—since there are still people who care less for a $50 binding on a dollar book than they do for good books bound with so much honesty and sincerity as are most rare now. Her binding is Love's Labor Won. One of the oldest and most famous binders in the United States told me he did not believe a book I showed him from her hands could be more substantially bound anywhere.

The Artemisia Bindery, in an attic of the big ranch-house, is almost entirely home-made—as is the binder's skill. It seems to me a very interesting achievement in every way, that of this plucky and able woman. The wonder is not that a woman should bind books—for many do so—but that anyone should bind them so adequately. [pp. 28–32]

The bindery at the ranch, including the sewing-press
and lying-press. (Courtesy of the Southwest Museum, Los Angeles.
Photo #N. 30606)

Lummis's lavish praise seems to have confirmed Idah's intention,
already expressed in advertisements she had placed in *Land of Sunshine,* to sell her ranchlands and relocate. By May of 1901, she had
sold most of her extensive holdings in Lassen Meadows for more than
$11,000 and moved to Los Angeles, accompanied by her parents. Not
only that, but she took up residence and set up her bindery at 231
East Avenue 41, in a rambling house set in a sycamore grove on the
edge of Arroyo Seco, three blocks from Lummis's own home. Idah
thus thrust herself into the leading cultural circle of Southern California. Among its members was an encouraging salon of local-color
fiction writers encompassing Charles Willard, Sharlot Hall, Mar-

garet Collier Graham, Mary Austin, and Eugene Manlove Rhodes, and artists like Ed Borein, Carl Oscar Borg, and Maynard Dixon. More far-flung contributors to *Land of Sunshine* included Mary Hallock Foote and Stewart Edward White. The energetic Lummis cultivated all of these talents and many others, while supporting organizations to rescue Indians, preserve Spanish landmarks, and hold gala street fiestas. In 1902 he renamed his journal *Out West* and then continued to issue it until 1910, by which time he was busy as head of the Los Angeles Public Library and making plans for the opening of the Southwest Museum.

Idah wrote more stories for the new journal and continued to publish the works of others—such as *The Hieroglyphics of Love* (1906), stories about Los Angeles's Sonoratown by Amanda Mathews Chase—but she also embarked on a larger program of publishing her own works. For her first book she gathered a group of lost-mine legends—some of which she had published in newspapers—amplified them, and interspersed them with evocative descriptions of the desert. She titled the collection *In Miners' Mirage-Land* and had a thousand copies printed by the Baumgardt Publishing Company of Los Angeles in 1904.

Thus, a quarter of a century before J. Frank Dobie was to make a comparable collection of Texas lost-mine tales in his *Coronado's Children,* Idah Strobridge was tilling ground only recently broken by John Van Dyke and Mary Austin. Although her book appeared a year after Mary Austin's more famous *Land of Little Rain,* Idah's lifelong intimacy with the desert reflects a quite different response to the region from Austin's. While Austin may have been the more talented writer, she had first seen the desert in 1888 as a twenty-year-old tourist riding the Union Pacific into post-boom California, and she inherited a ready-made reaction against the exploitation of the region. Her unhappy marriage to a teacher and part-time promoter, as well as having to raise a retarded child, apparently added to her alienation. In her writing, Austin came to reject society as much as to embrace nature and the Indians. Idah Strobridge's feeling for the desert is as intense as Mary Austin's but more realistic and less mystical.

The harshness of the desert is, for her, as much a cause of the human suffering and brutality there as any intrusions of "civilization."

In the writing of fiction, Strobridge and Austin seem about equally conventional, although several cuts above some of the other contributors to Lummis's journals. Idah's second book, *The Loom of the Desert,* published by her own Artemisia Bindery in 1907, collects a dozen stories written over a period extending from 1899 to 1907. As her title implies and foreword makes clear, these tales are heavy on plot and cruel twists of "Fate."

Several of the stories are romances as well, with predictable love triangles and parallelograms. But in spite of these magazine formulas of the times, there is more to these stories than that.

In one story, "The Revolt of Martha Scott," Idah even gives feminism a try, although here she lagged far behind Austin's example. Her heroine, married to an older mill operator out in the desert, forsakes her life of drudgery for a year-long fling in San Francisco and the Islands in the company of a man she does not love and then returns to duty, but without apology or remorse. Finally, her story "A Shepherd of the Silent Wastes" is also her most elaborate. In first-person voice, it recounts the lurid life story of Joe Burnham and his doppelganger, whose struggle with his good and evil natures leads him from Broadway to Istanbul, the Nile, and San Francisco's Chinatown, but only incidentally to Nevada. As Idah sought subject matter more conventionally exotic, her writing strayed from the hardiness of its sagebrush roots.

Idah Strobridge's third and last book, *The Land of Purple Shadows* (1909), is the most miscellaneous of them all. Lacking the thematic unity of *In Miners' Mirage-Land* and the generic consistency of *The Loom of the Desert,* it still contains some of her strongest writing. "The Quail's Canyon," "Subduing a Little Savage," "In the Days of Hank Monk," and "Old Campfire Days" are highly detailed narrative reminiscences of her life in Nevada. But some pieces, such as "One Day at Pacheco's," "Under the Campanerio," "Up-stream Under a Summer Moon," and "Jack Bruin: the Goatherd," are journalistic exercises focused on Old California.

Idah as author. (Courtesy of the Southwest Museum, Los Angeles. Photo #N. 30605)

With this collection, Idah published her last work, although in a letter to Eudora Garroute, dated 4 August 1909, she says "I am working on two or three others, principally 'The Passing of Old San Pedro' which is the subtitle, if it is to be used at all. But the name as it stands tells the story." [Calif. State Lib. MS] The piece does not seem to have seen print.

Idah found another outlet for her nostalgia in setting up a retreat called "The Wickieup" in San Pedro, located in a wing of an old bathhouse. As she told Kate Hall, a reporter for the Los Angeles *Examiner* in 1904:

> It is not alone the open which attracts me and the untrammeled natures of the people. It is the life utterly without pretense. I am not a city woman, neither do I like that country life which savors of the city. I despise the suburb. An existence wholly away from those conventional things hampered by man is what I long for. It is the life on the desert wholly apart from everything of pretense. I cannot give it up entirely and so I have furnished in fitting manner the 'Wickieup,' my substitute for the desert, down on the breakwater at San Pedro. The place is among the huts of the fishermen and it is there that I go every Saturday night. I sit at the fishermen's tables and they sit at mine and do you wonder that I love that beautiful expanse of water which stretches out before me, that vast sheet of blue relieved by motion, color and animate life? [28 August 1904]

Although she gave up writing at the age of 54, Idah Strobridge lived another twenty-two years, caring for her parents and actively involving herself in club work and genealogical societies. She was a member of the Friday Morning Club, the Southern California Press Club, and the League of American Pen Women among others. Working out of the extensive genealogical facilities of the Los Angeles Public Library, Idah prepared typescript genealogies of the line of Asa Standish in 1922 and one of the Johnson families of New England in 1925. She was affiliated with the National Genealogical Society, and state organizations in California, Connecticut, and New Jersey.

She died 8 February 1932 at the age of 76, leaving no immediate family, but only a cousin, Mrs. Hattie Chambers, with whom she had shared her Los Angeles home, and another cousin in Pomona. She was buried in Oakland at the Mountain View cemetery beside her parents, husband, and sons.

Idah Strobridge had lived more than one western life. After working fully her own desert ranch and mines, she took up fully the cultural world of coastal California. In the terms that Kevin Starr has taught us in *Inventing the Dream: California Through the Progressive Era,* Idah enjoyed both modes of Bohemia—the Arroyo and Pasadena. Having explored the crafts culture and nostalgia for the southwestern hinterland of Lummis's circle, she moved on, as Mary Austin and Robinson Jeffers had done. But in Idah's case, she forsook literature as well for her own version of gentility, clublife, and the genealogical societies. But it is in her "Wickieup" on the San Pedro breakwater that she can be glimpsed in her most distinctive mode, huddled once more with a book, the sulfur, and the snakeskins.

SOURCES

A Checklist of the Writings of Idah Meacham Strobridge

Manuscripts

Los Angeles, Calif. Southwest Museum. *The Tales That Winap Tells.* Three Paiute folktales: "The Great Blue Smoke," "The Great Rough Mountain," and "How the Cottontail Killed the Sun." Bound together and dated 16 August 1900.

Editions

In Miners' Mirage-Land. Los Angeles: [Artemisia Bindery, printed by the Baumgardt Publishing Company], 1904.

The Loom of the Desert. Los Angeles: [Artemesia Bindery], 1907.

The Land of Purple Shadows. Los Angeles: Artemesia Bindery, 1909.

Selected Articles in Chronological Order

Craiger, George W. [Pseudonym]. "Memorable Voyage of the Ship Orpheus." San Francisco *Chronicle,* 2 February 1896.

"Why Typewritten Manuscripts?" *The Editor* (September 1896), 97–99.

"A Neglected Corner." *Land of Sunshine* 8 (January 1898), 67–71.

"In Nanna's Palm." *Land of Sunshine* 9 (June 1898), 24–27.

"Greater Love Hath No Man." *Arena* 21 (March 1899), 335–50.

"The Happy Hunting Ground. A Paiute Doctrine." *Land of Sunshine* 11 (June 1899), 21–24.

"One Day at Pacheco's." *Land of Sunshine* 11 (July 1899), 101–104.

"The Glory of War." *Nevada Magazine* 1 (September 1899), 59.

"The First Night." *Nevada Magazine* 1 (November 1899), 219–32.

"How Christmas Came to Cyril Thorne." *Nevada Magazine* 1 (December 1899), 323–31.

"Brothers Aye, Brothers All." *Nevada Magazine* 1 (January 1900).
"Staging in the Sierras." *Land of Sunshine* 12 (February 1900), 169–72.
"The Blue-Eyed Chief." *Land of Sunshine* 13 (August 1900), 174–78.
"Lo's Turkish Bath." *Land of Sunshine* 14 (January 1901), 13–19.
"In Cañon Diablo." *Out West* 19 (July 1903), 66–71.
"The Enchanted Vale." *Sunset* 16 (January 1906), 277–80.
"A Shepherd of the Silent Wastes." *Out West* 27 (November 1907), 422–30.
"The Way of the Desert" and "Legend of the China Lily." In *Pathway to Western Literature,* edited by Nettie S. Gaines. Stockton: [no pub.], 1910.

Additional References

"An Accomplished Woman Miner." *Mining and Scientific Press* 71 (13 July 1895), 24.

Amaral, Anthony. "Idah Meacham Strobridge: First Woman of Nevada Letters." *Nevada Historical Society Quarterly* 8 (Fall 1967), 5–12.

Bingham, Edwin R. *Charles F. Lummis: Editor of the Southwest.* San Marino: Huntington Library, 1955.

Carpenter, Edwin H. "A Sagebrush Westerner: Idah Meacham Strobridge, 1855–1932." *The Branding Iron.* (Westerners, Los Angeles Corral Pub. 30, June 1955), [3–4].

———. "Idah Meacham Strobridge." *Biblio-Cal Notes* 12 (Fall/ Winter 1982), 14–16.

Hinkel, E. J. *Biographies of California Authors.* Oakland, 1942. V. 1, p. 214.

"Humboldt House Once Figured Prominently." *Nevada State Journal,* 9 March 1941.

Hylton, Jessie. "The Artistic Idea as Expressed by Early Nevada Authors." *Nevada Historical Society Papers, 1913–1916.* V. 1 (Carson City, 1917), 125–43.

Laird, Helen. *Carl Borg and the Magic Region.* [Layton, Utah]: Gibbs M. Smith, 1986.

[Lummis, Charles.] "A Sage-Brush Oasis." *Land of Sunshine* 14 (January 1901), 28–32.

"George W. Meacham—Obituary." *Los Angeles Times,* 20 December 1914.

"Mrs. Strobridge's Interesting Story." Reno *Evening Gazette,* 21 March 1902. From the *Los Angeles Times.*

Walker, Franklin. *A Literary History of Southern California.* Berkeley: University of California Press, 1950.

"A Woman Miner." *Scientific American* 73 (August 1895), 86.

IN MINERS' MIRAGE-LAND

MIRAGE IN THE DESERT

FROM THE PAINTING BY FRANK P. SAUERWEN

In Miners' Mirage-Land

by

Idah Meacham Strobridge

LOS ANGELES
MCMIV

TO THE MEN OF THE DESERT;
but more especially those miners who
have grown gray while waiting for
their dreams to come true, I dedicate
these stories that I found in that land
where I, too, dreamed dreams.

CONTENTS

FOREWORD

"The palpable sense of mystery in the Desert air breeds fables, chiefly of lost treasure. Somewhere within its stark borders, if one believes report, is a hill strewn with nuggets; one seamed with virgin silver; an old clayey water-bed where Indians scooped up earth to make cooking pots and shaped them reeking with grains of gold. Old miners drifting about the Desert edges, weathered into the semblance of the tawny hills, will tell you tales like these convincingly. After a little sojourn in that land you will believe them on your own account."

MARY AUSTIN,
In "The Land of Little Rain."

MIRAGES OF THE DESERT.

WAY back in the old days when the slow-moving ox team dragged its weary way, foot by foot, over the alkali flats and the long streatches of sun-baked soil, where the only growth was the gray sage and the greasewood—away back in those far days—the mirage, that Lorelei of the Desert, was there to lure men on to their destruction.

Great lakes of shining water, where little waves ran up to lap the shore; wide fields of clover and blue grass, that looked so green and cool under the burning sun; forests which reached miles away in a tangle of vine and tree—those were the visions that the Siren of the Dry Lakes showed to the water-starved emigrant of old, and—beckoning—led him on and on, in the pursuit of the unreal, until the picture grew fainter and fainter, and at last down the diminishing perspective of the vision—as he looked—he saw it fade away. The grassy fields where the oxen might have fed, the sparkling waters at which they might have drunk, the broad-leafed shade under which man and beast might have found refreshing rest, were gone! A tantalizing glimpse of Paradise in the great and awful desolation of those Desert days.

Many a poor traveler, led far astray by following the ever-calling, ever-retreating enchantress, has laid down

Mirages

of

the

Desert

at last to die alone in that vast waste, where his bones must bleach in the sun, and his dust must become the sport of the winds of the Desert.

I can recall instances innumerable of emigrant trains deceived by the mirage and led far out of their course, in the hope of reaching the lakes of water that looked so deep and pure.

Down through the valley of the Humboldt, in that part of the great American Sahara which the old emigrant knew so well, they traveled—they whose faces were set toward the land of gold and the setting sun. And there, as they passed along the banks of the long and tortuous Humboldt, they were told a fable that was believed by many a wayfarer of the early days;—that, except fish could be seen swimming about, the waters of the river were poisonous if one drank of them deeply. So people became afraid of it, and went far out of their route to avoid, if possible, drinking the fatal waters of the "River of Death," as it came to be called. Then, when alluring lakes and ponds, and lovely forests and fields spread out, a picture of enchantment before their gaze, is it any wonder that they eagerly hurried onward toward the prospect held out so invitingly toward them?

Only those who have suffered like disappointment can imagine the despair of beholding such a vision dissolve into thin air palpitating in heat waves over the wide plain—as far as the eye could see, only a shimmering haze.

The mirage is, in very truth, a part of the Desert itself—just as the sagebrush, and the coyote, and the little horned toads, and the sand-storms are part. To those who know Desert-land, the picture would be incomplete without them.

Perhaps the commonest form the mirage assumes is that of bodies of water—from tiny ponds only a few feet across, to great lakes so broad that the farther shore seems beyond the range of vision. I have seen such lakes under the heat of mid-day sun when the quivering air gave them the appearance of crested waves, so like those of reality that were it not for my acquaintance with the topography of the country, as well as the knowledge that I had of the strange forms the mirage takes, I should have felt tempted to believe in their tangibility.

In a few instances I have seen small boats on the surface, the reflection of them in the water being in perfect mimicry of nature's mirroring; and on one occasion, a great ship under full sail—though mistily seen, and seemingly far—rose and fell with the swell of the waves.

Such of these as I myself have seen, have always appeared near the centre of some large alkali flat, where, upon almost any hot spring or summer day, small bodies of water may be seen reflecting the heavens with a deeper blue than the sky was ever known to wear. Sometimes, on the far side of these ponds you may see a wavering border of———what? You look, and look yet again; and still you cannot tell what strange things they may be. Not trees; not human beings; neither are they creatures of the earth, nor of the air, that are moving on the opposite shore. It is something unreal, the presence of which you feel, but cannot explain; something you watch with a delighted fascination; something exquisitely intangible, like the dream of a dream, and as impossible to describe. It must be seen to be understood; no writer's pen, no painter's brush can faithfully portray it.

Early Spring mornings, when the sun rising from behind the purple range of mountains, still cold and dark on its western slope, has filled the valley with a soft, golden glow, and lighted the mountains across the way till they begin to take on that delicate tint which only early morning gives, then far down in the valley where the East Range rises up at the left of the southern gateway, the mirage runs riot with its fantastic fashioning.

The mountains alter their outlines so rapidly that the eye can scarce note all their changes. They change from great heights to a low chain of hills; and leap back again, to shoot in spires innumerable into the violet sky, or drop into a long, flat table-land with overhanging top; while, above—in the air—here and there float elongated islands that but a moment before were a part of the mountains beneath—mountains that are being pierced by gigantic caverns through which the sky can be seen. Then they disappear, and island and table-land once more unite; and again a myriad of pinnacles lift themselves from the mass of changing panorama, and the slender shafts reach far into the sky. Then—even as you are watching—one by one they dissolve, and the mountains have resumed their wonted shapes.

Farther down the valley (for this is a particular valley I know, that I am describing here, and for more than a score of years it was my home; and in my heart I have named it the only Home I have—for we loved each other, the Desert and I)—before the days of track and train—there was a station built for the accommodation of passing teamsters. The building had been constructed of time-stained lumber, torn out of the old houses of deserted mining camps in the adjacent mountains. The small, dull-toned, unpainted cabin stood, uncompromising in its plainness, in the midst of a broad, staring, white alkali flat, where the owner of the station had previously assured himself of a sufficient water supply. For the establishing of such stations depends largely upon one's being able to obtain an unfailing—if only fairly good—supply of well water. And the location of this station—here in the very centre of a barren, snow-white flat—was the result of his having found the only place where water could be got, by digging for it, within a distance of forty miles. Travel to and from the mines northward was increasing, and with it came an increase in the station-man's sales; for he not only had a "general merchandise store"—though of diminutive proportions—and conducted what he was pleased to call a "stable," but he set forth food for man as well. With his success, came the knowledge that it had created envy in the breast of another—one who would be a rival; for this other declared his intention of erecting at the same point on the road the emigrants traveled, a like establishment, and thus competing with him for their custom.

Much bitter feeling was expressed, and many hot words passed between them. Finally the station keeper made a threat to kill the other man at sight should he ever bring material there for the construction of a rival house. Matters stood thus for some time, each man waiting for some decisive move on the part of the other. Then the one who claimed prior right to the location, taking his four-horse team, went in to Virginia City for goods to replenish his stock, which the fast increasing Idaho travel was reducing to a small quantity.

On his return trip, when within a mile or two of home, he suddenly noticed opposite his own plainly built little cabin, a fine, large building of new lumber—the brightness of the fresh pine boards putting to shame his own unpretentious and almost shabby-looking house.

Mirages of the Desert.

Enraged at the thought that his rival had taken such an advantage as the week's absence had given him, he reached back into the wagon, and got out his Henry rifle. With the cocked weapon laid across his knees— revengeful and determined—he waited impatiently for the heavily laden team to draw near to the spot where he was resolved that his threat, made weeks before, should be put into execution.

There it stood! A two-story house of unpainted pine; its gable to the road, its front door invitingly open, its shutterless windows looking toward the South, as if watching his approach.

He saw it all as plainly as he saw his own poor little home across the way; then—when within less than a hundred yards of it—there was a shivering of the whole scene, and the "opposition" station disappeared into nothingness, leaving but the one building there—the small, solitary house that for several years thereafter stood without rival on the alkali plain.

With the going of the larger building, went also the station-keeper's desire for vengeance; and scarcely a traveller ever stopped at his place afterward who did not hear from him the story of the strange mirage. The name "Mirage" clung to the place, and finally it came to be so christened by the railroad company whose lines passed its door. A siding is there for waiting freights that you glimpse as you flash by in a train made up of "Pullmans;" but the railroad men—when you ask them—will call it "My-ridge." Shadow pictures waver about the place when the summer sun shines hot, but the station built of new pine has never reappeared.

Some localities seem specially adapted to the conditions which invite a mirage. I know of a bush—a large greasewood—out near the middle of a certain smooth, level flat that is over two miles broad and fully twice as long, that during the summer months seems always to be wrapped in the mystic mantle of a mirage. Sometimes it has no definite shape, but always the mirage-like effect is there. A road crosses this flat two hundred yards away, and after I first observed the bush, I took pains to notice it particularly, scarcely ever passing it when the days were full of shimmering heat that it did not take on some semblance of flesh and blood. So repeatedly did this seem to occur that I came to call it "My Ghost-Bush," and watched it with an interest that was generally rewarded by having some apparently living form evolve itself from the greasewood's scant and ragged branches.

It is apt to make the shivers run up one's spine to see a harmless looking bush, of a sudden, metamorphose itself into a tall man, and see the man come striding toward you with a long, swinging step; and then—while you are still intently gazing, and wondering where he could have sprung from on that barren Desert bit—as suddenly discover that he is walking away from you— and backwards, at that. An uncanny thing, you may be sure; yet one gets used to it, after a while, and to the knowledge that, after all, it is only one of the many Desert marvels. And dozens of times did I see this great, gaunt man go striding across the level, white plain, and then disappear as though touched by a magician's wand, leaving the lone greasewood standing there instead. Sometimes he seemed to be carrying a roll of blankets on his shoulders, as some poor wayfarers in Desert-land do; and at other times one could have sworn that he was visibly swinging a walking-stick as he went. There were days when the bush, instead of standing there so tall and thin, settled itself down into the semblance of some heavier body; and then one could see a sheep standing at the edge of a little pond as if

Mirages of the Desert.

nibbling at the grass that seemed to grow there. At times, it would lift its head as though it looked at you; then as the shimmering of the heat waves increased, it trotted away into the white glare of the summer sunlight, and was no more. Sometimes there were two objects instead of one; but whether moving away across the flat, or standing still by the little patch of imaginary water, their movements were always identical if the mirage was of two.

Once, I remember, it seemed to be an awkward, half-grown girl that moved there; and the point of her big gray shawl—too big, by far, for her slim body —was trailing behind her on the ground.

There have been gulls—ten or twelve seagulls—walking about in the shallow imaginary water, picking at imaginary weeds. And once when there was a large flock of them, and they began to melt into the ether, I found that there were real gulls among them—three of them—that had come far inland from their home by the salt sea, going toward the Lake that is Salt.

But all of these things that were of the mirage-world and without the breath of life, whether slim-built girl, or the man who was of sturdier mould, or the sheep, or the seagulls—all had the trick of moving when I moved, of standing still when I stood still. Then, when I had driven past a certain point in the road, they invariably dissolved, leaving only the heat glimmering across the landscape, and the "ghost bush" there, quiet and alone.

Once, in a rage at the mocking thing, I turned my horses' heads toward it, determined to drive onto it, over it, and crush it down. It irritated me to feel that I could not go by it there on the road without the senseless bush taking unto itself the likeness of some living, breathing thing. I drove hard and straight at it, and although there was not a particle of wind stirring the stifling air, yet that miserable bush was swaying back and forth as if waving defiance at me. Whipping up my team, I drove over it, the "off" horse crushing more than half its branches down to the ground. A shiver that ran over me, in spite of the heat of that Desert-day, for the thing had become so real to me as a creature of life, that I almost expected it to shriek out in pain as its crooked, misshapen branches cracked and snapped under the hoofs of the horses.

the start of the end — the branches of the west destroyed by the lever

It has never been my good fortune to meet any of the old-fashioned ghosts that go up and down the earth with rattling bones and a musty smell—the kind that leave a splotch of blood on everything they touch, but I doubt if they are any more uncanny than a gray wraith evolved out of a greasewood bush by the aid of a mirage.

We do not always recognize a mirage as such when we see one, or experience the "creepy" feeling that a meeting with ghosts is supposed to engender. Among the memories I have of things that were, in the gray country, is one of driving along a dusty road on a hot August day, and seeing some little distance ahead of me, through a blur of dust that seemed to rise from the road, a six-horse wagon driven by a man wearing a red shirt. The wagon, which looked to be heavily loaded with sacks of grain, appeared to have been once painted a bright blue, and the running-gear an equally vivid red—colors now dulled by dust and time. A cloud of fine, flour-like alkali arose about the wheels and around the horses' hoofs.

With my thoughts elsewhere, though with eyes upon this not unusual sight upon the traveled roads of Desert-land, I watched it for more than a quarter of an hour, as it seemed to jolt and bump along its way. Although

I was driving rapidly that I might reach it and pass it, and so be beyond the dust that seemed to be stirred up by the wheels, and which would soon be floating back and covering me, yet I did not seem to gain upon it. Finally I noticed that it moved only as I did. Then, when horses, and wagon, and driver, and the dust from the powdered white earth had disappeared, I realized that it had been but a mirage. Accustomed as I had long been to seeing them in all their varying guises, not for one instant had I suspected what it really was. I have counted it among the most remarkable mirages I have ever known of, because its coloring was so bright; the apparently new, vivid red shirt the man wore was a quite unusual bit of mirage color. For these Desert wraiths choose robes of dull grays, or browns that are dull and dim; unless it may be in the blue of sky and the water, or the green of grass and the trees.

Then, I remember once seeing the red dress of a woman reflected in a mirage that took the form of a small and shallow pond that seemed to lie between that part of a "dry lake" over which a road passed, along which she was driving with a companion, and another point half a mile away where I was driving along another—and parallel—road. The bright color of her dress, the man's darker clothing, the horses (one black, the other white), the wagon, were all reflected with wonderful exactitude in the simulated water. These people I knew; and afterward; when speaking to them about it, they too said they had seen the mirage of the pond lying between us, and had remarked upon the vividness with which my reflection was shown there. Although we were such a distance apart, yet each of us could see the movement of the horses' feet reflected in the water. Unlike the former mirage I had seen where the red had shown with such brilliancy, here the color was real—only the reflection of the woman's red dress in the mirage-lake being the unreality.

Of all the wonderful pictures painted by this artist of the atmosphere—and I have seen many—there was never one which in magnitude, in grandeur, in beauty of form and tinting, even remotely approached one which I witnessed in the spring of 1869.

It was about two hours after sunrise—the magic time the mirage chooses for its most ideal forms—when I happened to notice that the portion of Eugene Mountain known as the Woody Cañon district was undergoing one of those marvellous transformations so frequent in the rarified air and high altitude of that section. The change from the dull reddish hue of the rugged mountain to all of the loveliest tints that the mind can imagine, was rapid. The early morning sun had filled the valley with a warm yellow light, and one seemed to be looking through a golden veil at the gigantic castle that fashioned itself from the mountain's rocky top. Turrets, and round towers, and battlemented walls; graceful arches, and windows, narrow and long, were all there—parts of a structure stupendously magnificent in its beautiful gradations of color, violet, purple and lightest rose. But even as with subdued breath—lest a sigh of delight or a word ever so softly spoken might dispel it—I watched its rare and exquisite beauty, it faded away, and again the rough contour of Eugene Mountain loomed up where the mystical, mythical castle had been but a moment before. Such a gorgeous representation of magnificent architecture in such beautiful coloring never again was presented to the delighted quartette which witnessed that bewildering fantasy of Nature.

Mirages of the Desert

**Mirages
of
the
Desert**

To those who know the Desert's heart, and—through years of closest intimacy—have learned to love it in all its moods, it has for them something that is greater than charm, more lasting than beauty, yet to which no man can give a name. Speech is not needed, for they who are elect to love these things understand one another without words; and the Desert speaks to them through its silence.

To others—those who need words and want people in numbers—the Desert is but a gray waste of sand and sagebrush, lying in pitiful loneliness under a gray sky.

Utter desolation! To-day is like yesterday—to-morrow will be like to-day. The sun rises each morning upon a scene which never alters, except when a change is wrought by the mirage in its illusive, elusive mystery.

THE MYTHS OF THE DESERT.

UT the Desert showed another mirage than that of grass-bordered water-stretches, to the men who came a-search for gold in the Days of 'Forty-Nine; so that—even to this hour—some are still striving to reach it, away out there in the sand wastes.

The mines of old called men out of the East, to seek a fortune in the State that borders the sunset sea. And there they washed gold from the creek and river-bed in quantities sufficient, one would think, to stay the prospector's feet from wandering further. Yet many there were who—after crossing the plains—were lured back to sagebrush-land by the fabulous tales of gold and silver there; and so have lived more than a double score of years in the land of the mirage, seeking some mirage-mine.

Rich ledges in plenty are there, but not to the North in the lava country. Some knew where to find them; and the men who mined them have grown rich and gone away. Of them I do not speak. My tales, instead, are of those fanatical prospectors who are ever striving for the rainbow's end in their quest for rainbow-gold.

Into the gray Desert (a land of gray sage, and gray sand; of lizards, and little horned-toads that are gray; a land where the coyote drifts by you, like a fragment from gray fog-banks blown by the wind), half a century ago, they came—the prospectors—seeking silver or gold. And some yet seek, in places where there is none. Some are following the mirage still.

Once—long ago—my horse and I went away into the mirage-land of these old miners; and there I heard them voice the stories of their hopes—the dreams that they believe will some day come true. By camp-fire smoke, or in the dim light of sod cabins, I have sat in the silence the Desert teaches, and have listened as they talked, and believed while I listened. Yes, even believed; as you, too, will believe if you hear from their own lips the fables that seem so true during the hour you are under the story-teller's charm, with no sound breaking in save the crooning of the Desert wind or the cry of a lone coyote. One must sleep well, and dream of other things, before the coming of the time that will bring disbelief.

They are only miners' fables; but they sounded true. And for an evening and a day I believed them. And I am glad I believed. If I had not—if I had been a doubter—those hours would have lacked just what makes them now among my dearest kept memories. And if you, who read these re-told tales, are of those who have heard the Voice of the Desert speaking, I know you will understand.

THE SECRET MINE OF THE BROWN MEN.

The
Secret
Mine
of
the
Brown
Men

RIDING for weeks up and down trails that took me into cañons and over roads that crossed the alkali levels of the wide, still country tucked away under the northernmost shelter of Nevada, it was no difficult mental process to put myself back half a century in time's reckoning and feel that I was one of those Desert voyagers of long ago.

As they saw it, so can we see it today; so little has man disturbed the landscape. Nature's visible processes are slow, and few people find their way here, for mankind to make "improvements." The broad, far-reaching picture remains, as the still years slip by, mostly unchanged.

On the earth's well-traveled roads you never saw such pictures as these! Not only are they beautiful, but they are different—and all that implies! Look! Under a summer sun's shimmering light, distance paints the far ranges faintly in all the colors of the spectrum, while the near mountains rise about you, gray and grim. Over there is the blending of the mountain's blue and violet tintings; here a gray-banded cone rises, its western side furrowed and seamed like an old frontiersman's face. Between, lie miles and miles of drab-colored plain spotted with leper-patches of alkali—wide plains that reach from ridges of gaunt, gray slate

The

Secret

Mine

of

the

Brown

Men

to far-away hyacinthine hills. Someone tells you that those distant ranges are red-brown when you reach them; but now they are a lovely, delicate mauve, veiled as they are by the mists of distance.

And so, before you, day by day, as you go riding away out of noisyland into the big silence, you find thousands of pictures to delight the eye and charm the senses into a long-continued joy—such joy as only the Desert can give.

Turn your horse's head to the right, here! Ahead of you are the foothills—a double row of saffron-colored buttes, each capped with outcroppings of rough and craggy brown-black rocks. Ride over them, and you will see fissures where, down in the cleavage, are clay cliffs among buried coal cinders left by the great conflagration. Higher, the mountain is striped horizontal-wise in vivid coloring; each shade marked in broad, glaring bands, bench above bench, with the vigor and boldness of a painter who lays his colors on with a pallette-knife. Rocks run riot in their medley of coloring; striking—indescribable. You lope your horse along a "wash" leading down from the higher slopes, thick strewn with brightness as a springtime hillside in bloom. It is graveled with water-worn pebbles, brilliant and of variegated shades, with here and there big cobbles of the same. Not striped, not mottled, not merely faint tints of coloring, but of a uniform depth of rich purple, or blood-red, green, or yellow, or blue—every stone. So bright, and so many! Yet among them all is never a hint, so far as you can see, of galena, iron pyrites, or mineral of any sort—minerals of value or valueless ones that might suggest the proximity of others of real worth. In all your experience you have never come across a district so barren in its "indications." Yet among these vari-tinted mountains many a miner still is hunting for silver or gold that he heard of in the long ago—one of the many mythical mines that are believed in still.

Your eyes are never at rest, but go seeking new delights all the while, as you ride through the enchanted silence. Over there are vaporous mountains—soft, violet visions of mystic regions far, far beyond; here is all that is grotesque, freaks in color and formation. Such odd mountains, such fantastic hills, they are! Look at those lying northwest! Below, they are low and smooth—round buttes of lemon-yellow, shading into a glaring ochre; back of them, and higher, rise beetling crags that lift crests in battlement and turret, all ebony or burnt umber. On the one hand, perhaps, the hills are grimly gray; on the other, they are wrapped in wavering tints soft as the coloring on a wood-dove's breast.

The delight of it all, the charm, grows on you as the miles lengthen out; and you forget heat and fatigue and the comforts you left back where civilization waits your return. You only know that it is good—vastly good—to live! Just to feel yourself drawing the breath of life is enough, while taking your outing in this faraway corner, where you seem to have the whole earth and sky to yourself. What more would you? The biggest, most beautiful of pictures make the rim of the world here, to repeat themselves in wavering mirages on the levels that lie within the circle of the skyline.

It is, in truth, a land of mirages; but those you see dissolving into the ether, as you draw close to their fanciful outlines, are not the ones that were the lures bringing many a traveler into this enchanted land. Scarcely a day, riding through its length and breadth, did I journey there that I did not hear tales of fairy-weave about hidden gold—of mines that men search for year in and

The
Secret
Mine
of
the
Brown
Men

The
Secret
Mine
of
the
Brown
Men

year out, never finding, but always expecting to find tomorrow—the next day—next week—or the week after. They are always sure of standing on the very brink of discovery. You look about you, you look at them, and you wonder at their faith. To the average prospector, there is nothing suggesting either gold or silver thereabouts; yet among the old guard that brought Nevada into prominence as a mining State, are many who have grown old in the service they have given a useless quest. Scarcely a cañon of these rainbow-ranges alternated with others of Desert-gray, that does not have its story of a "lost mine." Dozens of such have I listened to in that country. At nightfall when we would sit outside the cabin door, an old man, between puffs on his pipe, would tell a tale he fondly believed; or on some rainy day before a huge sagebrush fire, have I hearkened as the story-teller poked at the coals with a poker made from a miner's "spoon"; or up on the heights, while I sat in the saddle and leaned down to some old prospector who declared his certainty that those very mountain heights held the long unfounded mine—his very own. Mirage-mines are they; yet the men who tell the myths, alas! believe them true.

One night, as the stars came out, after we had eaten by the campfire's warmth, at a camp made on the edge of one of the "dry lakes" in which the Desert abounds, looking into the glow of the greasewood coals, I heard this tale from one of its believers:

Years and years ago, over the California State-line, Job Taylor kept a trading post in Indian Valley. He was one of the earliest pioneers; and after establishing the post—much frequented by Indians who sometimes paid for their purchases in gold dust—he was greatly astonished one day at having payment tendered him, by one of the Indians, in nuggets of extraordinary size.

These, he declared (when relating the incident afterward), were as large as hen's eggs. The questions he put to the Indian as to the locality where they were procured, brought forth no answer. No satisfactory replies whatever were obtained from the brown man, who hastened to get away.

The following year the same Indian came again to the trading post; and again he offered nuggets of unusual size in payment for his purchases. Again Taylor importuned him to tell where they were found; but he met with no satisfaction. It was not until a year later that Taylor succeeded in making a sufficiently good impression on the Indian to encourage his confidence. Then he said that, for a certain amount of goods from the post, he would tell Taylor all he knew of the place; and for a further consideration he would take him there. The agreement being satisfactorily made, Capt. Wetherell—an old Indian fighter of experience—was induced to join them. Well equipped for such an undertaking, the three started out, setting their faces to the east, to find the place that the Indian described as containing so great a number of mammoth nuggets. It was a creek, he said—a fine stream filled with mountain trout, and sheltered in part by many trees.

From Indian Valley they went to Susanville, and then—keeping on the Honey Lake road—camped one night by the springs at Deep Hole. It was while they were there that the Indian said to them: "Two more sleeps, and we get there! I know."

Just at that time—the precise year I have forgotten—old Winnemucca, chief of the Paiutes (he for whom the town of Winnemucca was named), was camped on Granite Creek Mountain; and to him the Indian bore a message from some of his people, across the line in California. It was while they were at Deep Hole that the

The
Secret
Mine
of
the
Brown
Men

The

Secret

Mine

of

the

Brown

Men

Indian said: "I got go see ol' Winnemuc', an' tell um what them Injun say. You wait here. I come back pretty quick."

On the following day he returned to them, downcast, and the bearer of disheartening news. He had told the old chief, he said, of their expedition, and Winnemucca had become very angry—he was "heap mad," he said. Further, the chief declared he would have him killed if he took these men farther on their quest; for—he had argued to the younger man—if white men found gold there, they would come in numbers so great as to frighten away much of the game—the deer, the antelope, and the mountain sheep—on which the Indians principally relied for subsistence. The Indian would be the sufferer if the white man came; in no wise would he gain by their coming. Hence, the search must be abandoned.

Entreaties — threats — promises — bribes! they all availed nothing. The old man's edict was irrevocable, so it would be useless for the white men to go to him (as they discussed doing) for favor. The Indian himself would do nothing more. That, under the changed conditions, he would forfeit all the goods at the trading post that he had bargained for, seemed, to him, a matter of utter indifference.

So the two men made their way back to California; and neither Captain Wetherell nor Job Taylor ever saw the Indian again. Whether it was that the old chief had given him orders to shun the White Man lest the secret be wrested from him, or whether he had no more gold to offer in exchange for clothing and food, no one could say. Only of this were they sure; never again did he come to the post.

However, the following year, a young Indian—a mere boy—came with nuggets similar to those that had been previously offered to Taylor. The boy had no hesitation in talking about them and said, in reply to his questioners, that some of the old men of the tribe had gathered the gold, but that he, himself, had never seen the place from whence it was obtained. They had told him, he said, that he was yet too young to be shown the way to the cañon, though he had been taken by them to other cañons near by. But he declared that though he had never seen the exact place, he had attentively listened to the talk of his elders each time they returned with treasure, when the whole camp had gathered about in council as to the best method of disposing of it; and from their description of the cañon, and his own knowledge of adjacent localities, he was sure he could find the nuggets' hiding place.

The white man made tempting inducements for the boy to guide him to the spot; but he was reluctant to do so. He repeated the declaration of the old men of the tribe that he was "too young," and that they would "get heap mad" should he take white men there. But, finally, he admitted that he knew an old man who was in disfavor with the rest of the tribe, who had gathered some of the gold, and might be induced to act as their guide. "I take you go see him," said the boy; "then maybe he show you place. Him live by Deep Hole."

Taylor, Wetherell and the boy set out; and over the same road they had traveled when the older Indian was guide. At Deep Hole, too, they found the old Indian whom the boy declared they would find. They saw him, but that was all. There was more to be desired than the mere sight of the old gray-haired Indian, whom they believed to have taken nuggets from the

The

Secret

Mine

of

the

Brown

Men

The

Secret

Mine

of

the

Brown

Men

unknown cañon. Alien he might be from the rest of the tribe, yet he was loyal to their interests. The eager prospectors found him absolutely dumb when information was desired. He would give them no intelligent answers whatever. To all questioning they got but the stereotyped reply of the Indian who does not want to talk: "Me no savvy. Me no know." Nor could they get more than that from him through the two days they lingered there for that purpose. Every artifice to induce him to disclose his secret, failed. He had evidently been impressed by the warning of Chief Winnemucca; and tribal traditions constrained him to silence. And when an Indian elects to keep closed lips, the Sphinx is not more dumb.

Then the two men got the boy to one side, and sternly demanded some knowledge of the gold's locality. The little fellow was frightened at the threatening manner Capt. Wetherell assumed, and—half-crying—promised to take them there if he could. He was far from sure of the precise cañon it might be, but he knew of the locality, and had a general knowledge of the mountain itself. He would make an effort—he would try—maybe he could take them there; the things the old Indians had told in his presence, when returning to their camps with the great nuggets of gold, were not forgotten, and these memories would be his guide.

"Come on. I think may be so I fin' it," he said; and the journey was resumed.

Both men noticed that their route continued in the same direction indicated by the other Indian as being "two sleeps" further on. At the end of the first of these two days of travel, while lying in their blankets at night, supposing the boy asleep, Capt. Wetherell said to Job Taylor: "If that Injun fails to show us the place, I'll make short work of him!" It is to be doubted if the captain meant more than to express his emphatic annoyance at the way their progress was being discouraged by guides who deserted, and guides who would give no information as to things one wanted to know. But certainly the threat must have sounded ominous enough to one small guide to warrant his desertion. For the captain's indiscretion cost him and Taylor dear. Morning came; but the boy was gone.

Gone, as a whirlwind that dissolves itself in the Desert! And the place, so far as they knew, nor the men, ever knew him more. He had overheard the threat; and fearing, no doubt, that he might not succeed in the search, and in terror of possible results, at day-dawn he had put miles and miles between him and the rough-spoken white man who had planted terror in his young heart.

Frequent search was made afterward for the lost Indian diggings, but they keep their secret still. There is a cañon a mile and a half east of Ebling's, in Virgin Valley, in northeastern Humboldt county, that men declare to be the one the Indians worked in days of old. It is also believed by many to be the one where the famous "Blue Bucket" gold was found. The tale goes that these two lost placers are the same—the "Blue Bucket" mines, and those which the Indian has always kept hidden from the White Man.

Though it is now impassable for wagons, yet the older Indians living there, say that, years and years ago, when the first white men came into the country on their way to the West, many of them passed down the narrow and deep gorge above Ebling's, which though al-

The

Secret

Mine

of

the

Brown

Men

ways difficult, is now impossible to travel of any sort—even passage on foot may be won only at great risk of life or limb. No faintest trace of wagon road, nor even the slightest mark of trail is there. During the last forty years great masses of rock have been continually falling, and have choked the way. The few of recent years who have undertaken it afoot, have stories of uncounted hardships to tell.

It may be (if you choose to believe it so), that this is truly the cañon of the Indians' secret diggings. It may be that this is really the cañon of the lost "Blue Bucket" gold. It may be that these were, after all, but mirage mines; but whatever the truth, the search goes on—goes on.

THE CHARM OF THE DESERT.

VERY likely such a tale seems absurd to you, as you read it between the covers of a book, the while surrounded by the things that make a busy, people-full world. But do not give voice to that disbelief. Not even to yourself must you confess your own incredulity, lest it may prove a thorn in the flesh if you should go into Desert ways some day. For there may come to you some time a twilight hour that shall find you in greasewood-land, and a guest at the campfire of some one of those old prospectors whose guest I, too, have been. Then he himself, you may be sure, will tell you this story. He will tell it to you in almost the very words I have used; but it will have a quality which my own story-telling has not—that of carrying conviction to your heart.

For you will believe. Ay! you will believe it is true; you will believe that there is a marvel of gold there for the lucky one who is to find it.

There, at the end of day, by the drifting blue smoke from the sagebrush campfire—where he has boiled the coffee that you will declare the best that was ever brewed—with the Desert's weirdness creeping up to you with the dusk, while you eat of the strips of bacon your host has cooked and the bread he has baked in the ashes, you will gladly and greedily listen to the

**The
Charm
of
the
Desert.**

story again. And then—when you hear him tell it in the way that he told it to me—you will believe it true. The charm of the Desert will be all about you; the mystery of the Desert will move you in ways that you have never known. Strange thoughts will be yours, of things that—in that strange land—in your heart, you feel might very well be. And of the truth of what you may hear, you will not question.

There are those who have asked me: "What is the charm of the Desert? What is there in the Desert that makes you care for it so? What constitutes its hold on those who have love for its solitude?"

I would answer the last question first. Its hold upon its lovers is the very love they give. For to love is to hold out one's wrists for the shackles to be snapped thereon. It does not matter to what or to whom love is given, it is so—always. So I have answered you this question. But, the others—Its charm? And why does one care?

How can one convey meaning to another in a language which that other does not understand? I can only tell you the charm of the Desert, when you, too, have learned to love it. And then there will be no need for me to speak.

But this much I may say that you will understand: In the Desert all things seem possible. If you ask me, again, "Why?" then I cannot tell you; only I know it is so.

Perhaps that accounts for the faith of the old prospectors.

THE QUEST OF OLD MAN BERRY.

HE faith of the old prospectors! There is no other such blind faith in the world. Take up your map of the Western States. There, where the great Oregon lava flow laps over the State line of Nevada, in the northwestern corner, lies the Black Rock country. Out there in that sweep of gray sand and sage-levels, and grim heights—the scaling of which—taxes the soul sorely, I found him—the typical prospector, "Old Man Berry," or "Uncle Berry," they called him. Over eighty years old he was, and for more than fifty years of his life led by the lure of a mirage.

All day I had been traveling over alkali flats and greasewood-covered mesas, to reach—in late afternoon —the upper tablelands. They were dotted with mountain mahogany, and slashed with cañons where streams ran bordered with cottonwood and aspen.

It was already dusk when we began our descent of one of the larger cañons, and quite dark when we stopped at the ranch-house doorway, through which the lamplight streamed—the friendliest sight a Desert wayfarer ever "meets up with."

We had come upon one of those small ranches that are tucked away in the heights, where old prospectors are as sure to drift to, when not out in the

mountains with poll-pick and hammer, as though they
—like the ranchman's collie or the cat curled up on
the bunk—were among the assets of the place.

He was tall and spare—gaunt, you would have called
him; and you would have noticed at once how bowed he
was. But not as other old men on whom age has rested
a heavy hand. It was the head, not the back, that was
bowed—as though he had walked long years, and
far, with his eyes upon the ground. When he lifted
them quickly—looking directly into your own—you
found they were bright and piercing, with a keenness
that belonged to a man forty years his junior; and you
felt that his sight reached away beyond—to things not
of your reckoning.

We speak of beards that are "snow-white," and
and usually it is a misapplied term. His was really
white as snow—white as freshly fallen snow is white,
with thick and long hair to match. A patriarch of the
mountains, he; you would have declared.

Except as you noted his trembling hands, and saw
how heavily he leaned his weight against the staff he
carried as he walked, you did not feel he was old—
rather it was as though, of his own choice, he wrapped
himself in a dignity of years—wearing it as a monarch
wears his robes of state, in no wise to be counted as
the mark of flying Time.

Indeed, there was something royal about the old
man; and you might join the others (the ranch hands,
and the teamsters, and the cowboy crew) in good-
humored scoffing at the old man himself, as well as his
hobbies, when his back was turned. Yet, not you, nor
any man among them dared to jest ever so lightly to
his face. He commanded your respect. And you, too,
would have shown him the same deference as they did,
whenever he spoke. Somehow, one feels more or less

a coward to try to disabuse a man of his faith in a thing that he has believed in with all his soul for a lifetime. So it is the kinder way, even as it is the easier way, to listen as they tell of such things as you, perhaps, may doubt.

That night, after the supper dishes had been cleared away, and the others had gone out to sit in the darkness, and smoke, and talk over the day's work and the plans for the morrow, while the crickets sang their night-song to the stars, Old Man Berry and I sat by the bare pine table, by the wind-blown flame of a flaring kerosene lamp, while he told me of his quest for a mine he had been seeking for more than half a hundred years.

Back in the days of the young century when he had crossed the plains, while camping at the point of Black Rock, he had found a bit of "float." Small, it was, but so rich in gold that it scarcely seemed real. It was lying at the edge of the well-traveled road where it almost touches the foothills. He looked about everywhere for others of the same sort. That one wonderful nugget was all that he found.

The old man unfastened his shirt-front, and drew from his breast a buckskin bag—a crudely constructed affair that bespoke his own handiwork. It hung suspended from his neck by a buckskin string. Old Man Berry handled it as though it were something holy, turning it over and over, as though weighing it. Finally he untied the string, and turned the bag upside down. The nugget struck heavily on the boards of the table. It was a wonder! Enough, and more than enough to drive any man mad with the gold fever.

"Nuggets like these don't just happen anywhere— as if they were made in the sky, and let fall," he said. "They come from a ledge—carried down to the flats by the forces of Nature. They are like strangers down there—their home is in the mountains. This came from the mountains—the mountain back of Black Rock. There is a ledge there somewhere. Where—in what cañon or on what ridge? Maybe it is a long, long way from there; for 'float' travels a long way sometimes. Where is it—where? Where will I find it, and when? But I will find it! I'll find it, so help me God! Why, I have almost found it now—almost, but not quite. For I've found a place that tallies with the Frenchman's story, and what the Padre told. I may find it next week; and it will be **MINE**! There are tons and tons of gold like this, where this came from.''

He was talking fast and feverishly, and I saw he was no longer talking to me, but rather thinking aloud. He had forgotten me—his surroundings—everything, except the one thing he never forgot, sleeping or waking.

For a long time he sat there, turning his fetish over and over in his knotty and weathered hands. I hardly breathed as I watched him—never moving, my eyes on the nugget, too. Somehow I had caught sight of the face of the Siren, and was one with him, for the time.

Suddenly he seemed to remember me, and he hastily put the nugget back in the little bag, and slipped it again into his breast. I could hear the men lazily talking where they leaned back against the walls of the sod house; and an owl hooted over at the barn. The chirping of the crickets sounded shriller than ever from their cover in the tall weeds and nettles down by the creek. I heard it all as in a dream. There was something unreal in all the sounds. Nothing seemed real and believable, except the sight of the nugget of virgin gold, and the tale of Old Man Berry.

By and by, I heard him talking again—telling me

how, at that time, he had ventured to stay in the country for a few days, to prospect in the hope of finding the ledge. Not for long, however; for he dare not risk the savages, or draw too heavily on his food supply which was barely enough to see him through to California. The delay brought him no reward. He found no ledge; neither did he find any sign of mineral in all the district. He was forced to abandon, for the time being at least, his quest, and to push on to the sea. Once there, however, he was impatient to get back; and again he returned to the sagebrush country. Once more his quest brought him nothing, and he was forced to return to the coast. So he went back and forth between the sea and the sagebrush; and finally he came to stay. Now he had been here for so long, that he could not count the years. And, anyway, what did it matter? Few, or many, it was all the same to him.

"There are others—reliable people, I'd have you know—who know that there is gold here," he said. Then he went on to tell me the Padre's story:

Away back in the years that were gone, a California miner, while journeying through Mexico, took the opportunity offered him by a Mexican friend, to examine some of the old Spanish archives preserved there. The friend had noted in what he had read, that gold had been discovered in a locality that—as he rightly thought—would be crossed by the old emigrant road. Knowing this friend from the North was well acquainted with the country, he called his attention to it.

There—recorded by a Padre long dead—was an elaborate account of a wonderful find of gold, made by the Padre himself when he was a Desert-voyager through a country hundreds of miles to the North, in what was then Spanish possessions. The record gave latitude and longitude of the place, and noted many important

The Quest of Old Man Berry

landmarks, to guide the ones whom the Padre was to lead there when he could organize an expedition. But the Padre had fallen ill—was sick unto death, and had died. Yet not before he had made a map of the country, and which was on record with the description of his journey's discovery.

With these to assist him in his search, the miner started on his northward way into the country of the great plains. The Padre's description of certain boiling springs which this miner found, and camped at for a number of days, tallies precisely with that given by Fremont in his journal. The latter says:

"The basin of the largest one has a circumference of several hundred feet; but there is at one extremity a circular space of about fifteen feet in diameter entirely occupied by boiling water. It boils up at irregular intervals, and with much noise. The water is clear, and the spring is deep. A pole about sixteen feet long was easily immersed in the centre; but we had no means of forming a good idea of its depth. It was surrounded on the margin with a border of green grass," (the date of this entry was January) "and near the shore the temperature of the water was 206 degrees. We had no means of ascertaining that of the centre, where the heat was greatest; but, by dispersing the water with a pole, the temperature of the margin was increased to 208 degrees, and in the centre it was doubtless higher. By driving the pole towards the bottom, the water was made to boil up with increased force and noise. There are several other interesting places, where water and smoke and gas escape, but they would require a long description. The water is impregnated with common salt, but not so much as to render it unfit for general cooking; and a mixture of snow made it pleasant to drink."

Now the miner found the boiling springs that the Padre found, and that Fremont tells of. The latitude and longitude, as given by Fremont in his journal, is precisely that given by the Padre. Then the record of the Padre's travels tells how he went still farther north, and to what is now the Oregon State line, or very nearly so far. The miner and the companion on the trip followed as their compass led, while they neared the place where the holy father had seen the fabulous gold ledge, along the Honey Lake Valley road, as far as Buffalo Springs in Northern Nevada. There, their course took them away from the traveled road, and they struck out across an unknown country, going N.—N-E. To Pueblo Mountain it led them—not so far north as the road that goes through High Rock cañon, though up to the mountain's very edge.

But of ledge they found no sign. Yet when leaving there, the morning they were packing up their camp outfit, they found two small nuggets, which proved that there was gold there; and these nuggets were similar in appearance to the large one Old Man Berry had found.

How did they come there? "Uncle Berry" declared that they had been carried away from Black Rock mountain by some prospector, who had lost them from his pack while journeying farther north. Though why he should say that, I don't know; for he believes that there is a continuous ledge, over a hundred miles long, reaching from some point near Double Hot Springs, away to Pueblo Mountain—the Giant Ledge of the World!

So, though the nugget he had found and those found by the miner lay that distance apart, yet Old Man Berry declares they could only come from one and the same ledge.

Then he reminded me that Pueblo Mountain was

but a short distance from the place where Stoddard had found nuggets in the "Three Little Lakes of Gold," nor was it far from where the emigrants found the gold that came from the "Blue Bucket Mines"; so that it is easy to account for all the scattered bits of gold found through the length and breadth of that barren land. A mammoth ledge is there—miles upon miles wide, and hundreds of miles long—but only in one or two places does it show itself in croppings; and only by the few nuggets that men have found, has it ever made itself known.

Then the old man commenced telling of another proof (he calls it) of his theory. Years ago, a Frenchman who was traveling eastward through Surprise Valley, found a cave that was studded with gold. It lies about forty miles distant from the California State line. The Frenchman had gone in to seek shelter from a storm. The day was cold, and it was snowing bitterly, so that he built a fire of the roots and stumps of sagebrush that he brought in from outside. As the fire blazed up, and the light flooded the cavern, he saw scattered over the floor great nuggets of gold that shone in the fire-glow. The floor sloped away up to the rear, where the cave narrowed to a mere slit in the rock, and so barred a man from going farther. Taking up a firebrand, he thrust his arm in there as far as he could stretch it; it lit up the farther recesses, and he beheld there—far beyond his reach—innumerable nuggets of the shining yellow metal. It seemed unbelievable!

From the floor of that portion where he stood, he gathered all there were; and these he tied up in a cotton flour-sack, and fastened behind his saddle when he went away. The jogging motion of the horse, wore a hole in the sack, and many of these (in fact, most of them) he lost upon the way. When he missed them he retraced his steps as nearly as he could, but the drifting snow had covered up his horse's footprints, and he found none of those he had dropped. Some, however, remained in a corner of the sack that was tied with the buckskin strings of his saddle. These, he took with him to his home in Sacramento, where he lived with a couple named Butler. He was exhausted from the long trip, and ill from exposure. He became desperately ill. Until he died, he was nursed by Butler and his wife, to whom he gave the nuggets. And to them he gave a detailed description of the locality in which he found the wonder-cave of the Desert. He described the formation of the cave as being of water-worn pebbles and fine crumbled rock, embedded in a formation similar to concrete. All through that district he had found great cliffs and many caves—caves of all sorts. Just about there, he found a number that were in form like unto this one—as of water-worn rock that was burrowed full of holes. But in none of them, except this particular one, did he find gold. Here, they were either lying loose on the floor of the cave, or embedded in the soft rock, from which he dug many of them with his penknife—aiding the work by breaking away the rock with a loose stone.

He gave the Butlers a rough chart he made of the country. To the south, it showed the boiling springs that Fremont and the Padre found; and the dotted line he drew took one on the way to Pueblo Mountain. The Butlers went there, after their friend had died; and they spent many a month in a useless quest. But it did not lessen their belief that the cave of the wonder-gold is there—somewhere. They have the nuggets still, and will show them to you as proof.

A dozen other instances did Old Man Berry tell me,

The Quest of Old Man Berry

as we sat there in the little sod house, and the men gossiped and smoked outside. But by and by they came in, and then the old man would say no more. Perhaps he knew they were skeptics, and so would not invite derision.

The next morning, after I had gone down to the cabin from where I had slept the sleep of those who are elect to find rest under the arching, star-studded sky, I found myself the last one at the breakfast table. So that, when I had finished, and had gone outside again, I found the others gathered about the corral where they were assisting "Uncle Berry" get his horses hitched to what passed for a wagon. Such a marvel of inadequacy I never have seen, as the "team" he was to use in getting off into the Desert where the lure of the gold—a veritable mirage—was calling him!

Originally intended for a small delivery wagon, it had long borne no likeness to any sort of a vehicle whatever. There was no dashboard. There was no seat. The double-trees were home-made; and the tongue was a cottonwood pole. Missing spokes in the wheels were replaced by the limbs of the quaking asp; and the reach itself was pieced with a pole used as a splice. The tires were wired on with baling wire— wound round and round with the wire, till the tire itself was scarcely to be seen. Wire all over the wagon; wire to mend the harness. The reins were of bits of old straps fastened together; and wouldn't have held a runaway pair of kittens. He had a dry willow switch for a whip. One of the horses was too old to have been properly apportioned to anything in this world, except to the filling of a grave in a horse-graveyard. The other was a half-broken colt.

Again, he was starting off for Black Rock. Alone, of course; for he would have none with him on a trip

like this, lest they see where he went, and so—perhaps
—some time wrest the Mine of the World from him.
No; there were none he would trust. Did not a nephew
come out of the East to pave the way to becoming his
heir, against the hour the old man should discover the
ledge and——then die. And did not this same nephew,
who began by calling him "Dear Uncle Berry," end
by cursing him for an "old fool," and then go away
leaving the old man laid up with a crushed ankle—
Did he not, all the while, and secretly, try to find the
ledge for himself? No; he would have none of them.
He was sufficient unto himself. He needed no one.

The colt was acting badly, and two of the cowboys
were getting him into the harness—lightly dodging
his heels which he lashed out viciously at them, or
springing quickly aside as he reared and came down
"spiking" at them with his fore-legs.

After a good deal of manoeuvering, they got him
blindfolded, and finally into the harness. One of the
men held the colt by the head, while old "Uncle
Berry" climbed up and seated himself on his roll of
blankets, which—in lieu of any other—served as a seat.

There was a look of determination on his face that
did me good to see. It was the grim look that a face
takes on when its owner has the knowledge that he has
met a worthy foe, yet he has willed to fight to the end.
It stirred my blood with admiration to see him.

There he was—more than eighty-four years of age,
and yet able to climb cliffs, and peck away at the rock
that lies at the tops of the mountains. Why! they told
me, he would ride this unbroken colt—and did, often—
if the men would help him to mount.

Such goods as he got for his small needs, must come
from towns a hundred miles distant; and to them
(through the winter's snow-drifts, or under the Desert's

dizzying sun)—alone—in that old rattletrap of a wagon, would he go. Truly, the old man was the personification of "Western pluck."

He was thinly clad, and through the threadbare cotton shirt he wore, one could see the framework of the great, gaunt body. Somehow, the other men standing about (cowboys, and ranch hands, and teamsters), seemed puny beside him,—feeble though he was, and an octogenarian.

He nodded "good by" to us. Then—"Ready!" and a pause. "Let them go!" he said; and the man at the young horse's head, pulled off the blind and jumped back. The colt reared on his haunches—pawed the air with his hoofs, and leaped forward—almost jerking the old buckskin horse off his feet, as he went. Old Man Berry sat there—his feet braced far apart; his gray hair blowing back in the rush of wind that came up the cañon; his knotted hands gripping the reins; and that grim look on his face that made you feel that he, after all, was master of whatever he undertook.

So, down the steep cañon, through a cloud of alkali dust he went. And every instant I expected to see the old wagon go to pieces.

"God! but he's got pluck!" said one of the cowboys, turning away as "Uncle Berry" went out of sight round a bend. "They ain't nary thing that old feller won't tackle, just give him the chanst. He's clean grit, through and through!"

He was grit.

Two days later, when we came down to the ranch after a day of deer-hunting on the heights, there—at the haystack, contentedly feeding—stood Old Man Berry's horses. They were necked together just as he had left them when he had turned them out at night, to graze on the scant growth of artemisia down on the

Desert, and they—led by the instinct that guides home-lovers—had come straightaway to their mountain home. The horses were well and safe, but——Where was Old Man Berry?

There was not one of us who did not feel (though no one dared voice that fear) that down on the alkali flats somewhere—far from water—they would find Something that would be a horror to see.

The ranchman ordered work in the corrals stopped, and hurried the men on swift errands he directed. To the creek, to fill canteens and demijohns with water; to the house for blankets; to the barn for horses to be put to the wagon, and others to be saddled. Every man was to aid in the work of rescue. Scarcely one of them spoke, but all wore sobered faces. Not one among them but that loved the old man; "loco" though they declared him to be.

I watched them go down the cañon, as I had watched him go such a short time before. Then I went back to the sod-house, and wondered where they would find him, and how. Ah! that is the thought—when we know some one is astray in the Desert—that grips one's throat, making it hard for them to swallow. It is as though one's mouth was parched, and without moisture; and as though one had been long without water to drink. Strange, is it not? that our fears for another should in that way hold the prophecy of what is to come to them.

After an hour or two of restless wandering about the place, I, too, went down the road that led to the Desert. I wanted to sight, if I could, the coming of the men. Then—less than a hundred yards down the cañon—I came upon them. They were bringing Old Man Berry.

Alive. And quite determined to go back, just as

soon as he could arrange with some one for another wagon. Pluck to the last!

When he found his horses had gone, he started back on foot after them, thinking to find them but a short distance away. Following their tracks, for twenty-five miles he went up and down gullies—weary and faint for want of food; over sun-baked alkali flats where the warped mud-crust had dried in up-curled flakes like feathers blown forward on the back of some wind-buffeted fowl—(it showed where water had been); along foothills where he stumbled and fell, while the sharp stones cut into and bruised his flesh; through the burning sand where the sun seethed and bubbled in his brain, and he wondered if he was going mad.

It was the old story of the earth in those places where it is far between water-holes. He fought with Death in the Desert. Fought, and won!

The cowboys, after the fashion of their kind, cursed him roundly (but with a ring of tender feeling for the old man in every word they said), and they called him many kinds of an old fool for getting lost. All of which he took in the spirit in which it was meant. Yet more than one of them had wet eyes as he tried to talk to them with thickened tongue that was still black between his lips; and we saw that his palms—which he tried to hide from us—were all bruised and blood-stained from sharp stones where he had fallen.

He was pluck itself—yes, sheer grit; for he fought his way through to victory over age, and infirmities, and Death. Yet, the end is not yet. Some day—there on the sun-bleached levels—they will find him—Old Man Berry—when the Desert has taken its toll.

THE LOVERS OF THE DESERT.

FOR all the toll the Desert takes of a man it gives its compensation in deep breaths, deep sleep, and the communion of stars. It comes upon one with new force in the pauses of the night that the Chaldeans were a Desert-bred people. It is hard to escape the sense of mastery as the stars move in the wide, clear heavens to risings and settings unobscured. They look large, and near, and palpitant; as if they moved on some stately service not needful to declare. Wheeling to their stations in the sky, they make the poor world-fret of no account. Of no account you who lie out there watching, nor the lean coyote that stands off in the scrub from you and howls and howls.''

And she who wrote the words knows. She speaks from the heart that understands, because it voices the language of love for the vast, gray, silent mystery that means so little to those who flit by in a day and night of car travel, and then talk about ''how lovely'' the Desert is, and how ''it appeals'' to them. And to those I would say that the real Desert, and all its grave meaning, is farther away from them than it is from those who say nothing except that they do not know the Desert, and do not care anything about it. The Desert does not need such lovers. Its voice will never speak to those who call it either "artistic" or "restful." Yet there are many such—good folk, too; but they are those who use, for the decorations of their "cosy corners," Indian baskets and Indian blankets that they buy at the stores—and most of them made by white men or women. The Indian—his work and wares—have been the fashion for a little day among those who set the styles for the ornamentation or disfigurement of our homes; but I fear me his devotees (those who are devoted to him in this special way) are feeling that he is getting to be just a little bit—just a trifle passee. And they are already beginning to look about for another to take his place. There is just the shadow of a sign that they will choose the Desert. Suppose it should be? We who reverence and love the gray land, can only hope, with a hope that is half a prayer, that they will pass it by. Yet——If this thing should happen! What could we do—the Desert and I—to prevent it? The Desert and its lovers are helpless against vandals.

If you love the Desert, and live in it, and lie awake at night under its low-hanging stars, you know you are a part of the pulse-beat of the universe, and you feel the swing of the spheres through space, and you hear through the silence the voice of God speaking.

Then you will come to know that no better thing is in the world for man than just this—the close-touching of great things; the un-desire of the small, such as the man-crowded places give you; and just enough food and clothing and shelter to support life, and enough work to fill one's days.

Now, all this belongs to the old men of the Desert—the prospectors who have made the Desert their own.

So you do not know, neither do I dare say, how much of the joy of life these old prospectors find in following the mirage of a mine that leads them away to life's end with empty palms, till at last they lie down in the alkali wastes to be one with the great silence of the plains. If it gives them much of joy to deny themselves all that you would deem vital, as they live out the measure of their days, dare you give them of your unasked pity? Perhaps they know more of the joy of life than you, in all the devious ways your quest for happiness has led you, have ever found.

Sometime, your destiny may lead you there; and lying in your blankets some night under a purple-black sky that is crowded with palpitating stars, while the warm Desert-wind blows softly over you—caressing your face and smoothing your hair as no human hands ever could—and bringing with it the hushed night-sounds that only the Desert knows; then—all alone there with only God and the Desert—you will come at last to understand the old prospector and his ways. But not now; not till you and the Desert are lovers.

The Lovers of the Desert

FORMAN'S FIND.

OPEN Fremont's journal; turn to the entry he made on New Year's day, 1844, and here is what you will read:

"We continued down the valley between a dry-looking, black ridge on the left, and a more snowy and high one on the right. Our road was bad along the bottom by being broken by gullies and impeded by sage, and sandy on the hills, where there is not a blade of grass; nor does any appear on the mountains. The soil in many places consists of a fine, powdery sand covered with saline afflorescence, and the general character of the country is desert. During the day we directed our course toward a black cape at the foot of which a column of smoke indicated hot springs."

And so it was, that the great Pathfinder—journeying west through the unknown, eerie land, vast and sand-strewn—on that first day of a year now more than half a century dead, came to know that certain part of Nevada where rises a great, gaunt promontory, its bold front to the Desert, grand in its gruesome barrenness, that afterward came to be such a well-known landmark. Seemingly devoid of every vestige of animal or plant life, it stands there defiant of any softening touch of nature. Down where steam clouds from the hot springs show white like sea spume, the mountain's base is lapped by little hills that make creamy ripples against the other's black ruggedness.

On the following day after the entry just quoted, Fremont's journal bore these words: "At noon . . . . we reached the hot springs of which we had seen the vapor the day before. There was a large field of the salt grass here, usual to such places. The country otherwise is a perfect barren, without a blade of grass. . . . . . We passed around the rocky cape, a jagged broken point, bare and torn. The rocks are volcanic, and the hills here have a burned appearance—cinders and coal occasionally appearing as in a blacksmith's forge. We crossed the large dry bed of a muddy lake in a south-easterly direction and encamped for the night, without water and without grass, among sage bushes covered with snow. The heavy road made several mules give out today; and a horse —which had made the journey from the States successfully—was left on the trail."

On the sixth day of January Fremont tells of ascending a mountain "in the south-west corner of a basin communicating with that in which we encamped, and saw a lofty column of smoke ten miles distant, indicating the presence of hot springs."

In describing them, further on he says: "This is the most extraordinary locality of hot springs we have met during the journey."

After the Pathfinder, came others; and the way grew worn with many hoofs and wheels that moved westward. As the road became traveled, the places gained names; the "black cape" became Black Rock, and the twin hot springs at its point were known as Double Hot Springs, while the great cauldron of hot water across the valley bore the name of Granite Creek Hot Springs. Fremont gives the location of these latter as being in latitude forty degrees, thirty-nine minutes, forty-six seconds. His second day's camp from Black Rock was made in latitude forty degrees, forty-eight minutes, fifteen seconds. But one must remember that on January second and third his journeys were, each of them, short, as one day they traveled but eight miles, and on the other did not start out till afternoon—he having waited for the fog to lift.

These are the things we know. So much for Truth. Now to the Legend—if Legend it be.

If you go out these days into the Black Rock country, you will find dozens of camp-fire story-tellers who will relate it to you just as they did to me; and no one will vary in the telling—not in the slightest detail— from the way scores of others tell it.

One night, of the year eighteen hundred and fifty-two, an emigrant party crossing the plains camped at the foot of the mountain due west of, and in the next range from the one since known as Hardin Mountain. Being out of fresh meat, two or three of the men were chosen, as was the custom among emigrant parties, to go out afoot and hunt along the higher parts of the mountain for game. One of these men was named John Forman.

The following morning, Forman and two of his companions started out early after antelope, deer, mountain sheep, or such smaller game as they could find— going up the mountain at whose base they had made their camp, which was just across the valley from the point of Black Rock. Game being scarce on that side of the ridge, they ascended to the mountain top, intending to cross over to the farther side. On reaching the summit, where they could look down on the plain beyond, they saw what they thought to be smoke from Indian-made fires. Such were generally the signal fires of the hostiles, so the white men kept well away from points where their movements would attract attention. But they did not cease their search for game, while bearing up from the foothills, and working their way along on the side of the mountain.

Forman had dropped behind the others, and was considerably higher on the slope, when he stepped on some metallic substance that at once attracted his attention. It was entirely unlike anything else he had seen in that volcanic district—especially so in the top of this mountain of ashes and cinders, gray pumice and black lava. It protruded from the ground in a slab five or six feet in length, and was twelve or fourteen inches wide, at the lower end it stood at least sixteen inches out of the ground. Its surface was as though at some remote time it had passed through some extraordinary heat—as if it had been melted in the fires of a great furnace.

Forman hallooed to the others, who came back and examined it with him. It was not at all like any metallic stuff such as any of the three had ever seen. No one could guess what it might be; though Forman himself was half inclined to declare it melted silver. With their hunting knives they cut off bits of the metal which they carried away with them in their pockets as they continued their quest for game; for, though it might mean a fortune for each of them, meat was of more immediate importance to them all than a mountain range of solid silver, or even gold. So the hunters went on, climbing the mountain and clambering over the rocks; then, as the afternoon wore away, getting a better sight across the valley, they discovered that what they supposed to be Indian signal fires, was but the rising vapor from distant hot springs; springs that Forman—long afterward—came to know as Granite Creek Hot

Springs. They found no game on the barren heights, so went down to the valley again, and joined the rest of their party that night at Mud Meadows where camp had been made.

Some days after, during idle hours in camp, finding that the metal would melt when subjected to extreme heat, Forman took the bits he had cut from the great metal slabs found on the mountain, and molded them into bullets. What the metal was, he had not yet determined; but other members of the party had fully convinced him that—whatever it might be—it certainly was not silver.

Going down Pit river, in an encounter with hostile Indians, Forman found use for the bullets. He shot them all away.

In the varied excitement and interests incident to life in a strange and newly-settled country, he soon —in California—completely forgot the matter, until it was recalled to him later when he was shown some specimens of pure lead. Satisfying himself that it was identical with the mineral he had discovered five or six years before, he saw the gleam of fortune brightening those far off plains for him. His decision was formed at once. He would forsake the gold-seeking that had, thus far, but ill repaid him; he would return to the mountains where he had every reason to believe were tons of lead to be had with but little expenditure of labor or money.

He confided in no one. If it should prove, when he investigated it, to be after all some worthless metal (which he did not for one moment believe), there would be none but himself the loser, or to laugh at the misplaced faith. On the other hand, if a fortune was there awaiting the finder, then it would be all his own.

During the months that intervened before he could

arrange his trip, he became acquainted with a Missourian, who told him of a supposed lead mine away back on the desert, that was seen by one of Fremont's party in 1844. The discoverer had never thought it worth his while to return to it (he was too little impressed with it to know its real value); but he told the Missourian the latitude of the place they had encamped the night before ascending the mountain where he saw a huge, protruding slab of the metal. He also drew a rough map of the surrounding country. It was in latitude forty degrees, forty-eight minutes, fifteen seconds, he said; and across the valley rose a column of steam from immense hot springs, that looked—as one gazed down on it from the crest of the mountain, like the signal fire of hostile Indians. Forman listened with keen interest, thinking of his own discovery, and which he believed to be the same. The Missourian added that he intended going there in the following spring.

Forman kept his knowledge of the great lead mine to himself; but after hearing the Missourian's tale, his anxiety to go back to the Desert increased. He hastened his preparations, and early in 1859 he was back at the spot where he and his companions had encamped seven years before. He was back at the foot of the mountain that lies westerly from Hardin mountain, and in the very next range. Everything seemed familiar —he recognized every well remembered landmark. He was sure of success.

By the roadside, when arranging his own camp for the night, he noted that some one had camped there but a short time before—perhaps the previous day— as ashes and footprints showed. Early morning found him clambering over the mountain, stumbling over lava rock, or floundering through cinder and ash, as

(marginal note) **Forman's Find**

he directed his course to the farther side. At last he gained the summit, all out of breath and eager, and looked down again upon the "Indian signal fire" rising across the plain. But he saw something more—something he was unprepared for. He was not alone.

Just below him, where he knew the treasure lay, was the Missourian, going back and forth, up and down, over the ground as though seeking that which he was not able to find. Presently he looked up and saw Forman. Forman went down to him, and the result was the inevitable.

Each man accused the other of trespass, and hinted at treachery. Each of the men—friends before—eyed the other with suspicion. Then, covertly, they began looking for the slab of metal, each feeling himself handicapped in the search by the presence of the other, with whom he determined there should be no division of the treasure. So Forman and the Missourian alike carried on the search surreptitiously—or tried to—but, with another striving for the same possession, the quest was a failure. At last they departed from the place together; neither daring to trust the other there after he should himself be gone.

The next year the search was renewed by both men, but at different times; and renewed again and again in the aftertime. But after that first meeting on the mountain, they never chanced to encounter one another there; which was perhaps fortunate, for their animosity toward each other grew with the years.

Neither of them ever found the slab of pure lead that stood for a mine—or which to them represented a mountain that might well be, for all they knew, of solid lead, and might form the bulk of the mountain. Prospecting year after year, neither of them ever came upon any sign that spoke of lead in any form or any quantity. It seemed strange that neither of them, after so many years of searching should fail in their quest; for both claimed such accurate knowledge of the exact locality. Yet—if you will but think of it in so favorable light—the reason is not hard to find. Only you must not be of a sceptical turn of mind. It is this: The Missourian was forever declaring that Forman had covered it up to keep him from finding it.

And Forman always said the same of the Missourian.

Forman's Find

THE LESSONS OF THE DESERT.

The
Lessons
of
the
Desert

JUST a little flour, a piece of bacon, a handful of coffee, one's blankets, enough clothing for comfort—that is all. When one stops to think of it, it is astonishing to find how little one really needs, to live. It is only after you have been on a rough trip of weeks, when it was needful that you should debate well and long over not every pound, but literally every ounce of extra weight that you were to carry—casting aside all things but those that were vital to your absolute needs—that you came to realize how much useless stuff one goes through life a-burdened with.

I have a friend—an Indian—who tells me he would be more apt to think the White Man a great man, were he not forced to see he is a fool—for doing fool things. "Heap big fool," he says. He says that the White Man voluntarily strives for the acquisition of such things as bring but added care into one's measure of days; which is fool's work. Then he says; that to breathe full and strong, and to have a straight back, and carry the head high, one must not bear a load. And that to have long years of peace, and to live gladly, one must not do the things that "make worry."

So he asks me why the White Man (who thinks himself wise because of his different color) should—of his own free will—make of himself a burden-bearer; and so be less wise (in the eyes of the Brown Man) than his Indian brother, whom he—in his heart—calls a fool? But I have been unable to make answer to that; because I, too, have also asked myself: "Why, indeed!"

Now, the least of us know that the possession of one thing calls for the immediate acquirement of some other thing to supplement it. And then, to that one, must be added another to answer the new demands the latter creates. And the third calls even more insistently for a fourth; and so on—forever and forever—the last one calling for still another, if we are of those fools who listen to the cry of their folly for more, and yet more.

And, if we only found satisfaction in the pampering and pleasing of the tastes and desires we encourage! But we don't. So that the Indian has license to laugh at our ways, when we ourselves can give no rational excuse for what we are doing, and keep doing. We burden ourselves with things that we buy, with no other excuse for the act than——"They are the things other folk have!" So we go on getting and getting, whether we want them or no. Very like sheep that follow the sheep with the bell, are we.

And I wonder if he who follows the bell-wether is any wiser than that one who trails after the story of a will-o'-wisp mine that leads him across Desert valleys and rough mountain ridges where there is never a sign of gold? Which is the fool; and which is the wise man? And who has the right to judge?

You may jeer and deride as you will, but the old prospectors do not care. They go their ways, letting you alone; and they ask, in return, that you let them

alone also. They will give you help if you need it;
but they will ask nothing from you.

Their needs are so few that they want but little to
live; and that they can earn. They have little; but they
can earn a little by work. So it happens that those
who know them may give—now and then—of their
own stores, asking no toll for what they may do. Yet
the kindness does not go unpaid. For, you must remember that these live in the Desert; and the Desert teaches
one how to forget self. The help that an extra pair
of hands can give to those who live in the far places
where men do not congregate, is much; and for what
is done for a comrade there, one gets payment in labor
that is done with a willing hand—not because payment
is exacted or expected, but because there is that in the
blood of those who live there, that teaches them to be
grateful.

It is only in those places where human life is hived
in houses that touch elbows, so close are they huddled
together, that one holds out one's hand for the final
dimes and nickels in the payment of debts; or for the
ultimate and absolute settlement of each and every ob-
ligation incurred. True, when you have become one
with them that live there, you, too, fall into their ways;
yet it is a good thing to remember that there are places
—lonely and far though they be—where one may find
those who have souls that are not shrivelled and dry;
wrinkled and weather-worn men who are great of heart,
and who would give half of their little all to you in
your need, and with never a thought that payment was
due.

So, in this way, and because of the fellowship there,
the mirage-miners manage to live—to buy the few
things that even a simple life makes needful.

A little flour, a piece of bacon, a handful of coffee,

your blankets, and such clothing as the season calls you to wear.

Then to live in the big, still plains that inspire a big, serene life, learning the best the Desert can teach you —these things, namely:

That we are what we think and feel, not what others think and feel us to be; and that in such wise does God surely judge us. That mankind is a brotherhood, each needing the other, and that not one can be spared from the unit; brothers are we, born of a common parentage, and you shall know there is small difference between man and man, except in so far as they are good or bad —not as the veneer of environment makes them. That we shall be more censorious of our own faults—less critical of the failings or follies of others.

To feel that the best life is the simple life; and, if one can, to live it out in such a companionship somewhere that you may have the great stretches of earth as God gives; to read—as from printed pages—in the grains of the far-reaching sand; to listen to a speech that is voiced by the stars and the four winds.

All these belong to the men who live there; so that it is hardly worth while to try to make the old prospectors give up their quests and go back to the places where people live. Even if the fairy stories of the fabulous mines were true, and they should, some day, find each his own treasure, I doubt if the end of the search would bring joy. To have money in the Desert, makes little change in one's ways of living. And to go back to cities——! They are alien to all the cities could give. So, the joy of life, for them, lies in the search for—not in the finding of gold.

THE MARVELOUS HARDIN SILVER.

SINCE that far time when Fremont found himself under the lee of Black Rock, one gloomy New Year's day, the sullen and bare promontory has been guide and landmark to thousands of voyagers crossing the great American Sahara. Westward more than half a hundred miles from the Central Pacific Railroad's traveled ways that go through Humboldt County, Nevada, lies Quin River Desert—forbidding and grim—and Black Rock rises abruptly from its levels. It is a dark and unfriendly looking point, with all the gruesomeness Fremont describes; but through all the years the emigrant wound his way toward the State that sees the setting sun sink downward to touch salt water, it has been his unfailing friend. For once seen, there is no mistaking Black Rock for any other landmark ever described, and to the wayfarer across the vast, lonely land, it was compass and star. The range of mountains from which it juts is of gnarled and misshapen masses of lava rock mixed with miles of ashes. About, are vast stretches of alkali plain, of whitened hummocks of hardened earth, of wide reaches of sand flats swept into waves by the wind.

It is all fierce, hard and repellant. Farther away the mountains bear rocks that burst into color, and their broken and rainbow-hued bits besprinkle the "washes" in the foothills. Their graveled floors are thick strewn with variegated flakes of beauty—dark blue and light blue, purple and pink; a green that is like to emeralds, and ruby and amber in all their beauty of clarity and coloring. And where these jasper fragments are not, are burned and black volcanic boulders; and then you will come across places thickly strewn with fragments of vivid red rock—rock that is red as if blood-stained; and you say to yourself: "Why this is the waste and refuse from nature's great brick-yards!" so like unto that artificial building material does it seem.

All through this weird and wonderful valley, where white plumes of steaming springs wave here and there along the foothills, are things to hold your curious attention—acres of obsidian, others of petrified wood; turquoise, geodes, onyx, and a thousand other things beneath your horse's crunching hoofs, to make the riding of this range well worth your while.

Away back in 1849 a long train of emigrant wagons, fourteen in number, was crossing the plains on its journey to the West. Following the Humboldt river down the valley of the same name, at the Lassen Meadows they found so little feed for their stock, where the stock of the emigrant usually grazed for a day or so, that the travelers decided upon abandoning that route and, instead, crossing over toward Black Rock, and following the old Lassen road into California. But at Black Rock, also, they found but scant feed when they arrived. So they pushed on six miles farther to make camp, and rest, at those water demons called Double Hot Springs. About that steaming twin vent-hole of the old Earth's anger was always to be found grass green and growing—grass moist with steam-pearls, and of the tender hue of hot-house plants. Go there

The Marvelous Hardin Silver

when you will, you will find such sweetly fresh vegetation—sparkling with the ever-moist breath of the
springs—that you leave it with regret to take up your
journey again through the baked plain with its lep-
rous-like spots of alkali.

At Double Hot Springs they made a temporary camp
to give the stock the opportunity to rest and recover
from the journey thus far passed. Brown men with bow
in hand, and the soft tread of a wildcat, were all about
the emigrant in those days; but at the springs there
was no shelter under which an Indian could creep upon
them, so they made a halt of a number of days there.

Their next move was to Mud Meadows, around on
the farther side of the range.

Now it so happened that on the day they broke
camp there, three of the party were deputized to hunt
along the mountain ridge for game to replenish the
well-nigh depleted larders of the camp-wagons. It
was their custom to have two or three hunters—each
"crew" taking its turn—go out, when the meat supply was low, to kill such game as the country afforded.
These three were directed to hunt along the mountain tops, while the wagons worked their way up the
valley's edge to Mud Meadows where, later, they would
all meet.

One of the three hunters selected for that occasion
was a man named Hardin, a wheelwright and blacksmith by trade. He was an uncle of J. A. Hardin, of
Petaluma, California, a well-known cattle man of that
State and Nevada.

The hunters were to cross a near-lying mountain,
and then go over to the farther side to join the wagons.
In leaving their camp at Double Hot Springs they
crossed, first, a piece of tableland, and then made their
way to the higher parts of the mountain. No game

was seen. Keeping along the east side of the mountain for some distance, they finally worked their way upward to the summit, from whence they had an unobstructed view of the valley.

Then they discovered they had lost their bearings, for no sign of the wagons was to be seen. They were about to descend to the plain to find (where the wagons had passed) the wheel-tracks, and so follow them into camp, when they espied, away down the Desert, a team that had stopped on the road. The three hunters—glad in this lonely land, to find a fellow voyager—at once started down the mountain side, heading directly for the halted wagon below.

They had gone, perhaps, a third of the way when of a sudden they found themselves floundering through a soft, gray deposit like sifted ashes, in which at every step they sunk ankle-deep. And here in the powdery stuff, was embedded something which shone so brightly in the sun that their gaze was arrested, and the faraway team, for the time, forgotten. One of the trio had, years before, been in the Mexican War, and after receiving his discharge had been employed on the pack-trains of the famous Potosi mine for some time before leaving that country. He instantly recognized the great slabs of whitish metal as melted silver—and perfectly pure, so far as he could judge. It looked as though the awful fires that had scattered the lava rock over the land and burned and blackened the face of the country in some places—or blanched it in others in the blaze of flames we wot not of—had run the metal white-hot through the ashes that covered that side of the mountain for several hundred square feet. Everywhere it was sticking up—pieces protruding that were the size of bricks—others in uneven masses of four or five feet long.

One is slow to realize good fortune, and they could but vaguely comprehend the meaning of what they saw. Then gathering up all they could carry, they started down the mountain to the place on the plain where they could still see the wagon stopping by the way. Arriving there they found an emigrant and his wife and child, who had been overtaken by disaster, for their oxen—all but one yoke—were dead, and there were yet many miles to travel ere they could reach California. The man was engaged in trying to re-model his wagon to fit the circumstances of his misfortune. He was cutting down his wagon from a four-wheeler to a cart, that the remaining yoke of weak, half-famished cattle might be able to draw it, loaded with their most important belongings, the rest of the journey, on and into the Land of Gold.

The excited Hardin showed them his find, and told them of the uncountable wealth they had discovered; and then asked the emigrant to take as many of their precious slabs into California as his wagon (after being cut down) would carry. But in vain did he and his companions plead. Not even the promise that he should share equally with the others had any effect on the man who kept busy with hammer and saw. They poured out their glowing wonder-tale, but he remained unmoved.

"Silver!" he exclaimed, at last, straightening himself from his work. "Maybe 'tis, and maybe 'tisn't. But I wouldn't do what you ask, even if it was solid gold! If I can get through to California with my little family alive, and with such things as we must have, it will be all that I can do. I've got to leave the bulk of my belongings here on the road, because I can't carry them in a cut-down wagon. No, Friends, you'll

get no help from me; for all the silver in the world
wouldn't help me in my present predicament.''

Finding all importunities of no avail, they threw the
largest piece—the one Hardin himself had been carrying—down by the roadside. The remainder was then
divided among the three and they started for Mud
Meadows, where they arrived long after dark. There
they showed their marvelous ''find''; and the stir the
shining stuff made, as it was passed from hand to hand,
was excuse for the wild rejoicing of the two hundred
emigrants, which was continued by the camp fire,
more or less, all night. There was cause enough for rejoicing; for Hardin had declared there was enough of
that silver in sight to load all fourteen of the wagons.
So one and all declared that so soon as they could properly equip themselves for a return trip and the transportation of the silver, they would come back into this
Desert-land of treasure that seemed beyond the most
extravagant of dreams.

The following morning they left Mud Meadows, resuming their journey toward the West. Whether by
accident or not, no one can say, but some pieces of the
silver were left where they had camped that night, and
were found later by others making camp there.

The emigrants found no further signs of silver or of
other metals, and finally reached California, where the
story of Hardin's find spread, as the emigrants repeated
the tale. The three men, however, kept the secret of
the exact locality where they had found this marvelous deposit. They were impatient to return at once,
but the growing depredations of hostile Indians, as
well as other affairs, deterred them. As soon as all
arrangements could be made, and traveling in that land
of the murderous arrow was safe, they would go; but

The
Marvel-
ous
Hardin
Silver

it was many a month thereafter before they could put their plans into execution.

Among those who, on that memorable trip into the West, had seen the marvelous silver, was Steve Bass— so well known the West through—and his brother. They had seen it, handled it and had heard Hardin tell the tale over and over again. And Bass himself often told how he had seen Hardin melt some of the bits into silver buttons. Taking an axe handle—it being of hard wood that would not ignite easily—Hardin hollowed a little place in the side of it, and laid therein bits of the silver which he had previously cut from the larger pieces of the metal, with his pocket knife. He then covered these over with live coals, and by blowing steadily on them for some time, the silver was melted into a button—one that he carried in his pocket for years afterward. And subsequently, when telling the tale of the fabulous find to a collector of minerals and curiosities, he showed him this button. Interested in its history, the man bought it of Hardin and took it to England, where, no doubt, it is now in some collection of minerals and curios, on the shelves of an Englishman's cabinet.

Hardin settled in Petaluma and opened a wagon shop, doing blacksmithing and such work. Men congregated there in the early days to "swap" mining stories; and one day when some one began talking to Hardin of his discovery away back on the plains, a new-comer—a man named A. B. Jennison, who had just come in from Rogue River, to settle in the valley—exclaimed:

"Why, I've heard that same story told by another man—one of the three who found it. I knew him well. But he declares that he's found since he got to California that other men know of gold in quantities as great as was the deposit of that silver, and that he is going to look here for gold, instead of going back there to get a less valuable mineral—and perhaps be butchered by the Indians, in the bargain.''

Hostilities were increasing back on the emigrant roads where the brown man watched for the wayfarer from his hiding-place in the rocks, and the Desert country had no great attraction for miners who believed in like fortunes being found farther toward the West, and in more settled districts. But there were those whom the Hardin Silver lured, and of these was a doctor who had come to his knowledge of it through another source.

In 1859 this doctor came into the Honey Lake country, and took up his home in the lower end of the valley. He was a silent, uncommunicative sort of a man, and had no confidants. In those troublous times there were many desperate characters about, in that locality. If a man knew aught of any valuable possession —whether of something material or only a secret knowledge of things—he was very careful in his selection of those in whom he reposed confidence.

The doctor had no doubt of being able, some time, to trace his way back to a place on the plains where he had once seen something, the value of which he had not known till long afterward. The years went by, and he said nothing of it to any man. He was certain of a treasure-house there in the Desert; and the time would come when he would be able to go a-search for it, tucked away somewhere in the mountains. He could wait.

It was in 1852, when crossing the Desert near Mud Meadows, just after Hardin's party had passed through, that the doctor had found lying by the roadside where Hardin had dropped it, the larger piece of silver that the emigrant had refused to carry for him—that lone emigrant whom Hardin had left cutting down his wagon. At the time of finding it, the doctor had failed to recognize its value, and so had left it there. But—many months afterward—he came to know that it had been pure silver that he had held in his hands. Others who camped there later, and were questioned about it, knew nothing of any such thing being there; so that it is not known who took it away from the place where it lay in plain sight. Probably it was picked up by some one who knew as little of its value as did the doctor. Or it might have been some one who did indeed know its value, and to this day is seeking the place from whence it came—as so many other prospectors have done, and are still doing.

The doctor finally laid plans for the return trip to this spot where he so well remembered having seen the melted silver; but the very month set for his start found him sick—sick unto death. When he realized that recovery was impossible, he called two of his friends to him, and there on his death bed told Tommy Harvey and George Lathrop all he knew of it, and of the locality where it could, no doubt, be found. Even to the minutest particulars he described that place in Desertland where he had held in his hand what he believed to be the key to a treasure-house of uncounted wealth.

"If I could only have lived long enough to go there, myself," he said. "If it had only been safe for a man to go there at any time since I saw that country, I know I should have found the ledge itself—I know from what I have heard Hardin and others tell, that I could have gone directly to it."

So the doctor died—one of the many who believed in the mirage-mine—if it be but a mirage-mine, yet who knows?—and the two who went found nothing. The mountains were so many, and so bewildering.

Nor was the doctor the only one who, in crossing the plains, found evidence of the truth of Hardin's story, there where the old camping ground had been. One party of emigrants, in particular, made their camp near Mud Meadows, in the spring of 1852; and there they, too, found some of the smaller pieces of silver that Hardin and his companions had dropped. They gathered together all they could find, though it was but a small amount, and took it to the town of Shasta with them. There, it was bought by a jeweler by the name of Lewin, who paid for it by giving in exchange its weight in Mexican dollars. He displayed it in the window of his jewelry store; and there it was seen by scores of people—among them such men as L. D. Vary, Governor Roop, and others whose word was relied upon as of those who "speak of a verity," and who have many a time since told of having seen the Hardin Silver with their own eyes. It attracted much attention by reason of its romantic history, until the store was burned. Yet, in raking over the ashes when they had cooled, Lewin found it there—a melted mass of smoke-blackened metal.

Hardin dreaded (as who did not dread in those days when the Indian held the Desert?) to undertake the hardships and perils of a trip, even though it held out such glorious promise of fortune quickly made. People who crossed the plains in the old days were not eager to retrace their steps immediately, or to repeat their experiences. Hardin felt, too, that the treasure was safe though he might not go to it at once. But, finally—in 1858—he determined to hazard Indians and like evils, and to retrace his way to where in ashes and lava lay those great blocks of silver—no one knew how many, no one could guess.

On this trip he took with him, as a precaution

The Marvel-ous Hardin Silver

against any surprises from Indians, two men, one of whom was named Alberding. When, at length, they arrived at Double Hot Springs, Hardin looked ahead and saw Black Rock point—the monument he so well remembered—that was the landmark of the wondrous slabs of silver. Pointing to it, he said to his companions:

"Look ahead, boys! Do you see that spring on the hillside?" (It was afterward named "Ram's Horn Spring" by the later emigrants, and is known by that name today.) "Do you see the cañon that lies below it? I'll tell you this, now; I didn't find the silver below that place; nor did I find it more than half a mile above; and it is somewhere there at the left."

They all went to the spot he had indicated. They searched and searched. Up and down, back and forth, and retracing their steps again and again, as they looked for the strange ash deposit. Of silver there was no sign. Even ash there was none. The face of the mountain seemed completely changed. Waterspouts and cloudbursts are of frequent occurrence in that country, and now there were deep gullies and cuts that had not been there before. The whole surface of the mountain had altered beyond recognition.

Avalanches of broken, sliding rock had been set moving downward by the restless elements, and what had been bare ground before was now hidden under tons of boulders and smaller bits of rock. Avalanches of water had bared rocks once covered with earth. Moving—shifting—changing with the years, nothing was now the same. No sign of silver was ever seen in that mountain again, either then or thereafter.

So, at last, Hardin and his companions went away. He knew the silver was there; but it was to be his—never.

Others came, after them, and the search went on.

Several prospecting parties were there in 1859, and again in the '60's; and year after year, even down to our own day, do they go.

There have been those (guided by a divining rod that showed them, they aver, the exact spot where the stream of molten metal flowed and cooled in its bed of ashes) who have put minted silver by the thousands into the mountain in tunnels, and shafts, and inclines driven and sunk in absolute faith in the hidden treasure of the heights. Silver a-plenty has been sunk, but none ever brought to light.

Every summer sees one or more wagons, carrying prospectors, crawling across the furnace-hot alkali levels that border the Black Rock land. The mirage of Quin River Desert dances about them, as the mirage of Hardin Mountain beckons them on.

And though they always return with empty palms, hope is never absent from them; and they will tell you that some one, some day, somewhere in that grim, still mountain that even the birds shun, will find the lost treasure vault the three men stumbled on that day in the long ago.

Perhaps. I do not know. Such is the story of the marvelous Hardin Silver—the story just as I heard it out by the foothills of the grim old mountain, and by the dry Desert-sea that creeps up to its feet. If you had heard it in that strange land you would not have marveled at the strangeness of the tale, but would have had the faith that the others have had, no matter how you might have doubted when—afterward—you had shaken off the mystery and charm of the Desert.

I give you the story just as I got it. Believe it or not, as you choose.

> "I dare not say how true 't may be—
> I tell the tale as 'twas told to me."

The Marvelous Hardin Silver

THE LURE OF THE DESERT.

XCEPT you are kindred with those who have speech with great spaces, and the Four Winds of the earth, and the infinite arch of God's sky, you shall not have understanding of the Desert's lure.

It is not the Desert's charm that calls one. What is it? I know not; only that there is a low, insistent voice calling—calling—calling. Not a loud voice. The Desert proclaiming itself, speaks gently. And we—every child of us who has laid on the breast of a mother while she rocked slowly, and hushed our fretting with a soft-sung lullaby song—we know how a low voice soothes and lulls one into sleep.

You are tired of the world's ways? Then, if you and the Desert have found each other, surely you will feel the drawing of your soul toward the eternal calm —the brooding peace that is there in the gray country.

Does the beautiful in Nature thrill you to your finger-tips? When your eye is so trained that it may discover the beauty that dwells in that vast, still corner of the world, and your ear is attuned to catch the music of the plains or the anthems sung in deep cañons by the winds; when your heart finds comradeship in the mountains and the great sand-seas, the sun and the stars, and the huge cloud-drifts that the Desert winds set a-rolling round the world—when all these reach

your heart by way of your eye and your ear, then you
shall find one of the alluring ways that belongs to the
Desert.

Do you seek for the marvelous? Or do you go a-quest
for riches? Or simply desire to wander away into little
known rifts in the wilderness? By these lures and a
hundred others will the Desert draw you there. And
once there, unprejudiced, the voice by and by will
make itself heard as it whispers at your ear. And when
you can lay your head on its breast, and hear its
heart-beats, you will know a rest that is absolute and
infinite. Then, you will understand those who yearly
go a-searching for the mythical mines of mirage-land,
and those who have lived apart from others for a lifetime, and are forgot by all their kindred and friends
of a half-century ago. You will say: "It is the Desert's lure. I know—they cannot help it. And—yes!—
it is worth all the penalty the gray land makes them
pay!"

If you go to the Desert, and live there, you learn to
love it. If you go away, you will never forget it for
one instant in after life; it will be with you in memory
forever and forever. And always will you hear the
still voice that lures one, calling—and calling.

"The Desert calls to him who has once felt its strange
attraction, calls and compels him to return, as the sea
compels the sailor to forsake the land. He who has
once felt its power can never free himself from the
haunting charm of the Desert."

THE RISE AND FALL OF HARDIN CITY.

The
Rise
and
Fall
of
Hardin
City

HITE as bleached bones and level as a coffin lid, Quin River Desert fills the miles and miles of space lying between the Antelope and Black Rock mountain ranges. A sea of alkali, the Desert winds set waves of drifting sand lapping the western shore, where Black Rock point itself (that famous landmark for all who have voyaged here, from Fremont down to the lonely prospector of today), juts promontory-wise into the great silence. So vast and level it is, that Quin River itself—a considerable stream after the spring thaw has sent the snow-fed creeks rushing down the river—is but a varnish of moisture, miles in width, on the surface of the great plain where sun and wind soon combine to rub it all away.

A sea without a sail, save those that—like mine own —have gone drifting over its desolation into that wonderful beyond; that weird world made of strange rock forms and lavish splendor of color that lies a hundred miles away from the railroad, undisturbed and almost unknown. A land of marvels, of wonder upon wonder, where you may ride for hours, never out of sight of petrified tree stumps that stand like grim ghosts of dead centuries; where you may ride for days among hills honey-combed with caves whose linings are beautiful frescoes of color, or freaks in their oddity of form;

where you may ride for weeks among springs—warm, hot, or furiously boiling—never finding one that runs cold water. And riding so, you will find life a good thing. That is, if you have the eyes that see and the heart that beats in brotherhood to vast silence and space, and the thousand and one alluring things that we may find anywhere on the far edges of civilization—and surely here, where the world is rich in rare surprises as it waits you under the wide-arching, steel-bright Nevada sky.

So one day I beached my boat beyond the cliffs and rippled hills that cluster about the point of Black Rock; beyond those terrors, Double Hot Springs, whose wickedly boiling waters change their coloring—green as copperas, or blue as indigo—according as the light falls. Walking about their funnel-shaped rims, peering down into that inferno, you see the wheel-barrow that since the early '50's has balanced itself twenty feet under water on the edge of the shelf that is above a depth that is bottomless, and one falls to wondering what wayfarer on that great continental Desert-road brought it from out the far-away East to leave it here; and why.

Half a dozen miles beyond Double Hot Springs, stands—tall and alone—a chimney of squared, whitish stone blocks; sole relic of the buildings that once made Hardin City. About it the Desert is broken into hummocks of hard alkali ground that—being opened—yields the only fuel of the place. Hidden there are the roots of giant sagebrush long dead—roots that give no sign that sagebrush had ever thrived there till pick and shovel uncover them. That this particular spot was chosen for the townsite of Hardin City, was no doubt due to its plentiful, if peculiar, fuel supply.

Behind, are the Harlequin Hills—ribbed ridges of

The Rise and Fall of Hardin City

The
Rise
and
Fall
of
Hardin
City

color, motley, and unreal in seeming. And here it was
—just where, no man may say—in these hills that the
famous Hardin Silver was found, and lost—the marvelous Hardin Silver that has since sent many a man
half mad in his always fruitless quest. To this day
there are those of great faith who yearly seek the mythical silver in those mountains of strange geological
formations—so unlike any of their neighbor heights
and hills. Many are the men who, since the stir it made
in 1849, have been constantly searching; and not the
least well known among them have been Ladue Vary
and Leroy Arnold. Feeble, with palsied hands and
frost-white hair, these two men stir one's pity by their
useless faith.

It was years after the Hardin Silver excitement that
there journeyed down from Idaho a miner named
Frank Peed, bringing with him samples of ore from
the famous Poor Man's mine—bits that had that soapy
appearance peculiar to some rock from that district.
These pieces he showed to two men, O'Donnell and
Jennison, who at once declared it to be similar to, if
not identical with, ore that they had once seen near Hardin Mountain; but which at the time had not impressed
them as being valuable. Taking some three or four
pounds of samples from the Poor Man's mine for comparison, they at once went into the Black Rock country.
Soon they returned with a large quantity that seemed
of the same character, and suggested the same values.
An assay made by the assayer of the American Valley
Smelter, gave a return of $117. Other tests under the
direction of such men as Kingsbury, Bowman, and
Major Smith of the fort at Smoke Creek gave uniform
results.

Men were at once set at the task of taking out a large
amount of ore; and work, buoyed by hope, went for-

ward with the mining, as the miner's mirage beckoned them on. An assayer of good repute was engaged to work exclusively for that mine at a monthly stipend of $250. He devoted himself to the work with a wholeheartedness most commendable. The results he got from his assays were fabulous. Also, the results were unquestioned by the mine owners.

Encouraged by the assay returns, several tons of the ore were selected from that which had been taken out, for a working test, and one of the Thacker brothers undertook to haul it to Unionville, nearly—if not quite—a hundred miles away. It was worked at the John C. Fall mill at the mouth of Unionville cañon— the mill at the old Arizona mine that made Fall a several times millionaire, known all over the West—but Fall could not, for some inexplicable reason, cope with it. Nothing was obtained from the rock; and, as is usual in such cases, the mill received the full measure of censure and blame.

Disappointed, but not disbelieving, they determined upon another, if smaller, working test; so a man by the name of Giddings, with a thousand pounds or so, trudged with it into the Washoe country—to Dall's Mill. When the millmen there (experienced in the appraising of ores to the degree of being able almost to recognize values at sight) saw it, they at once declared the stuff to be worthless, and laughed at Giddings for bringing it all that great distance to be milled by them.

So, in pity for his delusion, they refused to work it. They declared it would be robbery on their part; and on his, time and money thrown away.

But Giddings was obdurate. He had faith in the rock; and he wanted it worked. And what faith so absolute, what belief so obstinate, as that of a man with a mine he believes in! At last the man who had charge

The
Rise
and
Fall
of
Hardin
City

of the mill—Hiskey—more to quiet Giddings than for any other reason, said they would take it; and having an entire distrust of there being any ore values whatever in the lot, agreed to make no charge for the milling should the result show any such values.

The rock was worked; the returns were—great! Hiskey proved himself a man of his word and made no charge for the milling.

Then the original owners of the mine, having taken others in with them to assist with capital in the construction of suitable works, began the erection of the mill and other necessary buildings. That was the founding of "Hardin City." Satisfied that they had "a big thing" at the foot of Hardin Mountain, they felt that the work was warranted. Major Bass, Judge Harvey, Larry Bass, Alvaro Evans and Chancellor Derby, as well as many others, had tests made time and time again, with the same uniform result. Perhaps eighty tons, as working tests, were milled by them— the net result being about $4,000 handed over to them in silver bullion. The more the tests, the greater were the returns. On an average, they ran higher than the average workings of the Comstock. Also, there was a greater amount of gold than the Comstock carried. It seemed in the face of such evidence that there was no good reason for disbelieving in the mine's genuine worth, and so the fame of the Desert's mining claim spread.

Soon a cluster of substantial adobe buildings were grouped around a mill modeled on precisely the style of Dall's—the one that had so successfully worked their second ore shipment. To reproduce as nearly as possible the mill they knew could, and did, work such ore as they had, was the thing to be done to ensure them unfailing results; so they secured the services of the furnace man from Dall's, together with two other men that understood perfectly the working of that mill in all particulars. With every hope of success the owners looked anxiously forward to the clean-up of their first run.

In the meantime a new assayer, Cheatham, had been engaged. The man's name was a misnomer, for he was honesty itself; and with the result of his first assay before them, came the first chill of fear, lest they had been over sanguine. The results obtained by Cheatham were not at all those got by his predecessor. The mine-owners began to look dubious, outsiders said things looked queer, and all awaited the start of the mill with the keenest of anxiety.

At last everything was complete—the ore was waiting, the machinery was set in motion, the stamps went to chunk-chunk-chunking the ore into powder. They were now to know the truth.

Several tons were run through. The result was—nothing!

Absolutely nothing! Not even a trace. Of metal of any sort, none! Not so small a particle as the point of a fine cambric needle did it yield.

Over and over again they tried. Always, the result was the same. The rock from Hardin Mountain was barren of ore values as a bit of Bath brick.

What was the explanation, then, of the bullion they had received from the run at Dall's Mill?

I, myself, can offer no explanation. I can only tell you what was told me. An old miner—Duffy, of Deer Creek—whose superstitions would put to the blush many a Southern mammy's faith in spooks and spirits, has solemnly averred to me that the mine had been placed under a spell by some evil spirit—changed by a

The
Rise
and
Fall
of
Hardin
City

The

Rise

and

Fall

of

Hardin

City

genius of ill from rich rock into worthless. "Hoo-dooed," he said.

But when I repeated this to one who had, in days of old, known the men and the mine, he only smiled and said that an assayer receiving $250 per month would naturally want to "hold onto his job," and (unconsciously, of course) would be optimistic.

"But the bullion that was worked at Dall's Mill?" I queried.

"Comstock."

"I don't understand," I said, rather bewildered.

"They hadn't made a thorough clean-up of Dall's Mill after running those rich old Virginia ores through, before they took hold of this ore, and these fellows got about $4,000 in bullion that originally came up to the light of day from out of Comstock shafts."

Its buildings are quite dismantled and destroyed. The winds of the Desert—the rains of the years have nibbled and gnawed at the adobes until only the faintest traces that they once were, remain. Of the mill itself, part of the whitish-gray stone of its walls, and most of the tall chimney, stand out in sharp relief, discernable miles away against the darker background of Hardin Mountain.

Duffy told me the other day that now the mill is haunted.

THE MEN OF THE DESERT.

I N THE Pine Forest range, tucked away in a cañon that is hard for a stranger to find, is a little group of cabins where some of the oldest prospectors in the State have made their homes for this many a year. There, away from kindred —even civilization—they have lived for a third of a century, seeking for the gold they have never found. They have isolated themselves from the rest of the world for half a lifetime, and have lived a life of hardest toil in that land of which such wondrous stories are told of mines of fabulous worth. It savors of romance to read of men going there to seek their fortunes; but to endure the hardships such quests involve is quite a different matter.

Apart from the world, and by the world long forgot, these men are in reality path-finders—blazing the way for future generations.

So the quiet years go by, while they go on looking for fairy-gold—for the mines that are found only at the rainbow's end. Yet, fairy-gold though it be, still will they keep on seeking the Three Little Lakes of Gold, and Forman's Find, and the silver that Hardin saw, or the long lost Blue Bucket mines. They are not miners, after all—only prospectors; for they have never had a mine. They have, for all their busy years, found nothing to be mined. So they are but prospectors, at most. Neither are they looking for mines. Only for a mine. Just one certain mine, that each one believes in—and each one has named as his. Only it is in dreamland still.

Some of these men have met starvation and thirst in the Desert, and have been down to the edge of things where Death claims his own—and have yet lived, coming back from the horror of it all, to tell of the hours of the Black Night, and to warn other men from the trail that leads that way. Some there are who have gone through battles of Indian warfare; and they will show you arrow-point scars, and those that came from slits in the flesh that were made by the "Redskins." That was when the State was a Territory; and they themselves were young. These men all have their stories to tell; and if you linger long in the land, you will find yourself often by their campfires, as the darkness falls on the foothills and they whittle from a square of tobacco that with which they crowd the bowls of their pipes. When a glowing greasewood coal is laid there, and the pipe is made to draw, you will hearken to things (as they tell them) worth crossing the world to hear.

But other men than miners live in this lava-land; and here have made homes. So small are the ranches, you scarcely call them by that name. You come upon them up on the heights where are found wee meadows wet by the mountains' melted snow, or the flow that comes down from hot springs. There men toil, and till the ground, and find life good. There one fills his lungs with air that is like wine in the blood, and his soul with the gladness of living. You will have to discover these places for yourself; for the roads that men make in that country mostly run through the valleys, and these skyland ranches do not lie on your route.

As you go journeying away over these little used highways, you note that the country can be in no wise changed from that which men found as they voyaged through here in the years of long ago.

Railroad steel has been laid, and the wires have been strung on poles set away to the North, and far, far to the Southward; but here there is nothing to mark human life in the land, except the dim and dusty road that is but little more than a thread through the valley's expanse.

Desert stretches reach to far mountains. Beyond are still other barren plains; beyond these yet other lonely mountain ranges. And these keep repeating themselves over and over again as you go— as you travel farther and farther away to the North.

A picture of vastness. And—as you view it from afar—one with no detail; only the great sky-touching mountain ranges, the wide Desert—and over them the immensity of the ocean-blue of the heavens, lending the picture its only vivid coloring. But go up into the mountains, and there you find a wealth of tint and tone. Go up into the mountains, and you will there find the men that are good to know—the prospectors who came into the country in the days of their youth.

THREE LITTLE LAKES OF GOLD.

EEP-DOMED heavens—a wide-reaching Desert. Above, the sapphire blue of a summer sky without one cloud—below the nun-grey of a Nevada plain without a vestige of verdure. And (at the rim where they meet and blend) distant mountains, dim and uncertain in outline and coloring.

Here you are far, far beyond the locomotive's whistle or the moaning of the railroad telegraph wires, with the plaintive chords drawn from them by the plain's winds. You travel farther still into the North, across those level, lonely sand-wastes, going toward vague mountains wrapped in violet and blue shroudings, and so bring them out of their uncertainty, until you reach the first waves of foothills that lap their feet; then the mountains' misty outlines are dissipated, and they stand in all their mightiness before you—ruggedly magnificent and quite unlike anything you imagined them to be. For you find there hidden cañons holding groves of leafy shade, and beautiful streams, deliciously cold on the hottest of summer days.

Cross the mountain chain, and there will be another Desert like unto this you have but just passed over. Then (as breastworks on its farther side) there are other mountains so like these that you grow bewildered in looking. Another wide plain, dry and deathly still; another great ridge, vague and uncertain.

Half a century ago—in 1851—a little party of emigrants, with faces turned toward the West, moved slowly along here in their ox-teams, and one night camped at what is now known as Massacre Springs. It was away up toward the northward of the traveled ways across the continent—in the "High Rock country"—on the emigrant road that crosses the upper part of Humboldt county. On awakening the following morning, they found that Indians creeping to their camp while they slept, and leaving them undisturbed, had stolen all their cattle. What to do? How to reach California? Their oxen were gone. Without draft animals, to press on to the West was an impossibility. There was nothing to do but to follow the trail of the stolen steers, and—relying on the white man's superior weapons—recover their stock, if possible.

So all the men of the party—five in number—set out, leaving behind them the womenfolk and little children. The cattle were easily tracked, for during the night a light rain had fallen, and their footprints, as well as those of the Indians, were sharp cut in the mud.

The day was dark and gloomy; clouds obscured the sun, and a fog settled over the whole valley. At times a drizzling rain fell; but the men tramped doggedly on, following the hoof-prints marked deep in the moist earth. After many hours of walking, they realized that they were further away from camp than was prudent for white men in a hostile Indian country; inasmuch as the women and children were entirely unprotected during the time they might be away. They halted, and conferred together. It was decided that two of them should, at once, return to camp, while the remaining three were to follow the trail of the stolen

Three Little Lakes of Gold

cattle until they were sighted; and then, watching their opportunity, if possible get possession of the oxen again and get them back to camp. Without recovering them the emigrants were helpless in a hostile country, unless they should chance to be picked up by some other party of passing emigrants—a contingency so remote as to be scarcely worth considering.

So they parted; two of them going back to camp, and the others to whose lot it fell to follow the stolen cattle, keeping on the plainly marked trail leading southward. Finally, these three found themselves in a beautiful and well-watered cañon, green with grass and shrubbery. The rocky cliffs that closed it in rose to great heights on either side; and down between the narrow gorge's walls plunged a creek in a succession of foaming cascades. Near the entrance of the cañon it leaped—a sheer drop of seventy-five feet—over a ledge of projecting rock in a beautiful waterfall to a hollowed place in the solid rock bed of the creek beneath. Then, separating into three streams, the waters formed as many pools below.

It was at the foot of the waterfall the three men stopped, and stooped to the basin hollowed there nearest the fall to drink. In its clear depths, among waterworn pebbles and black sand, one of the men (who had previously seen something of the California placers) saw pieces of gold—not simply gold-dust, but nuggets. Huge nuggets of the pure metal. He showed them to his companions, to whom native gold was an unfamiliar sight. All three immediately fell a-searching for more, and were rewarded in a short time by finding enough to fill a tin quart-cup which one wore tied to his belt. Besides this, they filled their pockets—and one of the men put as many nuggets into his handkerchief as he could well manage.

However, they feared the delay of hunting for gold might lose them their stock—which was infinitely more precious to them in their desperate condition than a mountain of gold—so realizing that each minute meant loss, as well as danger, to them, they reluctantly prepared to leave the spot that still lured them to stay. But men do not easily turn away from the sight of gold, no matter to whom it belongs; and this—uncounted wealth for all—was all their own. Theirs, for the simple task of taking. So, after filling the cup with the precious nuggets, and cacheing it at the foot of a tree (a dead pine that should serve as guide when they would come again) they yielded to the fascination of the gold's yellow shine, and turned again to the creek to gather, if possible, from one of the other wee lakes that had been less thoroughly searched, yet other bits of gold. They had scarcely clambered down the bank to the edge of the stream when a rain of lead came from the cliffs above them, and two of the three men fell—shot to death.

Indians had slipped softly upon them as they were searching in the gravel and sands; and the waterfall's roar had drowned any sound that otherwise might have warned them. Before the second volley of shots could come from those old-time, slow-loading guns, the remaining man had found opportunity to escape by darting quickly into the thick underbrush, and working his way carefully up the creek. Clever as the redskins were in following the trail of a white man, here was one who outwitted them by hiding among rocks that, in their search, they passed and repassed many times. Then slipping out, but keeping well under cover, he finally found himself in a large grove of aspens and cottonwoods. From there he made his way out of the cañon to the heights where he could see over the country. Mountains, mostly rugged and bare, were all about him, rimming the wide and barren plains; but far away to the southward he discovered a single timbered range. Toward it he directed his course. He had lost his bearings in his flight, and could not guess now in which direction lay the camp. He argued, too, that no doubt hours before the redskins had come down upon him and his companions, they had found the unprotected women and children and massacred them. Nothing ever was heard of them, or of the two men who had returned to camp, so that they too doubtless met their death at the hands of the savages, unless they perished in the Desert in an attempt to continue their journey on foot.

When the one survivor, of whom we know aught, saw the wooded mountain across the valley, he turned his steps that way. He must get out of the Indian-infested country as best he could, without food or any human assistance. Ahead of him were terrible miles to be traversed, and the demon of thirst to be battled with. Where trees were, there he knew was water; and about those mountain springs was greater chance of finding things that were edible. He must reach the tree covered heights.

He—Stoddard—began his awful journey. He still carried the handkerchief with its burden of gold, having kept an unconscious grasp on it through all the perils of his escape. Over mountain ridges he climbed, over sun-baked plains he wearily walked. Days and days he journeyed. How many? where? in what measure of suffering?—neither he nor any other ever knew. For when, at length, he wandered into Downieville, in California, it was a shrivelled mummy that men saw stumbling along in shreds of ragged clothing, barefoot and bareheaded, half-famished and with mind wholly gone. Delirious, he babbled of Indians, of eating roots and the berries of wild rose-bushes, of picking up nuggets of gold, of walking—walking—walking! He had a wild animal's fear of human faces—was hardly human himself. But still his bony fingers clutched a handkerchief, and in the handkerchief were the nuggets of gold.

Of those who first saw Stoddard when he staggered into Downieville, was old Major Downie himself—he for whom the town was named. To many a listener afterwards he related how he himself had seen Stoddard still tightly gripping the handkerchief as he came into the town—delirious, in the likeness of a skeleton, yet with the miser's grasp on his treasure.

When after long weeks of careful nursing, reason returned to him, he began—little by little—to recall the events of days directly preceding that of his arrival at the cañon of the "three little lakes," as he called the pools where the gold was found. Some things rose quite clearly before his mind; others he groped for through a fog of dimmed recollection. Gradually he came to remember that about noon of the day preceding the one when his companions had been killed, they had passed out of High Rock cañon, and that night had camped at Massacre Springs. Then, later, memory was further cleared of the haze, and he told of the loss of the cattle, of the trail they had followed, of the finding of the nuggets, of the Indians' attack upon them, of his comrades' fall, and his own escape, and—lastly—of directing his course toward the far-away mountain of water and food as well as shelter—that mountain to the southward, fully forty miles away.

Again memory failed him. As to the fearful days that lay between the time when he dragged his wearied feet over the dry Desert levels—going mad with an intolerable thirst, and, with blood-shot eyes, always

Three Little Lakes of Gold

looking toward the far-off heights dark with juniper and mountain mahogany—and the time when he found himself fed and clothed and cared for by the people of Downieville, his mind was a complete blank.

As to the truth of his assertions regarding the three little lakes of gold—if you doubted, there was the handkerchief heavy with the metal; a very tangible proof that somewhere back in Northern Nevada at the foot of a high waterfall in a lovely cañon, where three small pools and in them was gold.

Then the gold hunt began. That was in the spring of '52; and not yet is the search ended—not yet are the searchers done. Still men go to the big, quiet country away off there where the railroad, and the telegraph, and the daily mail do not find them. They search, and search, and search. Even in this year of grace do men go to seek the hidden treasure casket of the mountain.

Travelling away out there, on pleasure bent, I have myself met them on the road; and (after the fashion of wayfarers in a great silent country where few go, albeit they who meet are strangers) we have greeted one another as we met on the road, and we drew rein to talk together a bit there in the stillness of the wide alkali plains. I have found them bright with hope, and buoyed by the belief that they surely, this time, would find reward for their years of patient search. And I have seen them again, long afterward, jaded and worn with weeks of fatiguing toilsome travel. Less buoyant they were, less bright; but still hopeful that some day they would come upon the cañon (that lies less than a day's foot-travel from Massacre Springs) where a mountain stream falls sheer to its rocky bed below; and the stream—dividing—fills three tiny pools, and in the pools are nuggets of gold.

They search and seek—they grow old and gray in

the seeking, while the years slip softly by, as a gray coyote slips by one on the rabbit-trails that make a network of the gray earth there. Searching for what (we say) is not. Creeks they find in the cañons, that have divided and make three—four—a dozen little pools. But no waterfall plunges down the gorge from just above. The mountains have many beautiful waterfalls (if one but knows where to find them), but none that the old men have found sings to three little lakes down below. The sceptics (after their fashion) smile, but that does not hinder the faithful in their quest.

Dreamers? We declare them such. Yet suppose that some time one of their number should find the spot that Stoddard found back in the early 'fifties? What if one of the faithful should some day come back to tell us he has found, in a remote cañon away back on the plains, an old tin cup (so old and rusted that it broke apart as he lifted it), and that the cup was filled full to the brim with virgin gold? What then?

Three Little Lakes of Gold

THE BEAUTY OF THE DESERT.

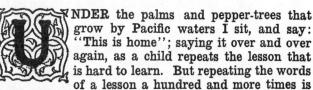NDER the palms and pepper-trees that grow by Pacific waters I sit, and say: "This is home"; saying it over and over again, as a child repeats the lesson that is hard to learn. But repeating the words of a lesson a hundred and more times is not learning it. And I do not know my lesson yet. I have driven my tent pegs here among California roses, and under a California sky. I have stretched the ropes tight, and have anchored them down—to stay. Yet this is not Home. If you would ask why, remember that the tent canvas was weathered in a Desert-wind, and the ropes bleached by a Desert-sun. Then, too, the tent stood there for long. Very long. And the tent pegs pull hard when driven long in one place. So—though there are roses and lilies about me, and the wind brings the salt smell of the sea—yet would I have the Desert-alkali in my nostrils and smell the smoke from a grease-wood camp-fire. You, who do not understand why I make such choice, are apt to ask: "Is it not a mirage you see—the charm of color, and form, and music that you say is in the Desert? We do not see these things. We only see uncouth fashioning, where you see magnificence or grace. The cry of a cougar—the coyote's wailing is uncanny to hear; yet you call it music. You

tell us there is color in the Desert; while we, who know, see nothing but the endless gray—gray always and always. We are wise with the wisdom of cities and many men, and therefore we know. It is but a mirage, this charm of the Desert.''

And so you wise ones decide for the ones whom you call poor fools, and say that the mirage they follow is like unto the one the wanderer a-thirst sees, or the old miner in his quest for rainbow-gold.

Well, is happiness, or beauty, or any of the things that give us joy anything more than a mirage? Do they exist except as we see them? And is it not well that we are thus unwise to believe in the non-existent? For when we shall have come to the door of death, and all of life is ended, we shall come to know that through all the years that have been ours, the heart was made glad by our faiths more often than by facts. So let me believe in the Desert still. We find in the world only what we, ourselves, bring into it. If we find love, and joy, and beauty, it is because we are capable of loving, and can feel joy, and can see beauty. They are not there, except as they are of us.

So, now, go your way and leave me and the old miners to our faiths—our fancies, if you will. At least, we have had much that you have missed.

Perhaps it is because of all this that I feel kinship with those who believe in the wonder-tales.

After you have come to know these men and their stories, and have lived long enough in the land they have made their own to understand why it is they cannot go away, you will have a tender regard for them and their welfare, no matter where your lot may be cast in all the after years. You will never forget ever so small a part of any of the stories that they have told you.

The
Beauty
of
the
Desert.

**The
Beauty
of
the
Desert.**

The seasons will come and go, you will make new friends and bury the old, and life will bring you fresh interests and let slip the things that you knew on other by-ways; but of these old men and their complete trust, there shall never come to you a forgetting. To the last chapter of your life, the memory of their own—and their stories—will be with you, to link you yet closer to the old days when you found the Desert and its men.

THE LOST BLUE BUCKET MINES.

NO STATE in the Union contains so great a variety of minerals and geological phenomena as Nevada. Not a county of the State is so rich in them as is Humboldt. And one may add that perhaps no other like area on the face of the globe so abounds in legends of "lost mines"—of fascinating tales of fabulous "finds" of every valuable mineral or precious stone that Mother Earth has ever given birth to—as that same county lying in the northeastern corner of the State. Go out there among the old prospectors for a month or more, and you will hear scores upon scores of stories of the marvelous findings of diamonds and rubies, of emeralds and turquoise, of copper and lead, of silver and gold. But mostly of gold. For the dream of the old-time prospector is always of finding gold in quantity so great that one would grow bewildered in its computation.

Simple hearted and credulous, there are dozens of them today looking for mines that have never existed, save in the lurid imagination of some legend-maker—some emigrant who crossed the plains in the late 'forties or early 'fifties, and at the end of his journey told eager listeners of his "find" away back, somewhere, in the barren-land. How many trusting ones among the listeners found death in the Desert through the lure of these legends, God only knows! But the unmarked graves that resulted are more than you would guess there could be—graves carelessly or wantonly dug by way of the wild tales told by men who (just to be the envied centre of a crowd of open-mouthed listeners) fabricated them for their own amusement. Such falsehoods led many a one away to bear the hardships and privations of years of Desert roving; perhaps to die at last in the lonely land, and to die there alone. Have you ever thought what it would be like, for a man to die in the Desert—perhaps a hundred miles from any other human being—alone under the staring sky, with no sight of moving things but the gray lizards and the little brown squirrels, and a lone coyote watching him from some rise a few yards away; with no sound but the coyote's wailing cry, and the moaning of the Desert wind. So many, many men have died in just this way; only we are apt to forget that it is ever so.

Over there in that half-explored, wholly interesting country, where the chief chain of mountains has been fashioned by the united work of the great lava flow and the erosion of the centuries into flattened tops, making a vast landscape of sky-touching tablelands—where the cliffs and chasms take on strange shapes and colorings—where the odd and unusual in mountain and plain is about you always and everywhere, there lies, still unfound by the prospectors, a cañon that these aged and earnest men will tell you is rich in nuggets of gold—the cañon of the "Blue Bucket" diggings.

In 1845 one of the earliest trains of emigrants crossing the plains, with Oregon for an objective point, was working its way down the banks of the Humboldt, and at Gravelly Ford—a noted point on the old road, where now is the station of Beowawe—separated into two parties; one continuing on down the Humboldt river, while the other took the road by the way of Black Rock into California. The latter party on reaching the Pacific Coast had startling stories to tell of their adventures upon the way, while going through that country that lies back from that river which in the early days was known as "Mary's River," instead of "Humboldt."

And this is what they told:

After leaving Black Rock—perhaps three or four days' travel beyond that grim, dark-hued promontory—they had passed through a cañon so deep and rough that "it seemed only a bird would be able to get out, once it found itself in a cañon." However, after successfully overcoming a deluge of difficulties that beset them, they finally made their way through. Yet, even so, in many places they had to take their wagons apart, and—piece by piece—hoist them up cliffs and down declivities by means of ropes. It was a fearful experience of trial and hardship, unusual even in Desert travel of the early times.

It was when directing their course toward the "Twin Sister" peaks of Oregon, though while yet in Nevada, that they had come upon this cañon, to them unknown and unnamed, even in any description given by other wayfarers who later came through the land. Neither had they any knowledge of it from other emigrants who had gone before. It seemed to be a side road, little used, and turning out from the one better known and more traveled. There, while the wagons were grinding their way over boulders and broken rock of all sorts and sizes, they found, in the shallow creek and in the ruts made by the wagon-wheels, what in their ignorance and inexperience they called "brass." They had heard of gold dust, of course; but this was not dust.

It must then be brass. But it was pretty, this "brass"; and it attracted the attention in particular of the women and children, who were mainly the ones to gather it. The men were too much interested in the matter of getting their party through this difficult pass to pay heed to pretty playthings found along the way.

The wagons, and the buckets hanging to their sides, were painted a vivid blue. And into the buckets were thrown the supposedly worthless nuggets. When crossing the Deschutes river the wagons were partially capsized, and many of the emigrants' belongings lost. Among such things as went to the bottom of the Deschutes were the buckets that carried the bright bits of metal. A very few pieces, however, had been cast into the wagons with other things, and were thus saved. These, with their other possessions, the emigrants carried into the country of their new homes—eastern Oregon, where many of them permanently remained. Some of them, though, later, went southward, and eventually —in 1848—found themselves at Sutter's Fort. They remained there during the first months of that year, and there they were shown gold dust and small nuggets. In them they recognized a metal that they had previously supposed to be "brass."

Doubtful if any of their old companions had kept the bits of yellow metal they had brought to the farther West with them, they nevertheless wrote, making inquiry. As soon as a letter could reach them, there came not only a reply, but bits of gold—nuggets from the place that was henceforth to be known as the "Blue Bucket district"—that had been preserved through the many past months by the children of the party who had kept them for playthings.

Comparison with the nuggets then being shown at Sutter Creek proved these playthings to be gold. Of a coarse sort, but without doubt gold. A party of ninety was organized and equipped for the journey, and at once started back, in spite of the warnings of friends that Indians were up in arms against the whites, and that traveling had become even more perilous than before. Regardless of the almost certain encounters with Indians, they set out. Of the ninety who left, full of courage and hope, not half lived to reach home. Long before they came to the country of the "Blue Bucket" diggings, Indians fell upon them, and only by a miracle did any of their number escape. Of the few who did reach California and Oregon again, only two of them were of the original party that knew the exact locality of the cañon of the "Blue Bucket" gold. With Indians on the warpath they were too disheartened to continue the search after their companions had been massacred; so that—wounded and sick—they went back to the coast. They were too discouraged with the result of their one trip to ever make an attempt at a second journey into greasewood-land and the home of the jack-rabbit. The Indians were there; let them have it.

But to Dr. Dane, as they lay sick at Yreka, they showed the nuggets they still retained, and to him they told the story of the emigrants' "find." They described the locality of the cañon, and gave him minute directions as to where one should go to find it. These men died, and for some time interest in the "Blue Bucket" gold lapsed. But years later, while engaged in placer mining, the Doctor heard that which quickened his interest. He had a small store at the place on the river where he was working his placers; and there an occasional traveler might find accommodations for the night.

To this stopping place there came a Hudson Bay trapper one day, asking for a night's shelter. He had just crossed the plains, he said; and was full of stories of interesting experiences. The morning after his arrival, he accompanied the Doctor down to the placer claims to see the (to him) novel sight of gold washing. Plunging his hand into the Long Tom, the Doctor took out a handful of black sand and gold, and poured it into the joined palms which the trapper held out to him. It was unusually good that morning, containing a large number of good-sized nuggets. The trapper looked at them curiously.

"Is that stuff sure-enough gold?" he asked.

"Well," answered Doctor Dane, amused at his surprise and ignorance, "it seems to satisfy the people from whom we buy anything. They give us, in exchange, anything we want for it. Doesn't that prove to you what it is?"

"If that's gold," the trapper replied, "I know where there's any amount of it! It's in a place I could easily find again, too, for I kept my horses in that cañon all winter—a fine, watered cañon back near the emigrant road that comes out by the way of High Rock. I didn't find it—the gold—until I went to get my horses in the Spring. There's lots of these gold pebbles in the creek—lots of 'em! Why, I could load my two horses with all they could carry, inside of an hour of hunting them and picking them up!"

He then went on to give the Doctor a detailed description of the country about there, and in particular the appearance of the cañon, which was a very long one, he said. The account he gave tallied precisely with the description of that cañon where the emigrants had found the famed "brass."

It was arranged that the trapper should immediately take the Doctor to the place; Indian depredations having become less frequent in occurrence. Doctor Dane, loth to make the long trip into an unknown country with an entire stranger, induced him to allow a third person to join their little party. From the first, the trapper had said he could easily retrace his way by means of his dead campfires to which they would come day after day. And as they went back into the Desert country, in no instance did he fail to show them where he had camped but a few days before. Nor in any way did he do aught to create suspicion that he was otherwise than perfectly honest in all his declarations.

Their route lay through a country that was strange to the Doctor, and it was not until he found himself at the head of Goose Lake Valley, through which he had passed on his way to the West, that he got his bearings. When they reached Wardner Hill, and while standing on its bare and level summit, from which point a magnificent view can be had of the whole surrounding country, the trapper said—pointing northward to where two peaks rose sixty or seventy miles away, and which are now known as "Steen" and "Pueblo" mountains—:

"There! That mountain to the right is the one; and the cañon is on this side. That is the place where I put my horses to graze. There is a creek in it that runs a big stream in the Spring; but in the Fall it goes 'most dry. The cañon is pretty level part of the way, and there's a fine lot of bunch grass all over it; but farther up, the walls are terrible high and it's so rough that it's about all a horse can do to get through it."

Two days' travel brought them there. And Doctor Dane found the place exactly as described. It fully answered the description given by the old emigrants, as well as that which the trapper had given before starting out. The three men were scarcely within the cañon

The
Lost
Blue
Bucket
Mines

ere they came upon evidence of a recent cloudburst. The creek banks were piled high with uprooted shrubs, rose-bushes and the bush of the wild gooseberry, buck-brush and willows, left there by the flood. The banks themselves were cut out, and drift and brushwood had made dams across the channel. Fresh-cut gullies were everywhere. The track of the storm's devastation grew rougher as the men penetrated farther and farther into the cañon. At last, riding was an impossibility, and they dismounted to clamber over the boulders or to creep around the cliffs. Even the creek's course had been changed in places, and a new channel made. The work the cloudburst had done was not a month old.

To find the spot where he had seen the nuggets was easy for the trapper, but of nuggets themselves there were none to be found. If gold had ever been there, it was either hidden by the storm's debris, or had been swept farther down by the violence of the flood's resistless waters. They searched and searched, but in vain. Having come unprepared to mine for gold after the usual placer fashion, the quest was for the time abandoned.

Had Doctor Dane doubted for one instant (which he never did), the trapper's sincerity, that doubt would have been wholly dissipated by seeing the persistence with which the trapper prosecuted his search; by the perseverance, later, when a start for home must be made, with which he entreated the Doctor to stay yet longer. He declared over and over again that the gold was there—he knew it; and Doctor Dane, during the days of their search, became more and more convinced that it was so. Yet they had to return to civilization without even one small nugget to reward them for their tedious and tiring trip, or their days of seeking for the "Blue Bucket" gold.

With another year, however, the quest was renewed —but not by these men. And the men who sought for it then were not more eager and confident than are those who go there today. For they who believe in the story, fairy-tale or not, as it may be, are growing in number with the years, and every year sees new converts.

Some go there boldly—organized parties for prospecting, willing the public should know of the object of their trip—others, half-ashamed of their own credulity, slip away by themselves into that land of space and stillness, and wander its mountain ways alone, lest others may know, and jeer at their faith. Men went last year to find the "Blue Bucket" mines; other men are there now. The years wax and wane; but time does not lessen their faith. Always and always will there be those who go up and down the length of Desertland seeking the mines that are myths; serving the Sorceress of the sand wastes until the day shall come when they lie down to rest on the old Overland Trail, where the bones of those who broke the way were buried in the long ago.

The
Lost
Blue
Bucket
Mines

A MEMORY OF THE DESERT.

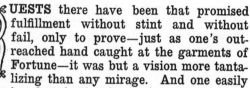UESTS there have been that promised fulfillment without stint and without fail, only to prove—just as one's out-reached hand caught at the garments of Fortune—it was but a vision more tanta-lizing than any mirage. And one easily sees visions, in that land of visible and invisible mysteries.

Once, there was one that I knew—one who was count-ed too sane to see visions and too wise to be deceived—who went a-search for diamonds, there in the Desert. Topaz, and turquoise, and other things of beauty are there, but of diamonds none have been found.

To one of the wee towns that make scattered dots on the map of Nevada southward from the Black Rock country, there came an old prospector; and he singled out this man, from all whom he knew, to take into his confidence and make half-owner in the wonderful diamond mines he had found. He brought with him a sack of the gems, to prove the truth of his assertions—a canvas bag full of sparkling white things that under the gaslight, as they were spread out, were beautiful enough to be real. Such a sight! Long, long after-ward I, too, saw them, and I did not wonder that ignor-ance of the diamond in its rough state, might very well help a man to believe in these—to think them the gems they looked to be. There must have been fifty pounds of the pretty, worthless baubles that were poured into a bright and new tin pan, and filled it well to the brim. It seemed impossible that they had not been cut by a lapidary, so perfect were they on all sides. Not crystals as we know them, pointed on one end only; but polished, and true, with facets cut by Nature on every side. The most beautiful crystals I have ever seen, and of a sort that I had never come across here in the West.

Out beyond the Quin River Desert, the Old Prospector found them, believing them to be diamonds of worth. They were lying about in quantities, sprinkling the sand wastes off there at the Desert's edge, where the sands gather together in dunes, only to scatter themselves broadcast, as grain is tossed from the hand of the sower. So the winds cover and uncover them; and to them, one day, came these men believing in their worth; and many a dollar that might have gone better ways, went toward the gathering of what came, later, to shame them for their simple credulity.

Others (and I among them, also) found copper out there—melted copper that I took from its home in the mountain, where it had been melted by the great conflagration. It seemed easy to believe the Desert's treasure-trove might well be there. It is so easy to dream of things that never present themselves to one in lands where strange things do not intrude. But here it would seem that any marvelous thing might very well be; the country is so weird—so unusual—so unlike our everyday world. You find yourself looking for all sorts of impossible things to happen. You find yourself saying: "Why not?"

But my handfuls of copper were all there were—there was never a sign of a ledge. Just melted bits from a "blow-out"—spewed out by the earth's internal fires, with its parent ledge leagues upon leagues away.

And a sulphur mine that I tried to conquer? Did it not become conqueror itself? It fought me with fire, though hidden, and so drove me away. Yet, I have heard that others have now gone there to do what I, in vain, tried to do. Will they succeed, or will they, too, be vanquished by the earth's better weapon? Or, will the Desert have gone back to its way of old, and become cool once more, as it was away back in the early 'sixties? I often ponder over it. It was a mystery then, it is a mystery still.

A DESERT MYSTERY.

YOU may try as you will to comprehend, in its entirety, the awful tragedy of Pelee and La Soufriere—to grasp it as something of modern times and real—yet, as you read, you are aware it seems as remote from our day as the stories of Pompeii and Herculaneum, and more than half fiction. It was too appalling a tragedy—too stupendous a death-roll, for the comprehension of any but those who afterward stood in the silence where once there was sound, and saw the fearful dead that bestrewed the places where once the living walked. Under the shadow of its black phophesy the people worked or played, loved and married, bore children and buried them— living out the measure of their days unheedful of the thing that was, some day, to come. None who live within a volcano's possible reach but know its danger; yet who will ever believe that he himself is to be in the pathway of its wrath?

And how thin the old Earth's crust is, over her mighty fires! And the warnings that she sends before her outbreaks—how little are they heeded! Man only believes in danger when that danger has come.

With my thoughts dwelling upon the Earth's vagaries; of the uncertainty of her temper where her fires burn the fiercest, I am reminded of a certain place where, once, I found a subterranean temperature that was tremendous.

It was a strange thing that I came upon, that time. Let me tell you of it.

It was in January, 1900, that I formed a partnership with a former associate in gold mining, to prospect for sulphur deposits in Northern Nevada. There are vast beds of pure sulphur (the largest in the United States, unless those of Louisiana that lie under the sea are included) lying west of north of the Central Pacific Railroad, and forty miles away from its threads of steel. They are the great Humboldt sulphur mines, so well known. Following that trend all the way to the Oregon line are scattered indications of sulphur throughout that weird and barren land that the great lava flow of the North has spread itself over.

For our initial work, we selected a district a short distance westward from the railroad station of Humboldt. As early as the late '60's I had had knowledge of small prospect hole at that especial place; and, as it was within a hundred and fifty yards of the railroad track (thus solving the problem of cheap transportation, which, in that land of long distances is the most serious drawback to the development of mines carrying small "values") we determined to begin our operations there.

Just prior to the laying of the Central Pacific's rails through the great gray valley of the Humboldt—the one-time-called "River of Death"—these beds were located by James Spence; and from the single prospect hole (an incline of not more than thirty feet in depth) he took some fifteen or twenty tons of sulphur. Two "mountain schooners" (Nevada's desert camel of the early days), driven by himself and Henry Childers, had carried the crude ore into Virginia City, where it became the property of Hy Barnes, and—an unprofitable speculation. I name these people to you because they were real people, even as the stories are real. In cabins and by camp-fires I have heard old miners tell these things so often that the names of these men are as familiar to me as my own. Hy Barnes could not dispose of it, and the months that came saw it lying there —a flaming yellow pyramid on the side of Mount Davidson. This was in Virginia City's palmy days. Later—for that must have been in '64 or '65—when the Central Pacific Railroad Company was building its snowsheds over the Sierra Nevada mountains, and bolt-holes were being drilled into the rock walls, to which the sheds cling like swallows' nests against a cliff, sulphur was needed for securing the bolts in place. Into these holes smoking-hot sulphur was poured as the iron rods were driven home, to hold them firmly; it having that unusual quality of non-shrinkage in cooling, peculiar to itself. The sulphur used in the work—two tons—was taken from the surface of the ground on the old Spence claim. No other work had ever been done there. So much was history. It was generally thought, by those interested in mining, that it had been simply a "blow-out" from some untraceable deposit, and that it was not worth the prospecting.

Although I knew of it earlier, I was too young to take any special note of it until about the year 1873. At that time it attracted my attention by reason of the very great number of freshly-shed snake-skins that lay about in the crevices of the gypsum and lava, the sulphur and ash. Dozens of them! Hundreds of them! And, paying heed to the fact, I observed thereafter that each spring they were replaced by others, while the old ones were blown away by the whirlwinds. Evidently it was a famous place for reptiles; yet it was a puzzle to me, always, that in such a quarry of snake-skins, I should never chance to see the snakes themselves.

Back in those years when I first knew sagebrush-land as home, I was an omniverous—if not always a discriminating—reader; and, on summer days when the desert sun shone hot and a particularly fascinating book fell into my hands, I at once sought some spot that offered both cool shade and quiet. What better place than just within the deserted incline of the old sulphur mine? There, surrounded by the white and yellow of gypsum and sulphur walls festooned with the silvery-white skins, I had a retreat all my own, and quite as full of charm to me as any rose-hung bower could have been to another girl—a girl not of the gray wastes and solitudes of the Desert. There, with eyes and heart deep buried in my books, I spent many and many a delightful hour, retreating farther and farther down the incline, as the afternoon sun found and followed me in there. For—burn as it might outside—it was always a delightfully cool place within the incline. There were times when, with an old broken shovel I found there, I dug into the bottom of the deserted prospect-hole for specimens of sulphur crystals —those delicate clusters of glittering yellow jewels that belong to fairyland—yet, dig deep as I would into the soft ash and gypsum, I never observed the slightest indication of heat. I know that in those days there was no indication of subterranean heat whatever.

Then—by and by—I left the Desert for a home at tide-water; and straightway forgot all about he sulphur beds, until years afterward, when I was reminded of them by hearing of a skeleton that had been found there.

In 1888 or '89, Samuel H. Kitto and Dan Merrigan,

two young men out for a jaunt one spring morning, came unexpectedly upon the bleached bones of an unknown man lying at the foot of a hollow cone that is commonly known as "the Crater," half a mile from the old prospect-hole. Nothing was found whereby the dead man might have been identified. There was no paper, no article of clothing—absolutely nothing except an open and rusty razor lying by his side. Of course the Coroner came, as the law provided; and there was the usual farce of an inquest on a fragment of what had once been human. Then the sun-and-storm-whitened bones were carried to the railroad station and buried in the little graveyard where the dead are mostly nameless—tramps killed by some passing train, or (as this one) a fleshless skeleton found far away from wagon road or railroad track. Their stories are unknown and their graves unmarked.

It was at "the Crater"—after doing some preliminary location work at the point where Spence had once worked the claim—that we decided to sink our first shaft. This cone is one of a number of such vent-holes that can be traced thereabouts—vent-holes for furnaces that were burned out centuries ago. Fires have burned and died; great mountain ranges have been lifted high on either side of the valley, down in which the vents are now all but covered by the valley's soil. Only this one lifts itself distinctive—rising sharply a few feet from the level of the plain, to be seen several miles away. The valley here is quite flat—broad, long, and a dead level. There are great alkali flats, absolutely bare and miles wide; but where the sulphur beds are, greasewood—short, scrubby and dead-looking—grows sparsely. Now and then the ground is sprinkled with gravel and flakes of quartz washed down from the mountains.

All the way from the railroad track (which here runs northeast and southwest) to the river, two or three miles away, one may find indications of sulphur. And when one comes to the river itself, one finds other cones, quite unlike these, are fantastically topped with a lime-crust that has resisted the erosion which has eaten the lower strata away. The same hard crust overlies the whole valley here for miles and miles, barely hidden under a thin veneer of soil. But down by the cones by the river's edge (the river of today, whose course is through the centre of the mile-wide channel of the great river of the dead years), one may easily trace the strata downward far below the crust's line. First, the mushroom-shaped lime topping, whose jagged edges in many places have taken unto themselves the semblance of grotesque, unkenned creatures —dragons and gargoyles, and strange open-jawed monsters that seem born of some nightmare. Next, a broad band of almost pure salt—two to three feet in depth; then gypsum and volcanic ash plentifully streaked with sulphur, down to the level of the ancient river bed. They are queer things, these cones that have been fashioned by creeks cut by short-lived floods born from the cloud-bursts on the high lands; and yearly erosion is eating them more surely away.

But none of these, in spite of the evidence of sulphur, are kindred with "the Crater." There, where we made our locations (which through their brimstone suggestiveness seemed to name themselves Aetna, Vesuvius, Popocatapetl, Yztaccihuatl, Mauna Loa and Kilauea), is lava and pumice in plenty; and in walking over the ground—especially if it be on a little rise— one hears the echo of his footsteps as though the sound were sent back from a great vault beneath—a hollow echo that tells of vast caverns underground.

I know too little of scientific lore to dare say what the conditions we found there may indicate; I can only tell what we discovered during our weeks of prospecting, and will leave to others the task of translating the signs that puzzle us still.

We began sinking the shaft in "the Crater" on the twenty-ninth of January. The only men working on the claims at that time were my partner and one of his sons. Later, the younger man's place was taken by an Indian—a young Paiute.

Though it is no part of this story, yet just here let me tell what we found during the morning of that first day's work. There, in "the Crater," but two or three feet down, we came on the skeleton of a man that had been thrust (not buried in decent wise—but jammed) into the hollow hole which the wind-drifts of each year had covered still deeper with the powdered pumice and gypsum and ash tossed down from the brim of the wee "crater."

The side of the skull was crushed in, and the body bent nearly double, as though hurriedly crowded into a hole too small for honest burial. The story? Who knows? Did that other—the one found years before but a few yards from this spot—did he——? But who can say? It is but another mystery of that great, gray land of mysteries.

The skeleton fell apart when unearthed and lay on the crater's edge, where it was cast up by the shovels, a heap of fragile brown bones that seemed more like strips and bits of wet pasteboard than anything else. The water-soaked ash (there had been an unusually warm period for January, and the snow of the valleys was melted, completely saturating the ground) and the moistened sulphur-stained formation we found there had communicated to the bones a peculiar flexibility; for they bent between our fingers like whale-bone. It was an uncanny thing to find at the very outset of our work; so we quickly buried them again, giving them sepulture in the "Popocatapetl's" location monument at the crater's rim. All but the skull and thigh bones—they were set aside to find place with many another strange thing that came out of the Desert in my strangely-lived Desert life.

We were still under the spell that the grewsome "find" had cast over us, when the shaft developed something even more mysterious—an unsolved mystery to this day, at least to the four persons who, so far as I know, are the only ones who have known of it.

After the last slabs of lava-rock had been replaced upon the monument, I dropped over the rim into the pit, and clambered down to the shaft. "The Crater" (such a baby crater it is!) was filled well to the top with a fine gray volcanic ash—dry on top, a bit moist from the rains beneath; while scattered through it were quantities of the rough, unfriendly rock that made the crust of the cone. In the centre of this was the hole that was yet too small to be dignified by the name of a shaft.

From the bottom of the excavation my partner scooped up a handful of the moist earth and asked me to hold out my hands. I did so, and he poured it in. It was warm!—perceptibly so. I was astounded—too puzzled to say anything; and I stood there holding it, looking stupidly at him for an explanation. He laughed; and then, throwing out a shovelful or two from the shaft, took from underneath some that was freshly uncovered.

"Here, take this!"

I don't remember what I said, but I cried out in astonishment as I let it fall. It was hot!—not just warm, but hot!

That was the beginning of what, for weeks and weeks, was to us a daily wonder. Seven or eight feet beneath the surface of the ground we would find this unexplainable heat. Not alone at that particular place, but over a five-mile area, we found like conditions. On the slope just below the old prospect hole we came on ground that was covered here and there with the so-called "petrified grass"—salt grass and the three-cornered stems of Paiute grass, over which, at some former time, lime-impregnated waters from hot springs had flowed. I tried to answer all the questions that came crowding in upon me, by saying to myself that, at some time in the remote past, there had been boiling springs here—springs that were now sealed up. But when I remembered that a quarter of a century before, the earth in the bottom of Spence's old incline was cold, I felt that such explanations were inadequate. Nowhere, in all our knowledge of the valley, had there ever been steam, or fire, or heat. I went into the camps of my Paiute friends and questioned the elders. None of them, nor their fathers, nor their fathers' fathers before them, had ever heard of a time when the valley had spit steam or fire; and their legends (told by father to son as they sit by the campfire, and memorized with infinite accuracy) date back to a time earlier than the white man's history.

Shaft after shaft was sunk, and sulphur in plenty was found. Some of it was crystalized; and much of it was colored like a California poppy. Elsewhere we found a snow-white marvel of sulphur—sulphur that turned yellow only when a lighted match was touched to it, and was ninety-five per cent pure! Now and then we came upon "black" sulphur—that glassy,

dark-green sort made by nature in those molds where
pressure is greatest. Where lime rock was, we found
pisolite and oölite in small quantities. That meant
there had been, at some time, boiling springs. But
such places were few. In the deeper shafts, volcanic
ash was found in undisturbed strata. Volcanic rock
and lava were everywhere; and the lava was frequently streaked with cinnabar. Sometimes a waxy formation would be encountered that discouraged work at
that point. It would not break, as rock ordinarily
will, from shots of giant powder; but was of a texture
that refused to be shattered when blasted, and was
too hard to be worked with picks. And everywhere
was that mysterious heat.

When we were some fifteen feet down the deepest
shaft we sunk, I wrote to the California Academy of
Sciences describing the conditions there (but not nam-
ing the locality) and asked if a similar state of affairs
was known to exist anywhere else in the world. They
were unable to give me any information on the subject,
but referred the letter to Prof. Branner, of Stanford
University. In reply to my brief outline of conditions
he wrote as follows:

"I regret to say that I do not know of any such place
as you mention in your letter. The temperature of
the crust of the earth varies so much, however, in different places that no fixed law has ever been found
for the downward increase of the temperature, except
of local application. In the Comstock mining region,
the temperature is one degree for every twenty-eight
feet, down to 3,000 feet; in the north of England, it
is one degree for forty-nine feet; in New South Wales,
it is one degree for eighty feet; in Leipsic, it is one
degree for fifty-six feet; at Grass Valley, Cal., it is
one degree for one hundred and seven feet; in the cop-

per mines of Michigan, it is one degree for two hundred and twenty-four feet, and so on.''

Up and down, back and forth, we prospected, sinking shafts where we could—tasting it, smelling it, testing it with a match. The whole district, so far as we investigated, is richly underlaid with sulphur; but everywhere that we sunk on the claims we found that strange heat—a heat too great to permit our continuing the work. Where the lava was encountered in greatest quantities, we uncovered the home of the snakes, for it was as full of bubble holes as a honey-comb is of cells. There, long, slim (and entirely harmless) snakes were housed in numbers that were appalling. When the explosions disturbed them from their winter's rest, they had crawled to the walls of the shafts, through the network of cracks that underlie the district, and, tumbling down to the bottom, coiled, and lifted, and writhed there, vainly trying to get out, and quite unpleasing things to see.

The weather turned cold—eight degrees below zero. But the temperature underground was growing hotter and hotter, the deeper the shaft was sunk. At eighteen feet each man who worked there suffered from frightful headaches, and the younger man had to return to his home in Sacramento. Their clothing—even their buckskin gloves—rotted as they worked, and their skin burned and stung. The drill's point in a few moments would become so hot that it caused discomfort to touch it with the bare hand. After a series of blasts had been put off, and the smoke had escaped from the shaft, a cloud of vapor would arise while the mercury marked zero at the top; and the rock thrown up from the bottom was so hot that it could not be handled at all bare-handed.

A
Desert
Mystery

Each night the giant powder froze. Each morning it was thawed in a few minutes by throwing it over a wheelbarrow load of rock and ash from the bottom of the shaft. Sometimes all the sticks of powder in the box would be frozen together, and the mass frozen to the box itself; but by the time the drill-hole was ready for it, the powder would be found thawed. Canteens of water, carried by the men coming to work, were frozen solid. Buried in the broken bits of rock a few moments, the ice would immediately melt. By and by—as the work progressed further downward—the drills became so hot that their temper was destroyed (and, incidentally, our own) and the men could make but little headway in their work. Still they kept on —changing shift every few minutes, and being hauled to the top with faces burning red, down which rivulets of sweat ran.

Some of the time it was, as has been said, zero weather; but on the warmest day the mercury marked fifty degrees. The shaft was down twenty-three feet. The mercury marked 120° when taken to the bottom of the shaft as soon as a man could descend after the shots had been fired. At twenty-nine feet it registered one hundred and forty degrees. The men—working five-minute shifts—sank a foot deeper; but the experience of the last one down was such that not one of them would again venture into that furnace of frightful heat, and the temperature after that last shot was not taken. They were satisfied with the knowledge already obtained—that the heat had increased something like ninety degrees in twenty-nine feet, at the point where the old Spence shaft was—where, more than five-and-twenty years ago, it was a cool and pleasant place to sit and read in on summer afternoons!

Are there fires underneath? Or sealed-up boiling

springs? Or gases that create heat? Or what? We had all sorts of theories, of course; and we talked together of the statements that had been made to us that there were places in the valley where the ground had settled unaccountably during the previous ten years; and we did a great deal of wondering. But all our speculations left us baffled and bewildered. And because we could not satisfy ourselves as to the causes, we said nothing of the affair to anyone else. The few folk who live within sight of the ground, and the hundreds that pass over it in railway cars every day, have never heard nor known of these things that would seem to me now (living here in rose-land by the sea, and "where things never happen") but a dream, did I not have, as proof of it really having happened, over the door of my den—where I can look up and see it as I write—the skull and crossbones of the man of "Popocatapetl."

A Desert Mystery

People came there to visit the "prospects," but not till after the deepest shafts had been partially refilled, that stray horses and cattle might not fall in them, to be killed or crippled. Some of the smaller shafts there were, in which (had they but closely noticed) some heat might have been observed. But much of the heat disappeared after the shafts had been exposed to the air for a while. So the visitors went away, discovering nothing unusual, at least up to the time when I abandoned the claims as impracticable for working.

Sulphur there is a-plenty, but it is guarded by an inferno of subterranean heat that puts it far beyond the reach of the miner's pick and drill. Will the heat that so strangely came, after a while subside? Who can say what may happen? I only know it is a place of serpents and sulphurous smells, of strange heat, of dead men's bones, and mystery. Such places are best let alone. I—for one—want no more of them.

THE TOLL OF THE DESERT.

 IRAGE of Water, or Mirage of a Mine! It matters not which it may be, the end is the same for him who follows after the Siren who is always in league with Death. All the years of his life the Old Prospector gives to the Desert his best and his all—gives hope, and joy, and love, even as he gave youth. He gives his very soul; then, finally, he commits his body to the Desert's keeping—to sleep there in its everlasting silence. It is the final toll that the Desert takes of a man. Cruel? Nay, the Desert is kind; for in death the body rests where the heart found its joy in life. What lover could ask more?

The sands, that knew his every footfall, cradle him. The everlasting mountains—the heights he loved—stand watch and ward. And the night-wind, that was with him when he lay out under the stars, shall sing his slumber-song now, as some Indian mother croons over the babe that, in the twilight, falls asleep at her breast. In such wise, does the Old Prospector find rest in the Desert.

In such wise, would all lovers of that land meet the end. To go to sleep there under the white stars; to go away into the land of dreams, lying in the arms of the Desert; to rest—and rest— and rest, through all time, through centuries of silence and solitude! What would you that one (loving the land) should have, when the Night comes, that could be more desired? They who have lived long there ask for no other burial, be assured.

And of this, too, you may be sure. If you have gone into the Desert and found its Soul, you have climbed more than half-way up the ladder that reaches Godward. Therefore, I say, these men who live there are not men without religion; though creeds they may not (and probably do not) claim as theirs. But it is not a far thing from reverence, as one knows it in a temple, to stand with voice hushed and ear inclined, while God and the Desert speak together. Not once a week—on the Sabbath—is this so. But it is part of what comes to one (though unconsciously, mayhap) daily. They know it, but give it no name.

So you will understand that he who has lived there —if he has lived a life that has harmed no man—dies unafraid. To spend many years of one's life there, in the gray land, takes away the coward fear of Death. That is because one has learned to measure all things in the balance of just proportion; and then one comes to see how small is the atom, Self. More! This truth is taught in Nature's wisdom—that all things are best. He has led the life he believed was best; and he believes it is best that so he should die.

"Earth to earth, dust to dust, ashes to ashes." If you come upon some Desert grave one day as you ride along any of the roads of old days, and if the words of the burial service come to you as you draw rein there, do not hesitate to add: "In sure and certain hope of the Resurrection." For none died without religion—as all great silence and space teaches religion—and few died without hope.

And this shall you remember. Though the Desert in its time takes full toll of the men who go there; yet never do they give unwillingly.

GRAVES OF THE DESERT.

GRAVES of the Desert! Forgotten graves. How many there are! In lonely places by the wayside, where civilized man has not yet succeeded in making "two blades of grass to grow" where once there was but the wide sweep of shifting, drifting sands; where still are found Desert stretches, alternating with the green oases which follow in the white man's wake across the plains, there are the graves of men fifty years dead—graves that bear silent testimony to the march of those battalions of America's heroes who were first to tempt the unknown in a land that once seemed God-despised.

Forgotten graves—dug in the sand and alkali that lightly covers the great inland Western states, whose priceless foundations—sunken far into the bowels of the earth, thousands of feet below the drab, sad-colored soil—were laid by the gnomes in those aeons when the world was being created in marvelous ways.

And the gnomes quarried huge masses of solid silver, and hewed and cut them cunningly, fashioning them into great polished cubes. These they laid for the far Western states to rest upon. And the blocks were cemented together with mortar made of molten, shining gold. Then over it all they spread the sand

and the soil and hid their handiwork, leaving it for man to uncover in the ages to come, when on these foundations he should upbuild the States.

Up and down the valleys, never resting, the whirl-winds go—those dancing dervishes of the Desert. They blow the sands hither and thither, back and forth unceasingly, as they spin giddily around year after year in their mad dance. Sometimes it seems as if they have almost brushed aside the sands and bared the foundations of these Silver States—these States of Gold. But a stronger whirlwind comes hurrying up the valley and buries the treasure deep again.

The little winds, as they go spinning on tiptoe round and round and round, until you are dizzy with the watching, whirl fast and mad; but, whirl as they will, whirl they never so madly, they are not strong enough to blow the sands away. And the people go back there to the

> "tending of cattle and tossing of clover;
> the grazing of cattle and growing of grain,"

in those places where Nature helps them make another oasis; and they will tell you that they are waiting for a wind that is in leash now; a great wind that will come out of the East.

Long they have watched and waited, and the sands are not yet blown away. Still they hope, as we all hope for the thing our heart leans to; and they will tell you that surely, some day, the East wind will come, sent by a power that will say, as it speeds it on its more than a thousand miles of journeying over mountain, and upland, and plain: "Go, blow the sands aside! brush them away, that the States may be built up from the foundations which the gnomes laid!"

These are the things they will tell you. Are they

Graves of the Desert.

right, or are they wrong? Are they prophets, or only men who pray? Do they see into the future, or are they but dreamers? Who knows?

But, all the while the whirlwinds are tossing the sands about, and uncovering and covering over again the dead men's bones—men who made a way across States that, unknown to them, were built upon foundations of precious metals. And those who faltered and fell by the way in their quest for gold as they struggled to push on to California—California by the sea—little dreamed of the wealth beneath their feet.

They strung themselves out—a living thread—across the plains, over half a hundred years ago; today the engine's whistle shrieks from shore to shore. Progress provides us the luxuries of the modern mode of travel, and in journeying westward from States far beyond the Rocky Mountains' jagged ridge, here and there, after entering that vast tract which belongs to the great West, looking from the windows of the Pullman sleeper one may see faint traces of an old wagon road running parallel with the railway's double line of steel. It is not the road which is nearest the track— that is the newer road made by a newer people—but the old one traced there by the emigrants of fifty years ago, in their half a twelvemonths' journey across the Great American Desert. At first one does not see it; the track is not visible in the grass-covered Nebraska soil, when the train, after crossing the great river at Omaha, puts behind it all things having a likeness to the East.

Looking from the window as one rushes by, he sees bits of a rolling plain, where—here and there—tall and scattered trees having the semblance of gray ghosts in the late afternoon light, go hurrying across the landscape, their slender branches outlined against a gold and glowing horizon, where red and fiery piled-up clouds fill full the western sky. Long stretches of shallow water, left by late rains, glisten amidst the growth of tall grasses, and in the reedy places—shaded by bush and tree—are grouped great flocks of ducks that in the fading daylight seem of a velvety blackness—scenes to thrill the heart of a hunter and charm the eye of an artist. Then the dusk's gray mantle drops slowly down and spreads over the sleeping world. Night has come—night on the plain—ere one has noted its approach, the while the train is rushing on into the darkness and the Western land. Graves of the Desert

On and on till the dawning of day; on and on throughout the long, hot, dusty daylight hours; each revolution of the wheels of the mighty creature whose sinews are of steel, and whose blood is of fire, has plunged one farther and farther into that vast land which was once but the land of sand and sage, and of silence. Human progress has plowed and planted here and there, civilization has made grain to grow in many of the waste places, and has garnered where once was but the illimitable Desert.

Cities have sprung up out of the once silent plains, and a hundred thousand homes of the living now line the great pathway which was marked out by the skeletons of the dead.

Half a century ago it was the land of the dried-up alkali lakes; of the far-reaching sage; of the biting, white dust; of the ever-beckoning mirage; of the strangely slender, cloud-touching whirlwinds which come writhing and winding and twisting their way up the valley to meet you, and greet you with a whisper of unknown things, and then pass on, twisting and swaying and whirling, to mingle with the mystery of the Desert.

Into this land, more than fifty years ago, an army of heroes voyaged. Across the dried-up sea, whitened by salt and alkali, their Desert-ships drifted on and into the farther West. The courage that was theirs to dare the dangers they met upon the way, the hardships they encountered and endured, have passed into the great volumes of unwritten history.

We know of the many who reached Pacific shores, but who can count those who died like that other weary traveler of whom a loving brother wrote: "He lay down by the wayside; and using his burden for a pillow, fell into that dreamless sleep that kisses down his eyelids still." Time is levelling the cairns which mark their resting places, and those mile-stones of their great and awful journey are being scattered and destroyed.

Along the road marked out by their slow-moving ox-teams, which stretched its weary way from the Missouri river to the Sacramento, the graves of those who fell by the roadside marked its course. Even unto this day the old road is traceable, although but little used. Not everywhere may it be seen from the car windows; for in some places the railroad leaves it miles and miles away to the right or left. Yet, through that vast plain lying between the Rockies and the Sierras, one sometimes sees it close beside the track for a long distance; then, to avoid a grade, it winds around a rise in the plain and disappears.

The railroad has cut a tunnel through the rise, and where the ground is levelled it has laid its track of pine and steel; but in those long past days no shovel was struck into the earth, save to hollow out the shallow graves wherein were laid away the bones of those who are asleep in the Sahara of America.

Wherever these graves are found—if it be in a locality where there are rocks about—one will see that they are heaped with stones. After the soil had been scraped into a long, low mound—the one form into which earth is shaped to wear the sign of pathos— stones were closely piled upon it to keep the dear dead from the ghouls of the Desert; for coyote and badger alike disinterred them unless they were protected in this way.

So, if you will do as I have done, and—in the saddle—ride over mile after mile of the old emigrant road where it winds in and out among the gullies along the foothills, or where it dips further down into the lowlands, or as it trails along the mesa, or stretches out straight across the hard, alkali flats; or where it follows the banks of the muddy Humboldt, crossing and recrossing the bends where the old fords are, you will surely chance upon some long-neglected mounds which tell their silent stories of the sufferings and privations of those whose names must forever remain unknown. Sometimes a roughly-lettered board was placed at the head, but oftener it was "a grave without tombstone or token. The new years of this century find very nearly all of the boards fallen or lost. Even the piled-up stones are being scattered. The graves are suffering the neglect which comes to all forgotten things; perhaps many of these dead men were themselves forgotten two-score years ago.

"None come who knew them. There are none to say
Where lived they, whom loved they, ere they passed
    away.
They sleep with none to marvel o'er them, save
Some stranger musing by the sunken grave.''

Riding along the road one day, where it winds its way down the valley of the Humboldt, I came upon two half-hidden graves. They were just above the

river bank, near an old-time emigrant ford. The head-
boards had rotted and fallen; the sagebrush—tall and
thick—hid them from the passer-by. The brief in-
scription told but little:

John Knudson,
died Sept. 13th, 1854,
aged 43 years.
From La. Co., Wis.

The words had been cut in a small board, evidently
part of some box taken from their scanty store, and
then nailed across the top of another narrow piece.
It had, no doubt, once been set firmly in the ground.
A bit of board had also been at the foot; but, like the
other, it, too, had broken off and fallen. The other
grave bore these words—cut clearly, and with great
care—on the little headboard:

John Walling,
Died
by drowning
September 1st, 1859.
Aged 28 years.

The lettering in the storm-stained, weather-checked
wood had been cut so beautifully true and even that
one is certain that it was the work of someone to whom
the dead man was dear; for only loving hands could
have been so painstaking. The graves were sunken;
the stones were scattered. I went away; and when
I came again it was to bring some one to re-set the
boards at head and foot, and with a shovel heap the
earth into the shape it bore when other hands than
strangers' had done the same office for the dead forty
years before.

Who were they? Were any of their kindred with
them when, with their journey but half done, they
stepped aside from the trail made by the path-finders

of the West, to stay in the barren valley, while the others went on to the land of promise by the Golden Gate? Or did they leave wives and children far behind them in the safer East, while they braved the perils of the plains to reach the land of gold for the sake of the wealth they would find, and all the great and good things it would bring to the dear ones at home? Or did mothers and children mourn, and wonder at the silence; and so die with their questioning ever unanswered? Who is there that dare say what that silence meant to them?

These are but two among the many hundreds barred along the route of the old emigrant road; and how pitifully alike would be the histories of their trials by the way, could we but know them all!

Almost all of these graves are nameless; yet in this valley there is at least one that bears a name, and is a grave well known. It bears the name of "Lucinda Duncan" upon a large, white cross, erected by the railway company when its roadbed was being made ready for the rails more than thirty years ago. It is "The Maiden's Grave," near Beowawe; and they placed the cross above the young girl sleeping in the valley, ere they passed on.

But the names of the dead lying in the numberless graves are, for the greater part, unknown; and age and sex can only be vaguely guessed at.

Here is one who was, perhaps, the captain of his caravan; a beloved leader of the men who manned some Desert-ship. How disheartened the survivors were when they had lain him away and had to push on under the burning, blistering skies without the companionship, the leadership, or the cheering encouragement of their trusted guide! Their ship was without a captain or pilot in this sea of gray, shoreless sand.

Could they carry it safely into port? they asked. And we, half a hundred years later, wonder—did they?

Here is a smaller, shorter grave, that holds, perhaps, the remains of some youth, hopeful and enthusiastic in his first venture into a new life; impatient at the slow pace of the weary oxen, dragging the wagons so few—so very few—miles each day toward the golden West he was so eager to reach.

Or perhaps it might have been a woman; one of those brave souls who, cleaving to the men of her household, left behind her all the dear associations of a lifetime to enter upon a new experience, and, hand in hand with father or hunband or son, went out into the unknown new country to share the work, the sickness or the dangers of the uncertain venture. No fear of the savages, who crept down upon many a one and left the victim murdered and mutilated by the road; no fear of disease that might claim them before the journey's end; no fear of any of the perils which made more than one man turn back before the journey had well begun, could keep these women from joining their dear kindred in the six months' march that reached almost from sea to sea. O men, men! how little you know the place you hold in the hearts of the women who love you!

There were many such grand and loyal women who went out beyond the pale of civilization, whose presence helped their men-folk onward, whose bravery spurred them forward to reach their golden goal, when heart-sick and weary they would have given up the struggle in despair.

These men were brave; yet there were times when courage failed them. As their hopes of reaching the sea faded in the face of unforeseen dangers met on the way, and they came to feel that, after all, the earth was only a place in which to dig graves, these women lifted them up with hopeful words and helpful deeds and carried them through to the end.

Here is a tiny mound of stones; "a little grave, a little, little grave, an obscure grave." What this one holds, we know. But no one can ever guess the anguish of that mother who laid her baby here, nor how she suffered as she looked backward, ever backward, as the ox-teams carried her away. Before that day, she had complained because the oxen went so slowly; but afterward their pace was never slow enough. Every step was making the tiny mound grow fainter to her sight, as the journey was resumed, when the wee little one had been lain away. How she looked, and looked, back to the place where they had halted a day! And as she looked, she kept whispering to herself: "To-morrow I shall not be able to see it at all." Backward, all the while backward, did she turn her face to the spot where "baby" was;—the little child that was yet too young to have another name. The mother forgot then that she had ever looked forward. Oh, how fast the oxen went! If they would but go slower, so that she could see the little, low mound in the Desert a while longer! It seemed to her that all those great stones they had piled there, had been heaped upon her heart— her poor, bruised heart—because of the load there that was so, so heavy. All her life long her heart would ache, her whole body would throb with pain—wrists and palms and finger-tips—with the intensity of her longing to know once again the sound of its voice, the sight of its face, the touch of its satiny, rose-leaf hands. Oh, to know again the thrilling touch of soft, warm, baby fingers laid upon her cheek—the touch of moist baby lips laid against her breast!

Graves

of

the

Desert.

Never again! She was going alone out of the Desert —out of the Valley of Death; going, and away back there by the roadside she had left a little grave.

Graves—graves—graves; how many there are! They are scattered all along the roadside from the far-away East to the farthest West; and yet not all who died on the old emigrant road received burial. The bodies of many, pierced by Indian arrows, never found sepulture, but, scalped and mutilated, were left by savage hands to the birds and coyotes, their bones bleaching there in the sun year after year.

Forgotten and neglected graves of the Desert! For more than fifty years they have been a part of that vast silence; visited only by the snows of winter or the rays of the burning summer sun. No one comes to mourn them. None come to lay flowers above their dead.

The afternoon sun goes down, shooting arrows of fire into the heavens, above a banner of crimson and gold. A curtain of blood-red grandeur fringed with flame is flung athwart the west in the magnificence of a Desert sunset—the like of which is not seen elsewhere in all the world—and as the sun sinks lower and lower behind the purple mountains, heaven above and earth beneath are all aglow with color. The sun's rays touch the highest peak of the range that guards the eastern side of the valley, and the snow-covered crest thousands of feet above is crowned by the dying sun with a diadem of more than regal splendor.

Slowly the wonderful light spreads over the landscape, changing the foot-hills to ruby, and the valley to rose, with an indescribable wealth of shading, and seeming to make every bush and briar burst into blossom with flowers of exquisite beauty. It falls with equal glory on green tree and gray shrub; on the clover-sweet oasis of a later growth and the Desert that the earth knew of old. And down near the river where the emigrant road runs, where are the graves of emigrants of the early days, where the graves of Walling and Knudson were made, the lovely light creeps in waves of pink and violet, and lines that are faintly blue; and ere the night comes, Nature, who never forgets her children, even in the Desert's solitude, though man forget brother man, has covered them over as with a pall of beautiful blossoms.

Graves
of
the
Desert.

And here ends "In Miners' Mirage-Land,"
as written by Idah Meacham Strobridge,
with cover design and chapter decorations made by J. Duncan Gleason, and
published by the Artemisia Bindery, which
is in Los Angeles, California, at the Sign
of the Sagebrush; and completed on the
Nineteenth day of August, One thousand
nine hundred and four. ✂ ✂ ✂

THE LOOM OF THE DESERT

"The boy swayed backward — backward." — Page 10

The Loom of the Desert

by

Idah Meacham Strobridge

LOS ANGELES
MCMVII

MARRIED: In Newark, New Jersey, Thursday, evening, June the Second, 1852, Phebe Amelia Craiger of Newark, to George Washington Meacham of California.

———————

To these—my dearest;
the FATHER and MOTHER who are my comrades still,
I dedicate
these stories of a land where we were pioneers.

CONTENTS

FOREWORD

There, in that land set apart for Silence, and Space, and the Great Winds, Fate—a grim, still figure—sat at her loom weaving the destinies of desert men and women. The shuttles shot to and fro without ceasing, and into the strange web were woven the threads of Light, and Joy, and Love; but more often were they those of Sorrow, or Death, or Sin. From the wide Gray Waste the Weaver had drawn the color and design; and so the fabric's warp and woof were of the desert's tone. Keeping this always well in mind will help you the better to understand those people of the plains, whose lives must needs be often sombre-hued.

MESQUITE.

MISS GLENDOWER sat on the ranch house piazza, shading her eyes from the white glare of the sun by holding above them—in beautiful, beringed fingers—the last number of a Boston magazine. It was all very new and delightful to her—this strange, unfinished country, and each day developed fresh charm. As a spectacle it was perfect —the very desolation and silence of the desert stirred something within her that the Back Bay had never remotely roused. Viewed from the front row of the dress circle, as it were, nothing could be more fascinating to her art-loving sense than this simple, wholesome life lived out as Nature teaches, and to feel that, for the time, the big, conventional world of wise insincerities was completely shut away behind those far purple mountains out of which rose the desert sun.

As for becoming an integral part of all this one's self—Ah, that was a different matter! The very thought of her cousin, Blanche Madison, and Roy— her husband—deliberately turning their backs on the refinements of civilization, and accepting the daily drudgery and routine of life on a cattle ranch, filled her with wondering amazement. When she fell to speculating on what their future years here would be, she shuddered. From the crown of her sleek and perfectly poised little head, to the hollowed sole of her modishly booted foot, Miss Audrey Glendower was Bostonian.

Still, for the short space of time that she waited Lawrence Irving's coming, life here was full of charm for her—its ways were alluring, and not the least among its fascinations was Mesquite.

She smiled amusedly as she thought of the tall cowboy's utter unconsciousness of any social difference between them—at his simple acceptance of her notice. Miss Glendower was finding vast entertainment in his honest-hearted, undisguised adoration. She had come West for experiences, and one of the first (as decidedly the most exciting and interesting) had been found in Mesquite. Besides, it gave her something to write of when she sent her weekly letter to Lawrence Irving. Sometimes she found writing to him a bit of a bore—when topics were few.

But Mesquite—— The boy was a revelation of fresh surprises every day. There was no boredom where he was. Amusing; yes, that was the word. There he was now!—crossing the bare and hard beaten square of gray earth that lay between the ranch house and the corrals. Though he was looking beyond the piazza to where the other boys were driving a "bunch" of bellowing, dust-stirring cattle into an enclosure, yet she felt it was she whom his eyes saw. He was coming straight toward the house—and her. She knew it. Miss Glendower knew many things, learned in the varied experience of her eight-and-twenty years. Her worldly wisdom was more—much more—than his would be at double his present age. Mesquite was twenty.

He looked up with unconcealed pleasure in her presence as he seated himself on the piazza—swinging his spurred heels against each other, while he leaned his head back against one of the pillars. Miss Glendower's eyes rested on the burned, boyish face with delight. There was something so näive, so sweetly childish about him. It was simply delicious to hear his "Yes, ma'am," or his "Which?" Just now his yellow hair lay in little damp rings on his forehead, like a baby's just awakened from sleep. He sat with his big, dust-covered sombrero shoved back from a forehead guiltless of tan or freckles as the petals of a white rose. But the lower part of his face was roughened by wind and burned by the sun to an Indian red, making the blue eyes the bluer—those great, babyish eyes that looked out with a belying innocence from under their marvelous fringe of upcurling lashes. The blue eyes were well used to looking upon sights that would have shocked Miss Glendower's New England training, could she have known; and the babyish lips were quite familiar with language that would have made her pale with horror and disgust to hear. But then, she didn't know. Neither could he have understood her standpoint.

He was only the product of his environment, and one of the best things that it had taught him was to have no disguises. So he sat today looking up at his lady with all his love showing in his face.

Then, in the late afternoon warmth, as the day's red ball of burning wrath dropped down behind the western desert rim of their little world, he rode beside her, across sand hills where sweet flowers began to open their snow-white petals to the night wind's touch, and over barren alkali flats to the postoffice half a dozen miles away.

Mesquite

There was only one letter waiting for Miss Glendower that night. It began:

"I will be with you, my darling, twenty-four hours after you get this. Just one more day, Love, and I may hold you in my arms again! Just one more week, and you will be my wife, Audrey. Think of it!"

She had thought; she was thinking now. She was also wondering how Mesquite would take it. She glanced at the boy as she put the letter away and turned her horse's head toward home. Such a short time and she would return to the old life that, for the hour, seemed so strangely far away! Now—alone in the desert with Mesquite—it would not be hard to persuade herself that this was all there was of the world or of life.

As they loped across the wide stretch of desert flats that reached to the sand hills, shutting the ranch from sight, the twilight fell, and with it came sharp gusts of wind that now and then brought a whirl of desert dust. Harder and harder it blew. Nearer and nearer—then it fell upon them in its malevolence, to catch them—to hold them in its uncanny clasp an instant—and then, releasing them, go madly racing off to the farther twilight, moaning in undertone as it went. Then heat lightning struck vividly at the horizon, and the air everywhere became surcharged with the electric current of a desert sand storm. They heard its roar coming up the valley. Audrey Glendower felt her nerves a-tingle. This, too, was an experience! In sheer delight she laughed aloud at the excitement showing in the quivering horses—their ears nervously pointing forward, and their nostrils distended, as with long, eager strides they pounded away over the wind-beaten levels.

Then the storm caught them at its wildest. Suddenly a tumble-weed, dry and uprooted from its slight moorings somewhere away on the far side of the flats, came whirling toward them broadside in the vortex of a mad rush of wind in which—without warning—they were in an instant enveloped. As the great, rolling, ball-like weed struck her horse, Miss Glendower took a tighter grip on the reins and steadied herself for the runaway rush into the dust storm and the darkness. The wild wind caught her, shrieked in her ears, tore at her habit as though to wrest it from her body, dragged at the braids of heavy hair until—loosened—the strands whipped about her head, a tangled mass of stinging lashes.

She was alone—drawn into the maelstrom of the mad element; alone—with the fury of the desert storm; alone—in the awful darkness it wrapped about her, the darkness of the strange storm and the darkness of the coming night. The frightened, furious horse beneath her terrified her less than the weird, rainless storm that had so swiftly slipped in between her and Mesquite, carrying her away into its unknown depths. Where was he? In spite of the mastering fear that was gaining upon her, in spite of her struggle for courage, was a consciousness which told her that more than all else—that more than everyone else in the world—it was Mesquite she wanted. Had others, to the number of a great army, ridden down to her rescue she would have turned away from them all to reach out her arms to the boy vaquero. Perhaps it was because she had seen his marvelous feats of daring in the saddle (for Mesquite was the star rider of the range), and she felt instinctively that he could help her as none other; perhaps it was because of the past days that had so drawn him toward her; perhaps (and most likely) it was because he had but just been at her side. However it might be, she was praying with all her soul for his help—for him to come to her—while mile after mile she rode on, unable to either guide or slacken the stride of her horse. His pace had been terrific; and not until it had carried him out of the line of the storm, and up from the plain into the sand hills, did he lessen his speed. Then the hoofs were dragged down by the the heavy sand, and the storm's strength—all but spent —was left away back on the desert.

She felt about her only the softest of West winds; the dust that had strangled her was gone, and in its place was the syringa-like fragrance of the wild, white primroses, star-strewing the earth, as the heavens were strewn with their own night blossoms.

Just above the purple-black bar of the horizon burned a great blood-red star in the sky. It danced and wavered before her—rising and falling unsteadily—and she realized that her strength was spent—that she was falling. Then, just as the loosened girth let the saddle turn with her swaying body, a hand caught at her bridle-rein, and——

Ah, she was lying sobbing and utterly weak, but unutterably happy, on Mesquite's breast—Mesquite's arms about her! She made no resistance to the passionate kisses the boyish lips laid half fearfully on her face. She was only glad of the sweetness of it all; just as the sweetness of the evening primroses (so like the fragrance of jasmine, or tuberose, or syringa) sunk into her senses. So she rested against his breast, seeing still—through closed eyelids—the glowing, red star. She was unstrung by the wild ride and the winds that had wrought on her nerves. It made yielding so easy.

At last she drew back from him; and instantly his

arms were unlocked. She was free! Not a second of time would he clasp her unwillingly. Neither had spoken. Nor, after resetting the saddle, when he took her again in his arms and lifted her, as he would a little child, upon her horse, did they speak. Only when the ranch buildings—outlined against the darkness—showed dimly before them, and they knew that the ride was at an end, did he voice what was uppermost in his mind.

"Yo' don't—— Yo' ain't—— Oh, my pretty, yo' ain't mad at me, are yo'?"

"No, Mesquite," came the softly whispered answer.

"I'm glad o' that. Shore, I didn't mean fur to go an' do sech a thing; but—— Gawd! I couldn't help it."

But when lifting her down at the ranch-house gate he would have again held her sweetness a moment within his clasp, Miss Glendower (she was once again Miss Glendower of the great world) let her cool, steady voice slip between:

"The letter I got tonight is from the man I am to marry in a week. He will be here tomorrow. But, I want to tell you—— Mesquite—— I want you to know that I—I shall always remember this ride of ours. Always."

Mesquite did not answer.

"Good-night, Mesquite." She waited. Still there was no reply.

Mesquite led the horses away and Miss Glendower turned and went into the house. Being an uneducated cowboy he was remiss in many matters of courtesy.

When Lawrence Irving arrived at the Madison ranch, his host, in the list of entertainment he was offering the Bostonian, promised an exhibition of bronco riding that would stir even the beat of that serene gentleman's well regulated pulse.

"This morning," said Madison, "I was afraid that I wouldn't be able to get my star bronco buster out for your edification, Lawrence, for the boys have been telling me that he has been 'hitting the jug' pretty lively down at the store for the past twenty-four hours (he's never been much of a drinker, either), but when I told him Miss Glendower wanted to show you the convolutions of a bucking horse, it seemed to sober him up a bit, and he not only promised to furnish the thrills, but to do the business up with all the trimmings on—for he's going to ride 'Sobrepaso,' a big, blaze-face sorrel that they call 'the man killer,' and that every vaquero in the country has given up unconquered. Mesquite himself refused to mount him again, some time ago; but today he is in a humor that I can't quite understand—even allowing for all the bad whiskey that he's been getting away with—and seems not only ready but eager to tackle anything."

"I'm grateful to you, Rob," began Irving, "for——"

"Oh, you'll have to thank Audrey for the show! Mesquite is doing it solely for her sake. He has been her abject slave ever since she came."

Both men laughed and looked at Miss Glendower, who did not even smile. It might have been that she did not hear them. They rose and went out to the shaded piazza where it was cooler. The heat was making Miss Glendower look pale.

They, and the ranch hands who saw "Sobrepaso" ("the beautiful red devil," Mrs. Madison called him) brought out into the gray, hard beaten square that formed the arena, felt a thrill of nervous expectancy— a chilling thrill—as Mesquite made ready to mount.

The Loom of the Desert

The horse was blindfolded ere the saddle was thrown on; but with all the fury of a fiend he fought—in turn —blanket, and saddle, and cincha. The jaquima was slipped on, the stirrups tied together under the horse's belly, and all the while his squeals of rage and maddened snorts were those of an untamed beast that would battle to the death. The blind then was pulled up from his eyes, and—at the end of a sixty-foot riata —he was freed to go bucking and plunging in a fury of uncontrolled wrath around the enclosure. At last sweating and with every nerve twitching in his mad hatred of the meddling of Man he was brought to a standstill, and the blind was slipped down once more. He stood with all four feet braced stiffly, awkwardly apart, and his head down, while Mesquite hitched the cartridge belt (from which hung his pistol's holster) in place; tightened the wide-brimmed, battered hat on his head; slipped the strap of a quirt on his wrist; looked at the fastenings of his big-rowelled, jingling spurs; and then (with a quick, upward glance at Miss Glendower—the first he had given her) he touched caressingly a little bunch of white primroses he had plucked that morning from their bed in the sand hills and pinned to the lapel of his unbuttoned vest.

Mesquite had gathered the reins into his left hand, and was ready for his cat-like spring into place. His left foot was thrust into the stirrup—there was the sweep of a long leg thrown across the saddle—a sinuous swing into place, and Mesquite—"the star rider of the range" had mounted the man killer. Quickly the blind was whipped up from the blood-shot eyes, the spurred heels gripped onto the cincha, there was a shout from his rider and a devilish sound from the mustang as he made his first upward leap, and then went

The Loom of the Desert

madly fighting his way around and around the enclosure.

Mesquite sat the infuriated animal as though he himself were but a part of the sorrel whirlwind. His seat was superb. Miss Glendower felt a tremor of pride stir her as she watched him—pride that her lover should witness this matchless horsemanship. She was panting between fear and delight while she watched the boy's face (wearing the sweet, boyish smile—like, yet so unlike—the smile she had come to know in the past weeks), and the yellow curls blowing back from the bared forehead.

"Sobrepaso" rose in his leaps to great heights—almost falling backward—to plunge forward, with squeals of rage that he could not unseat his rider. The boy sat there, a king—king of his own little world, while he slapped at the sorrel's head and withers with the sombrero that swung in his hand. Plunging and leaping, round and round—now here and now there—about the enclosure they went, the horse a mad hurricane and his rider a centaur. Mesquite was swayed back and forth, to and fro, but no surge could unseat him. Miss Glendower grew warm in her joy of him as she looked.

Then, somehow (as the "man killer" made another great upward leap) the pistol swinging from Mesquite's belt was thrown from its holster, and—striking the cantle of the saddle as it fell—there was a sharp report, and a cloud-like puff (not from the dust raised by beating hoofs), and a sound (not the terrible sounds made by a maddened horse), and the boy swayed backward —backward—with the boyish smile chilled on his lips, and the wet, yellow curls blowing back from his white forehead that soon would grow yet whiter.

*   *   *   *   *

Miss Glendower did not faint, neither did she scream; she was one with her emotions held always well in hand, and she expressed the proper amount of regret the occasion required—shuddering a little over its horror. But to this day (and she is Mrs. Lawrence Irving now) she cannot look quite steadily at a big, red star that sometimes burns in the West at early eve; and the scent of tuberoses, or jasmine, or syringa makes her deathly sick.

Mesquite

THE REVOLT OF MARTHA SCOTT

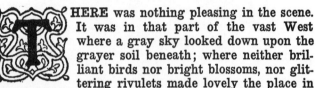

HERE was nothing pleasing in the scene. It was in that part of the vast West where a gray sky looked down upon the grayer soil beneath; where neither brilliant birds nor bright blossoms, nor glittering rivulets made lovely the place in which human beings went up and down the earth daily performing those labors that made the sum of what they called life. Neither tree nor shrub, nor spear of grass showed green with the healthy color of plant life. As far as the eye could reach was the monotonous gray of sagebrush, and greasewood, and sand. The muddy river, with its myriad curves, ran between abrupt banks of soft alkali ground, where now and then as it ate into the confining walls, portions would fall with a loud splash into the water. A hurrying, treacherous river—with its many silent eddies—it turned and twisted and doubled on itself a thousand times as it wound its way down the valley. Here, where it circled in a great curve called "Scott's Bend," the waters were always being churned by the ponderous wheel of a little quartz-mill, painted by storm and sunshine in the leaden tones of its sad-colored surroundings.

On the bluff above, near the ore platform, were grouped a dozen houses. Fenceless, they faced the mill, which day after day pounded away at the ore with a maddening monotony. All day, all night, the stamps kept up their ceaseless monotone. The weather-worn mill and drab adobe houses had stood there, year after year, through the heat of summer days, when the sun blistered and burned the whole valley, and in winter, when the winds of the desert moaned and wailed at the windows.

Today the air is quiet, save for the tiny whirlwinds that, running over the tailings below the mill, have caught up the fine powder and carried bits of it away with them, a white cloud, as they went. The sun, too, is shining painfully bright and burning. By the well a woman stands, her eyes intently following a chance wayfarer who has turned into the Sherman road—in all the waste, the only moving thing.

How surely human beings take on themselves the reflection of their surroundings! Living in the dull solitude of this valley that woman's life has become but a gray reflection of its never ending sameness. As we look, we fall a-wondering. Has she never known what it is to live in the way we understand it? Has nothing ever set her pulses tingling with the exultation of Life? Does she know only an existence which is but the compulsory working of a piece of human machinery? Has she never known what it is to feel hope, or joy, or love, in the way we feel it—never experienced one single stirring emotion in the whole round of her pitifully barren life? Is it possible that she has never realized the poverty of her existence?

Yet, she was a creature meant for Life. What a beautiful woman she is, too, with all that brilliance of coloring—that copper-hued hair, and those great, velvety eyes, lovely in spite of their apathetic stare. What a model for some painter's brush! Such beauty and such apathy combined; such expressionless perfection of feature; "faultily faultless, icily regular, splendidly null—dead perfection."

Martha Scott is one of those women whose commanding figure and magnificent coloring are always sufficient to attract the admiration of even the most indifferent. No doubt now in her maturity she is far more beautiful than when, nearly twenty years ago, she became Old Scott's wife. A tall, unformed girl then, she gave no promise of her later beauty, except in the velvety softness of the great eyes that never seemed to take heed of anything in the world about her, and the great mass of shining hair that had the red-gold of a Western sunset in it.

There had been a courtship so brief that they were still strangers when he took her to the small, untidy house where he had come to realize that the presence of a woman was needed. He wanted a wife to cook for him; to wash—to sew. And so they were married.

The sheep which numbered thousands, the little mill —always grinding in its jaws the ores brought down the mountain by the snail-paced teams to fill its hungry maw, these added daily to the hoard Old Scott clutched with gripping, penurious fingers. Early and late, unceasingly, he worked, and chose that Martha should labor as he labored, live as he lived. But, as she mechanically took up her burden of life, there came to the sweet, uncomplaining mouth a droop at the corners that grew with the years, telling to those who had the eyes to see, that while accepting with mute lips the unhappy conditions of her lot, she longed with all her starved soul for something different from her yearly round of never-ending toil.

Once—only once—in a whirlwind of revolt, she felt that she could endure it no longer—that she must break

away from the dull routine which made the measure of
her days; felt that she must go out among happy human beings—to be in the rush and whirl of life under
Pleasure's sunshine—to bask in its warmth as others
did. She longed to enjoy life as Youth enjoys; herself
to be young once more. Yes, even to dance as she
had danced when a girl! In the upheaval of her passionate revolt, flushed and trembling, she begged her
husband to take her to one of the country balls of the
neighborhood.

"Take me wunst!" she pleaded, her eyes glistening
with unshed tears; "only this wunst; I won't never ask
you no more. But I do want to have one right good
time. You never take me nowheres. Please take me,
Fred, won't you?"

Old Scott straightened himself from the task over
which he was bending and looked at her in incredulous
wonder. For more than a minute he stared at her;
then, breaking into a loud laugh, he mocked:

"You'd look pretty, now, wouldn't you, a-goin' and
a-toein' it like you was a young gal!"

She shrank from him as though he had raised a lash
over her, and the light died out of her face. Without
a word she turned and went back to her work.

Martha Scott never again alluded to the meagre
pleasures of her life. She went back to her work of
cooking the coarse food which was their only fare; of
mending the heavy, uncouth clothing which week-day
and Sunday alike, was her husband's only apparel; of
washing and ironing the cheap calicoes, and coarse, un-
bleached muslins of her own poor, and scanty ward-
robe, fulfilling her part as a bread-winner. The man
never saw that he failed in performing the part of a

good and loving husband; and if anyone had pointed out to him that her existence was impoverished by his indifference and neglect, he still would have been unable to see wherein he had erred. He would have argued that she had enough to eat, enough to wear; that they owned their home—their neighbors having no better, nor any larger; he was laying aside money all the time; he did not drink; he never struck her. What more could any woman ask?

That the home which suited him, and the life to which he was used, could be other than all she desired, had never once occurred to him. As a boy, "back East" in the old days, he had never cared for the sports and pleasures enjoyed by other young people. How much less, now that the natural pleasure-time of life was past, could he tolerate pleasure-seeking in others!

"Folks show better sense to work an' save their money," he would say, "than to go gaddin' about havin' a good time an' comin' home broke."

Together they lived in the house which through all their married life they had called "home;" together they worked side by side through all their years of youth and middle age. But not farther are we from the farthest star than were these two apart in their real lives. Yet she was his wife; this woman for whom he had no dearer name than "Marth'," and to whom—for years—he had given no caress. She looked the incarnation of indifference and apathy. Ah! but was she?

A few years ago there came a mining expert from San Francisco to examine the Yellow Bird mine; and with him came a younger man, who appeared to have no particular business but to look around at the country, and to fish and hunt. There is the finest kind of sport for the hunter over in the Smoky Range; and this fellow, Baird—Alfred Baird was his name—spent much of his time there shooting antelope and deer.

He was courteous and gentle mannered; he was finely educated—polished in address; he spoke three or four languages, and was good to look at. He stayed with the Scotts for a time—and a long time it proved to be; a self-invited guest, whether or no. Yet all the while he did not fail to reiterate his intentions to "handsomely remunerate them for their generous hospitality in a country where there were so few or no hotels." He assured them he was "daily expecting a remittance from home. The delay was inexcusable—unless the mail had miscarried. Very annoying! So embarrassing!" And so on. It was the old stereotyped story which that sort of a fellow always carries on the tip of his tongue. And the wonder of it all was that Scott—surly and gruff to all others—was so completely under the scamp's will, and ready to humor his slightest wish. Baird used without question his saddle and best horse; and it was Scott who fitted him out whenever he went hunting deer over in the Smokies.

By and by there came a time when Scott himself had to go away on a trip into the Smoky Range, and which would keep him from home a week. He left his wife behind, as was his custom. He also left Alfred Baird there—for Baird was still "boarding" at Scott's.

When old Fred Scott came back, it was to find the house in as perfect order as ever, with every little detail of house work faithfully performed up to the last moment of her staying, but the wife was gone. Neither wife, nor the money—hidden away in an old powder-can behind the corner cupboard—were there.

Both were gone—the woman and the gold pieces; and it was characteristic of Old Scott that his first feelings of grief and rage were not for the loss of his wife, but for the coins she had taken from the powder-can. He was like a maniac—breaking everything he had ever seen his wife use; tearing to pieces with his strong, sinewy hands every article of her clothing his eyes fell upon. He raved like a madman, and cursed like a fiend. Then he found her letter.

"Dear Fred:—

Now I'm a going away, and I'm a going to stay a year. The money will last us two just about that long. I asked Mr. Baird to go with me, so you needn't blame him. I ain't got nothing against you, only you wouldn't never take me nowheres; and I just couldn't stand it no longer. I've been a good wife, and worked hard, and earned money for you; but I ain't never had none of it myself to spend. So I'm a going to have it now; for some of it is mine anyway. It has been work —work all the time, and you wouldn't take me no- wheres. So I'm a going now myself. I don't like Mr. Baird better than I do you—that ain't it—and if you want me to come back to you in a year I will. And I'll be a good wife to you again, like I was before. Only you needn't expect for me to say that I'll be sorry be- cause I done it, for I won't be. I won't never be sorry I done it; never, never! So, good-by.

Your loving wife,

Martha J. Scott."

If, through the long years, he had not been blind, he could have saved her from it. Not a vicious woman —not a wantonly sinning woman; only one who— weak and ignorant—was dazed and bewildered by the possibilities she saw in just one year of unrestricted freedom to enjoy all the pleasures that might come within her reach.

To be sure, it did seem preposterous that a young

and handsome man, with refined tastes and education, should go away with a woman years older than himself, and one, too, who was uncouth in manner and in speech. However strange it looked to the world, the fact remained that they eloped. But both were well away before it was suspected that they had gone together. Old Scott volunteered no information to the curious; and his grim silence forbade the questions they would have asked. It was long before the truth was known, for people were slow to credit so strange a story.

The two were seen in San Francisco one day as they were buying their tickets on the eve of sailing for Honolulu. She looked very lovely, and was as tastefully and becomingly gowned as any woman one might see. Baird, no doubt, had seen to that; for he had exquisite taste, and he was too wise to challenge adverse criticism by letting her dress in the glaring colors and startling styles she would have chosen, had she been allowed to follow her own tastes. In her pretty, new clothes, with her really handsome face all aglow from sheer joy in the new life she was beginning, she looked twenty years younger, and attracted general attention because of her unusual eyes and her magnificently-colored hair.

She was radiant with happiness; and there was no apparent consciousness of wrong-doing. Baird always showed a gracious deference to all women, and to her he was devotion itself. The little attentions that will charm and captivate any woman—attentions to which she was so unused—fed her starved nature, and for the time satisfied without sating her. They sailed for the Islands, and were there a year. They kept to themselves, seeking no acquaintance with those around them —living but for one another. And those who saw them, told they seemed thoroughly fond of each other. He was too much in love with himself and the surroundings which catered to his extravagant tastes, to have a great love for any woman; and she was scarcely the person, in spite of her beauty—the beauty of some magnificent animal—to inspire lasting affection in a man like Baird. He was shrewd enough to keep people at a distance, for unless one entered into conversation with her she might easily be taken for the really cultivated woman she looked. Yet the refined and aesthetic side of Alfred Baird's nature—and there was such—much have met with some pretty severe shocks during a twelvemonth's close companionship. Too indolent to work to support himself, he bore (he felt, heroically) any mortification he was subjected to, and was content in his degradation. But the woman herself was intensely happy; happier than, in all her dreary life, she had ever dreamed that mortals could be. She was in love with the beautiful new world, which was like a dream of fairy-land after her sordid life in the desolate valley. That Hawaiian year must have been a revelation of hitherto unimagined things to her. Baird's moral sense was blunted by his past dissipations, but her moral sense was simply undeveloped. In her ignorance she had no definition of morality. The man was nothing to her except as an accessory to the fascinating life which she had allowed herself "while the money lasted."

When the twelve months were run she philosophically admitted the end of it all, and parted with him —apparently—without a pang. If, at the moment of parting, any regrets were felt by either because of the separation, it was he, not she, who would have chosen to drift longer down the stream. The year had run its course; she would again take up the old life. This could not last. Perhaps—who knows?—in time he might have palled on her. No doubt, in time, his weak nature would have wearied her; her own was too eager for strong emotions, to find in him a fitting mate.

Whether, at the last, she wrote to her husband, or if he came to her when the year came to its end, no one knows. But one day the people of the desert saw her back at the adobes on the bluff. She returned as suddenly as she had disappeared.

She seems to have settled into the old groove again. She moves in the same apathetic way as before the stirring events of her life. In her letter she said she would not be sorry. It is not probable that she ever was, or ever will be; but neither is it likely that she has ever seen the affair from the point of view a moralist would take. Her limited intelligence only allowed her to perceive the dreariness of her own poor life, and when her longings touched no responsive chord in the man whom she had married, she deliberately took one year of her existence and hung its walls with all the gorgeous tapestries and rich paintings that could be wrought by the witchery of those magic days in the Pacific.

Fires have burned as fiercely within that woman's breast as ever burned the fires of Kilauea; and when they were ready to burst their bounds, she fled in her impulse to the coral isles of the peaceful Western sea, and there her ears heard the sound, and her heart learned the meaning of words that have left no visible sign upon her—the wondrous, sweet words of a dream, whispered to her unceasingly, while she gave herself up to an enchantment as mad and bewildering as that of the rhythmic hula-hula.

If she sinned, she does not seem to know it. Going about at her work, as before, the expressionless face is a mask; yet it may be she is moving in a dream-world, wherein she lives over once again the months that were hers—once—in the far Hawaiian Isles.

AN OLD SQUAW

SHE had been lying by the stone wall all day. And the sun was so hot that the blood beating in her ears sounded like the White Man's fire-horse that had just pulled a freight train into the station, and was grunting and drinking down at the water tank a hundred yards away. It was getting all the water it wanted; why couldn't she have all the water she wanted, too?

Today they had brought her the tomato can only half full. Such a little drink! And her mouth was so hot and dry! They were starving her to death—had been starving her for days and days. Oh, yes! she knew what they were doing. She knew why they were doing it, too. It was because she was in the way.

She was an old squaw. For weeks she had been half dead; she had lain for weeks whimpering and moaning in a corner of the camp on a heap of refuse and rotting rags, where they had first shoved her aside when she could no longer gather herself up on her withered limbs and go about to wait upon herself.

They had cursed her for her uselessness; and had let the children throw dirt at her, and take her scant share of food away and give it to the dogs. Then they had laughed at her when one of the older grandchildren had spat at her; and when she had striven to strike at the mocking, devilish face, and in her feebleness had failed, they had but laughed the louder while she shrieked out in her hatred of them all.

Her children, and her children's children—her flesh and bone! They were young, and well, and strong; and she was old, feeble and dying. Old—old—old! Too old to work. Too old to do for herself any longer, they were tired of her; and now they had put her out of the wick-i-up to die alone there by the stone wall. She knew it—knew the truth; but what could she do?

She was only an old Paiute squaw.

At first they had given her half the amount of food which they allowed her before she had grown so feeble. Then it was but a quarter; and then again it was divided in half. Now—at the last—they were bringing her only water.

One day when she was faint and almost crazed from hunger, one of the boys (her own son's son) had come with a meat bone and thrown it down before her; but when she reached out with trembling, fleshless hands to grasp it, he had jerked at the string to which it was tied, and snatched it away. Again and again he threw it toward her; again and again she tried to be quick enough to close her fingers upon it before he could jerk it from her. Then (when, at last, he was tired of the play) he had flung it only an arm's length beyond her reach, and had run laughing down to the railroad to beg nickels from the passengers on the train. When he had gone a dog came and dropped down beside her, and gnawed the bone where it lay. She had crawled out into the sunshine that day, and lay huddled in a heap close to the door-flap at the wick-i-up entrance. The warm sunlight at first felt good to her chilled blood, and she had lain there long;

but finally when she would have dragged her feeble body within again, a young squaw (the one who had mated with the firstborn son, and was now ruler of the camp) had thrust her back with her foot, and said that her whining and crying were making the Great Spirit angry; and that henceforth she must stay outside the camp, for a punishment.

Ah, she knew! She knew! They could not deceive her. It was not the Great Spirit that had put her out, but her own flesh and blood. How she hated them all! If she could only be young again she would have them put to death, as she herself had had others put to death when there were many to do her bidding. But she was old; and she must lie outside, away from those who had put her there to starve, while in the gray dusk they gathered around the campfire and ate, and laughed, and forgot her. She wished the cool, dark night might last longer, with the sage-scented winds from the plain blowing over her. But morning would come with a blood-red sun shining through the summer haze, and she would have to lie there under the furnace heat through all the long day-light hours, with only a few swallows of water brought to her in the tomato can to quench her intolerable thirst.

They were slowly starving her to death just because she was old. They hated squaws when they got old. They did not tell her so; but she knew. She, too, had hated them once. That was long ago. Long, long ago; when she was young, and strong, and swift.

She was straight then and good to look at. All of the young men of her tribe had striven for her; and two had fought long—had fought wildly and wickedly. That was when the White Man had first come into the country of her people, and they had fought with knives they had taken from the Whites. Knives long, and shining, and sharp. They had fought and slashed, and cut each other till the hard ground was red and slippery where they stood. Then—still fighting—they had fallen down, down; and where they fell, they died. Died for her—a squaw! Well, what of it, now? Tomorrow she, too, would die. She whom they, and others, had loved.

Once, long ago—long before the time when she had become Wi-o-chee's wife—at the Fort on the other side of the mountain, where the morning sun comes first, there had been a White Man whose eyes were the blue of the soldier-blue he wore; and whose mustache was yellow like the gold he wore on his shoulders.

He, too, was young, and straight, and strong; and one day he had caught her in his arms and held her while he kissed her on mouth and eyes, and under her little round chin. And when she had broken away from him and had run—run fast as the deer runs— he had called after her: "Josie! Josie! Come back!" But she had run the faster till, by and by, when he had ceased calling, she had stolen back and had thrown a handful of grass at him as he sat, with bowed head, on the doorstep of the officers' quarters; his white fingers pressed tight over his eyelids. Then when he had looked up she had gone shyly to him, and put her hand in his. And when he stood up, looking eagerly in her eyes, she had thrown her head back, where she let it lay against his arm, and laughed, showing the snow-white line of her teeth, till he was dazzled by what he saw and hid the whiteness that gleamed between her lips by the gold that swept across his own.

That was long ago. Not yesterday, nor last week,

nor last month; but so long ago that it did not even awaken in her an interest in remembering how he had taught her English words to say to him, and laughed with her when she said them so badly.

She did not care about it, at all, now. She only wanted a drink of water; and her children would not give her what she craved.

Always, she had been brave. She had feared nothing—nothing. She could ride faster, run farther, dare more than other young squaws of the tribe. She had been stronger and suppler. Yet today she was dying here by the stone wall—put out of the camp by her children's children to die.

She would die tomorrow; or next day, at latest. Perhaps tonight. She had thought she was to die last night when the lean coyote came and stood off from her, and watched with hungry eyes. All night he watched. Going away, and coming back. Coming and going all night. All night his little bright eyes shone like stars. And the stars, too, watched her there dying for water and meat, but they handed nothing down to her from the cool sky.

Oh, for strength again! For life, and to be young! But she was old and weak. She would die; and when she was dead they would take her in her rags, and—winding the shred of a gray blanket about her (the blanket on which she lay)—they would tie it tightly at her head and at her feet; and so she would be made ready for her last journey.

Dragging her to a waiting pony she would be laid across the saddle, face down. To the stirrups, which would be tied together beneath the horse that they might not swing, her head and feet would be fastened —her head at one stirrup, her feet at the other.

Then they would lead the pony off through the

greasewood. Along the stony trail across the upland
to the foothills the little buckskin pony would pick
his way, stumbling on the rocks while his burden
would slip and shake about, lying across the saddle.
Then they would lay her in a shallow place, and
heaping earth and gravel over her, would come away.
That was the way they had done with her mother,
with Wi-o-chee, and the son who had died.

Tomorrow—yes, tomorrow—they would take her to
the foothills. Perhaps the coyote would go there
tomorrow night; would go there, and dig.

He had come now, and stood watching her from
the shelter of the sagebrush. He was afraid to come
nearer—now. She was too weak to move even a
finger today, yet he was afraid. He would not come
close till she was dead. He knew.

Once he walked a few steps toward her, watching
her all the while with his little cruel eyes. Then he
turned and trotted back into the sagebrush. He knew.
Not yet.

*　　*　　*　　*　　*　　*　　*　　*

All day the sun had lain in heavy heat on the tangle
of vile rags by the stone wall. All day the magpie,
hopping along the wall, watched with head bent sidewise at the rags that only moved with the faint breathing of the body beneath. All day long two buzzards
far up in the still air swung slowly in great circling
sweeps. All day, from early dawn till dusk, a brown
hand—skinny and foully dirty—clutched the tomato
can; but the can today had been left empty. Forgotten.

When it grew dark and a big, bright star glowed in the West, the coyote came out of the shadows of the sagebrush and stood looking at the tangled rags by the stone wall.

Only a moment he stood there. He threw up his head, and his voice went out in a chilling call to his mate. Then with lifted lip he walked quickly forward. He was no longer afraid.

An
Old
Squaw

GREATER LOVE HATH NO MAN

YES, you're right, Sid; in these days of multi-millionaires, nothing that is written with less than eight figures is considered 'wealth.' Yet, even so, I count this something more than a 'tidy little sum' you've cleaned up—even if you do not. And now tell me, what are you going to do with it?''

The man sitting at the uncovered pine table in the center of the room opened his lips to answer, checked himself as if doubtful of the reception of what he might say, and then went on nervously sorting and rearranging the handful of papers and letters which he held. However, the light that came into his eyes at Keith's question, and the smile that played around his weak lips, showed without a doubt that the "tidy little sum" promised to him at least the fulfillment of unspoken dreams.

He was a handsome man of thirty—a man of feminine beauty rather than that which is masculine. And though dressed in rough corduroys and flannels, like his companion, they added to, rather than detracted from his picturesque charm. Slightly—almost delicately proportioned, he seemed to be taller than he really was. In spite of his great beauty, however, his face was not a satisfying one under the scrutiny of a close observer, for it lacked character. There was refinement and a certain sweetness of temperament there, but the ensemble was essentially weak—it was the face of a man of whom one felt it would not be well for any believing, loving woman to pin her faith to.

Keith, sitting with his long legs crossed and his big, strong hands thrust deep into his trousers' pockets, watched the younger man curiously, wondering what manner of woman she could have been who had chosen Sidney Williston for her lord and master.

"Poor little neglected woman," thought Keith, with that tender and compassionate feeling he had for every feminine and helpless thing; "poor little patiently waiting wife! Will he ever go back to her, I wonder? I doubt it. And now to think of all this money!"

Williston had said but little to Keith about his wife. In fact, all reference to her very existence had been avoided when possible. Keith even doubted if his friend would ever again recognize the marriage tie between them unless the deserted one should unexpectedly present herself in person and claim her rights. Williston—vacillating, unstable—was the kind of a man in whom loyalty depends on the presence of its object as a continual reminder of obligations. Keith was sure, however, that the woman, whoever she might be, was more than deserving of pity.

"Sidney means well," thought Keith trying to find excuse for him, "but he is weak—lamentably so—and sadly lacking in moral balance." And never had Williston been so easily lead, so subservient to the will of another as now, since "that cursed Howard woman'' (as Keith called her under his breath) had got him into her toils.

Lovesick as any boy he was befooled to his heart's content, wilfully blind to the fact that it was the old pitiful story of a woman's greed, and that her white hands had caresses and her lips kisses for his gold—not for himself. Her arms were eager to hold in their clasp—not him, but—the great wealth which was his, the gold which had come from the fabulously rich strike he had cleaned up on the bedrock of the claim, where a cross reef had held it hidden a thousand years and more. Her red lips were athirst to lay kisses—— On his mouth? Nay! on the piles of minted gold that had lain in the bank vault since he had sold his mine. The Twentieth Century Aspasia has a hundred arts her sister of old knew naught of; and Williston was not the first man who has unwittingly played the part of proxy to another, or blissfully believed in the lying lips whose kisses sting like the sting of wild bees—those honey-sweet kisses that stab one's soul with needles of passionate pain. All these were for the gold-god, not him; he was but the unconscious proxy.

Keith mused on the situation as he sat in the flickering candle-light blown by the night wind that—coming in through the open window—brought with it the pungent odor of sagebrush-covered hills.

"Strange," he thought, "how a woman of that particular stamp gets a hold on some fellows! And with a whole world full of other women, too—sweet, good women who are ready to give a man the right sort of love and allegiance, if he's a half-way decent sort of a fellow with anything at all worthy to give in exchange; God bless 'em!—and confound him! He makes me angry; why can't he pull himself together and be a man!''

Bayard Keith was no saint. Far from it. Yet, for all his drifting about the world, he had kept a pretty clean and wholesome moral tone. Women of the Gloria Howard class did not appeal to his taste; that was all there was about it. But he knew men a-plenty who, for her sake, would have committed almost any crime in the calendar if she set it for them to do. There were men who would have faced the decree of judge and jury without a tremor, if the deed was done for her sake. He himself could not understand such things. Not that he felt himself better or stronger than his fellows; it was simply that he was made of a different sort of stuff.

Yet, in spite of his manifest indifference to the charm of her large, splendid beauty—dazzling as the sun at noon-day—and that marked personality which all others who ever came within the circle of her presence seemed to feel, Keith knew he could have this woman's love for the asking—the love of a woman who, 'twas said, won love from all, yet giving love to none. Nay, but he knew it was already his. His very indifference had fanned a flame in her breast; a flame which had been lit as her eyes were first lifted to his own and she beheld her master, and burning steadily it had become the consuming passion of this strange creature's existence. Hopeless, she knew it was; yet it was stronger than her love of life. Even stronger than her inordinate love of money was this passion for the man whose heart she had utterly failed to touch.

That he must know it to be so, was but an added pain for her fierce nature to bear. Keith wondered if Williston had ever suspected, as she played her

Greater
Love
hath
no
Man

part, the woman's passionate and genuine attachment to himself. He hoped not, for the two men had been good comrades, though without the closer bond of a fine sympathy; and Keith's wish was that their comradeship should continue, while he hoped the woman's love, in time, would wear itself out. To Williston he had once tried to give a word of advice.

"Drop it, Keith," came the quick answer to his warning, "I love her."

"Granted that you do, why should you so completely enslave yourself to a woman of that type?"

"What do you mean by 'that type?' Take care! take care, Keith! I tell you I love her! Were I not already a married man I would make Mrs. Howard my wife."

"Oh, no, you wouldn't," Keith answered quietly. "Howard refuses to get a divorce, and you know very well she cannot. Besides, Sid, it would be sheer madness for you to do such a thing, even were she free."

"It makes no difference; I love her," was again the reply, and said with the childish persistence of those with whom reiteration takes the place of argument.

Keith said no more, though he felt the shame of it that Sidney Williston's fortune should be squandered on another woman, while—somewhere off there in the East—his wife waited for him to send for her. Keith's shoulders shrugged with impatience over the whole pitiful affair. He was disgusted at Williston's lack of principle and angered by his disregard of public censure. However, he reflected, trying to banish all thoughts of it, it was none of his business; he was not elected to be his brother's keeper in this affair surely.

As for himself, he believed the only love worth having was that upon which the foundation of the hearthstone was laid. He believed, too, that to no man do the gods bring this priceless treasure more than once. When a man like Keith believes this, it becomes his religion.

Through the gateway to his big, honest heart, one summer in the years gone by, love had entered, and —finding it the dwelling of honor and truth—it abided there still.

Thinking of Williston's infatuation for Gloria Howard, he could but compare it to his own entire, endless love for Kathryn Verrill. He recalled a day that would always stand out in bold relief from all others in memory's gallery.

In fancy now he could see the wide veranda built around one of the loveliest summer homes of the beautiful Thousand Islands. Cushions—soft and silken— lay tossed about on easy chairs and divans that were scattered about here and there among tubs of palms and potted plants. On little tables up and down the veranda's length were summer novels open and face downward as their readers had left them, or dainty and neglected bits of fancy-work. Cooling drinks and dishes of luscious fruits had been placed there within their reach. Keith closed his eyes with a sigh, as the memory of it all came back to him. Here, amid the sage and desert sands, it was like a dream of lost Paradise.

It had been a day of opalescent lights, and through its translucence they (he and—she) could see the rest of the party on the sparkling waters, among the pleasure craft from other wooded islands, full of charm, near by. Only these two—he and she—were here on the broad veranda. The echo of distant laughter

Greater Love hath no Man

came to them, but here was a languorous silence. Even the yellow-feathered warblers in the gilded cages above them had, for the time, hushed their songs.

Kathryn Verrill was swinging slowly back and forth in one of the hammocks swung along the veranda, the sunlight filtering through the slats of the lowered blinds streaking with gold her filmy draperies as they swept backward and forward on the polished floor. Her fingers had ceased their play on the mandolin strings, and there was now no sound about them louder than the hum of the big and gorgeous bumble-bee buzzing above their heads. Summer sweetness anywhere, and she the sweetest of it all! Then——

Ah, well! He had asked her to marry him, and the pained look that came into her face was his answer even before he heard her say that for two years she had been another's—a secretly-wedded wife. Why she should now tell her carefully guarded secret to him she herself could hardly have told. No one else knew. Her husband had asked that it should be their dear secret until he could send for her to come to him out in the land of the setting sun, where he had gone alone in the hope that he would find enough of the yellow metal grains so that he could provide her with a fitting home. Her guardian had not liked the man of her choice—had made objections to his attentions. Then there was the clandestine marriage. And then he had gone away to make a home for her. But she loved him; oh, yes! he was her choice of all the world, her hero always—her husband now. She was glad to have done as she did —there was nothing to regret, except the enforced separation. So she was keeping their secret while feeding her soul with the hope of reunion that his rare letters brought. But she had faith. Some day— some day he would win the fortune that would pave the way to him; then he would send for her. Some day. And she was waiting. And she loved him; loved him. That was all.

All, except that she was sorry for Keith, as all good women are sorry to hurt any human creature. No loyal, earnest, loving man ever offers his whole heart to any true and womanly woman (it matters not how little her own affections are moved by his appeal, or if they be stirred at all) that she does not feel touched and honored by 'the proffered gift. Womanly sympathy looked out of her gentle eyes, but she had for him no slightest feeling of other attraction. Keith gravely accepted his fate; but he knew that Love (that beautiful child born of Friendship—begot by Passion) would live forever in the inner chamber of his heart. To him, Kathryn Verrill would always be the one woman in all the world.

He went out of her life and back to the business routine of his own. In work he would try to forget his wounds. Later there were investments that turned out badly, and he lost heavily—lost all.

Then he came West. Here, in the Nevada mountains, he had found companionship in Sidney Williston who, like himself, was a seeker for gold. A general similarity of tastes brought about by their former ways of living (for Williston, too, was an eastern man) had been the one reason for each choosing the companionship of the other. So, here in the paintless pine cabin in Porcupine Gulch, each working his separate claim, they had been living under the same roof for nearly two years; but Fate, that sees fit to play us strange tricks sometimes, had laid a fortune in Williston's hands, while Keith's were yet empty.

Greater
Love
hath
no
Man

Sidney Williston's silence, when asked what he would do with his wealth, was answer enough.   It would be for Gloria Howard.   There he sat now, thinking of her—planning for her.

Millers, red-winged moths and flying ants fluttered around the candle, blindly batting at the burning wick and falling with singed wings on the table.   The wind was rising again, and the blaze at times was nearly snuffed out, moth-beaten and blown by the strong breeze.

All the morning the sun had laid its hot hand heavily on the earth between the places where dense white clouds hung without a motion in the breathless sky.   The clouds had spread great dark shadows on the cliffs below, where they clung to the rocks like time-blackened and century-old lichens.   But in the shadowless spots the sun's rays were intensely hot, as they so often are before a coming storm; while the fierce heat for the time prostrated plant life, and sent the many tiny animals of the hills to those places where the darkest shadows lay.   Flowers were wilting where they grew.   White primroses growing in the sandy soil near the cabin had but the night before lifted their pale, sweet faces to the moon's soft light— lovely evening primroses growing straight and strong. Noonday saw them drooping weakly on their stalks, blushing a rosy, shamed pink; kissed into color by the amorous caresses of that rough lover, the Sun. Night would find them faded and unlovely, their purity and sweetness ruthlessly wrested from them forever.

As the sun climbed to the zenith, there was not the slightest wind stirring; the terrible heat lay, fold on fold, upon the palpitating earth.   But noon came and brought a breeze from out of the south.   Stronger and stronger it swept toward the blue mountains lying away to the northward. It gathered up sand particles and dust, and shook them out into the air till the sunlight was dulled, and the great valley below showed through a mist of gold. All the afternoon the atmosphere was oppressively hot, while the wind hurried over valley and upland and mountain. All the afternoon the dust storm in billowy clouds hurried on, blowing—blowing—blowing. A whistling wind it was, keeping up its mournful song in the cracks of the unpainted cabin, and whipping the burlap awning over the door into ragged shreds at the edges. The dark green window shades flapped and rattled their length, carried out level from their fastenings by the force of the hot in-blowing wind.

Then with the down-going of the sun the wind died down also. When twilight came, the heavens were overcast with rain-clouds that told of a hastening storm which would leave the world fresh and cool when it had passed. The horizon line was brightened now and again by zigzags of lightning. Inside the cabin the close air was full of dust particles.

Sidney Williston tossed a photograph across the table, as he gathered his papers together preparatory to putting them away.

"There's my wife's picture, Keith," he said; "I don't think I ever showed it to you, did I?"

Keith got up—six feet, and more, of magnificent manhood; tall, he was, and straight as a pine, and holding his head in kingly wise. Leisurely he walked across the bare floor, which echoed loudly to his tread; leisurely he picked it up.

It was the pictured face of Kathryn Verrill!

He did not say anything; neither did he move. . .

If you come to think of it, those who sustain

Greater Love hath no Man

great shocks seldom do anything unusual except in novels. In real life people cry out and exclaim over trifles; but let a really stupendous thing happen, and you may be very sure that they will be proportionately silent. The mind, incapable of instantly grasping the magnitude of what has happened, makes one to stand immovable and in silence.

Keith said nothing. His breathing was quite as regular as usual, and his grasp on the picture was firm—untrembling. Yet in that instant of time he had received the greatest shock of his life, and myriad thoughts were running through his brain with the swiftness of the waters in the mining sluice. He held the bit of pasteboard so long that Williston at last looked up at him inquiringly.

When he handed it back his mind was made up. He knew what must be done. He knew what he must do—at once—for her sake.

When two or three hours later he heard Williston's regular breathing coming from the bed across the room, he stole out in the darkness to the shed where the horses and buckboard were. It was their one vehicle of any sort, and the only means they had of reaching the valley. With the team gone, Williston would practically be a prisoner for several days. Keith had no hesitation in deciding which way his duty lay. It was thirty miles to the nearest town; to the telegraph; to Gloria Howard; to the railroad!

As he pulled the buckboard out of the shed and put the horses before it, the first raindrops began to fall. Big splashing drops they were, puncturing the parched dust as they beat down upon it. Flashes of lightning split the heavens, and each flash made the earth—for the instant—noon-bright. When he had buckled the last strap his hands tightened on the reins, and he swung himself up to the seat as the thunder's batteries were turned loose on the earth in a tremendous volley that set the very ground trembling. The frightened horses, crouching, swerved aside an instant, and then leaped forward into the darkness. Along the winding road they swept, like part of the wild storm, toward the town that lay off in the darkness of the valley below.

It was past midnight, and thirty miles lay between him and the railroad. There was no time to spare. He drove the horses at a pace which kept time with his whirlwind thoughts and his pulses.

He had been cool and his thoughts had been collected when under another's possible scrutiny. Now, alone, with the midnight storm about him, his brain was whirling, and a like storm was coursing through his veins.

The crashing thunder that had seemed like an avalanche of boulders shattered and flung earthward by the fury of the storm, began to spend itself, and close following on the peals and flashes came the earth-scent of rain-wetted dust as the big drops came down. By and by the thunder died away in distant grumbling, and the fiery zigzags went out. There was the sound of splashing hoofs pounding along the road; and the warm, wet smell of horses' steaming hides, blown back by the night wind.

Fifteen miles—ten—five miles yet to go. Not once had Keith slackened speed.

When at length he found himself on the low levels bordering the river, the storm had passed over, and ere he reached the town the rain had ceased falling. A dim light was breaking through the darkness in places, and scudding clouds left rifts between which brilliant stars were beginning to shine.

Greater Love hath no Man

As he drove across the bridge and into the lower town, he woke the echoes of a watch-dog's barking; otherwise, the town was still. At the livery stable he roused the sleeping boy, who took his team; and flinging aside the water-soaked great-coat he wore, he walked rapidly toward the railroad station at the upper end of the town. The message he wrote was given to the telegraph operator with orders to "rush." It read:

"I have found the fortune. Now I want my wife. Come."

He signed it with Sidney Williston's name.

"Is Number Two on time?" he asked.

"An hour late. It'll be here about 4:10," was the reply.

Leaving the office, he went back to the lower town. Down the hill and past the pleasant cottages half hidden under their thick poplar shade, and surrounded by neat, close-trimmed lawns. Leaf and grass-blade had been freshened by the summer storm; and the odor of sweet garden flowers—verbenas, mignonette and pinks—was wafted strongly to his nostrils on the night air. They were homes. He turned away from all the fragrance and sighed—the sigh of renunciation. Crickets were beginning to trill their night songs. Past the court-house he went, where it stood ghostly and still in the darkness; past the business buildings farther down, glistening with wet. He turned into a side street to the house where he had been told Gloria Howard lived. At the gate he hesitated a moment, then opening it, went inside. Stepping off the graveled walk, his feet pressed noiselessly into the rain-soaked turf as he turned a corner of the cottage, and—going to a side window—rapped on the casing.

There was silence, absolute and deep. Again he rapped. Sharply this time; and he softly called her name twice. He heard a startled movement in the room, then a pause, as though she were listening. A moment later her white gown gleamed against the darkness of the bedchamber, and she stood at the open window under its thick awning of green hop vines. Her face was on a level with his own. Her hair exhaled the odor of violets. He could hear her breathing.

"Gloria,"————he began, softly.

"Who are you————what is it?" Then, "Keith! You!" she exclaimed; and in a moment more flung wide the wire screen that had divided them.

"Sh!"————he whispered. "I want to speak to you. But————hark! listen!" He laid his hand lightly on her lips.

She caught it quickly between both her own, and laid a hot cheek against it for an instant; then she pressed it tightly against her heart.

The night watchman patrolling the streets was passing; and they stood—he and she together—without movement, in the moist, dusky warmth of the rain-washed summer night, until the footsteps echoed faintly on the wet boards half a block away; the sound mingling with the croaking of the river frogs. Keith could feel the fast beating of her heart. The wet hop leaves shook down a shower of drops as they were touched by a passing breeze.

"Gloria,"————he spoke rapidly, but scarcely above his breath————"I am going away tonight————(he felt her start) away from this part of the country forever; and I have come to ask you to go with me. Will you? Tell me, Gloria, will you go?"

(margin: Greater Love hath no Man)

She did not reply, but laying a hand on his still damp coat-sleeve, tried to draw him closer, leaning her face towards his, and striving to read in his own face the truth of his words.

Had there been light enough for him to see, he would have marvelled at the varying expressions that followed in quick succession across her face. Surprise, incredulity, wonderment, a dawning of the real meaning of his words, triumph as she heard, and then—finally—a look of fierce, absorbing, tigerish love. For whatever else there might be to her discredit, her love for him was no lie in her life. She had for this man a passion as strong as her nature was intense.

"Gloria, Gloria, tell me! Will you leave all—everything and everybody—and go away with me?" he demanded impatiently. "Number Two is late—an hour late tonight, and you will have time to make yourself ready if you hasten. Come, Gloria, come!"

"Do——you——mean——it, Bayard Keith?" she breathed.

"I mean it. Yes."

She knew his yea was yea; still she missed a certain quality in what he said—a certain something (she could not say what) in his tone.

She inhaled a long breath as she drew away from him.

"You are a strange man—a very, very strange man. Do you know it? All these many months you have shunned me; yet now you ask me to cast my lot with yours. Why?"

"Because I find I want you—at last."

His answer seemed to satisfy her.

"For how long?" she asked.

Just for the imperceptible part of a second he hesitated. His answer would be another unbreakable link in the chain he was forging for himself. Only the fraction of a second, though, he paused. Then his reply came, firm and decided:

"Forever, Gloria, if you will have it so."

For answer she dropped her head on her folded arms while a dry, hard sob forced its way through her lips. It struck upon the chord within him that always thrilled to the sight or sound of anything, even remotely, touching grief. This sudden, unexpected joy of hers was so near akin to sorrow—ay, and she had had much sorrow, God knows! in her misspent life—it was cause enough for calling forth the gentle touch he laid upon her bowed head.

"Don't, Gloria, girl! Don't! It isn't worth this, believe me. Yet, if you come, you shall never have cause for regret, if there's anything left in a man's honor."

He stroked her hair silently a moment before he said:

"There are some things yet to be done before train time; so I must go now. Will you be there—at the station?"

"Yes."

So it was that the thing was settled; and Keith accepted his fate in silence.

An evil thing done? Perhaps. Evil, that good might come of it. And he himself to be the sole sufferer. He was removing this woman beyond Sidney Williston's reach forever. When the weak, erring husband should find himself free once more from the toils which had held him, his love (if love it was) would return to the neglected wife; and she, dear, faithful, loving woman that she was, would never, thank heaven! guess his unfaithfulness.

Bayard Keith did not feel himself to be a hero.

Greater Love hath no Man

Such men as he are never vainglorious; and Keith had no thought of questioning Life's way of spelling "duty" as he saw it written. He was being loyal for the sake of loyalty, a sacrifice for love's own sake than which no man can make greater, for he knew that his martyrdom would be in forever being misjudged by the woman for whose dear sake it was done. He would be misjudged, of course, by Sidney Williston, and by all the world, for that matter; but for them he did not care. He was simply doing what he thought was right that he himself should do—for Kathryn Verrill's sake. Her love had been denied him. Now he must even forfeit her respect. All for love's sake. None must ever know why he had done this hideous thing. They must be made to think that he—like others—had yielded to a mad love for the bad, beautiful woman. In his very silence under condemnation lay security for Kathryn Verrill's happiness. Only he himself would ever know how great would be his agony in bearing the load he had undertaken. Oh, if there might be some other way than this! If there could be but some still unthought-of means of escape whereby he could serve his dear lady, and yet be freed from yoking his life with a woman from whom his whole being would revolt. How would he be able through all the years to come —years upon years—to bear his life, with her?

As he walked past the darkened buildings he breathed heavily, each breath indrawn with a sibilant sound, like a badger at bay. Yet he had no thought of turning aside from his self-imposed immolation.

No one was astir in the lower town, save himself and the night watchman. Now and then he passed a dim light burning—here a low-turned burner in store or bank building; there the brighter glow of lamps behind the ground glass of some saloon door. Half way up the long street leading to the upper town he heard the rumble of an incoming train. Was Number Two on time, after all? Was a pitying Fate taking matters away from him, and into its own hands? Was escape being offered him?

If he hurried—if he ran—he could reach the station in time, but—alone! There would be no time to go back for Gloria Howard. He almost yielded for a moment to the coward's impulse to shrink from responsibility, but the thought of Kathryn Verrill, waiting by the eastern sea for a message to come from the man she loved, roused him to his better self. He resolutely slackened his pace till the minutes had gone by wherein he could have become a deserter; then he went on up to the station.

"No, that was a freight train that just pulled out," said the telegraph operator. "Number Two will be here pretty soon, though. Less'n half an hour. She's made up a little time now."

Keith went to the office counter and began to write. It was not a long letter, but it told all there was to say:

"Sid: I have wired to your wife to come to you, and I have signed your name. By the time this reaches you she will be on her way here. It will be wiser, of course, for you to assume the sending of the message, and to give her the welcome she will expect. It will be wiser, too—if I may offer suggestions—to travel about with her for a while; to go away from this place, where she certainly would hear of your unfaithfulness should she remain. Then go back with her to your friends, and live out the balance of your life, in the old home, as you ought. I know you will feel I am not a fit one to preach, for I myself am

Greater Love hath no Man

going away tonight, taking Gloria Howard with me. I know, too, how you will look at what I am doing; but I have neither excuses nor explanations to offer.

                                        Bayard Keith."

That was all.

When he had sealed and directed it, he went to the livery stable and waked up Pete Dudley.

"See here, Pete," he said, "I want you to do something for me."

"Sure, Mr. Keith!" said Pete, rubbing his eyes.

"Here's a letter for Mr. Williston out at our camp in Porcupine Gulch. I want you to take it to him, and take the buckboard, too."

"All right, I'll go in the morning."

"No, no! Listen! Not till day after tomorrow. Wait, let me think——You'd better wait a day longer——go the next day. Do you understand?"

"I guess I savvy. Not till Friday. Take the letter and the buckboard. Is that the racket?"

"Yes, that's what I want, Pete. Here! Take them to him without fail on Friday. Good night, Pete. Good bye!"

Keith walked back to the station and went in the waiting-room, where he sat down. His heart felt as heavy as lead. He had burned all his bridges behind him, and it made his soul sick to contemplate the long vista of the coming years.

As he sat there, the coward hope that she—Gloria—might not come, shot up in his heart, trying to make of him a traitor. He said to himself: "If—— if——" Presently he heard the train whistle. He got up and went to the door. He felt he was choking. Daylight was coming fast; day-dawn in the eastern sky. The town, rain-cleansed and freshened, would soon awake and lift its face to the greeting of another morn.

The ticket-office window was shoved up. It was nearing train time.

Greater
Love
hath
no
Man

"Hello, Mr. Keith, going away?"

"Yes, I want a—" he hesitated.

"Where to?"

But Keith did not answer. A ticket? One, or two? If she should not come—— Was Fate——? What was he to do? But, no! Yet he hesitated, while the man at the window waited his reply. Two tickets, or only one? Or not any? Nay, but he must go; and there must be two.

Then the train thundered into the station, and almost at the same moment he heard, through the sound made by the clanging bell, the rustle of a woman's rich garments. He turned. Gloria Howard stood there, beautiful and eager, panting from her hurried walk.

"Where to?" repeated the man at the window.

"San Francisco—two tickets," said Keith.

" 'Two,' did you say?" asked the man, looking up quickly at him and then glancing sideways at the radiant, laughing woman who had taken her place so confidently at Keith's side.

Keith's voice did not falter, nor did his eyes fall: "Two."

But the telegraph operator smiled to himself as he shoved the tickets across the window sill. To him, Keith was simply "Another one!" So, too, would the world judge him after he was gone.

Bayard Keith was no saint; but as he crossed to the cars in the waxing light of day-dawn, his countenance was transfigured by an indescribable look we do not expect to see—ever—on the face of mortal man.

"For her dear sake!" he whispered softly to himself, as he looked away to the reddening East—to the eastward where "she" was. "For the sake of the woman I love."

And "greater love hath no man than this, that a man lay down his life for his friends."

IN NANNA'S PALM

T all happened years ago. Before there was any railroad; even before there were any overland stages crossing the plains. Only the emigrant teams winding slowly down the valley on the road stretching westward.

Some there were, though, that had worked their way back from the Western sea, to stop at those Nevada cañons where there was silver to be had for the delving.

The cañons were beautiful with dashing, dancing streams, and blossoming shrubbery, and thick-leafed trees; and there grew up in the midst of these, tiny towns that called themselves "cities," where the miners lived who came in with the return tide from the West.

There in one of the busiest, prettiest mining camps on a great mountain's side, in one of the stone cabins set at the left of the single long street, dwelt **Tony** and his cousin Bruno—Italians, both. Bruno worked in the mines; but Tony, owning an ox team, hauled loads for the miners to and from the other settlements. A dangerous calling it was in those days, because an Indian in ambush had ever to be watched for when a White Man came down from the cañons to travel alone through the valley.

Tony was willing, however, to take risks. Teaming brought him more money than anything else he could do; and the more he earned, the sooner he could go back to Nanna—to Nanna waiting for him away on the other side of the world.

He and Bruno both loved her—had loved her ever since the days when, long ago, in their childhood, they had played at being lovers down among the fishing boats drawn up on the beach of their beloved Italian home. Black-browed Bruno had then quarreled with him in jealous hatred time and again; but the little Nanna (who loved peace, and to whom both playfellows were dear) would kiss each and say:

"Come! Let us play that you are my twin brothers, and I your only sister!" And so harmony would be restored.

Thus it went on, and at last they were no longer little children, but men who love a woman as men may love. And Bruno's parents came to the father and mother of Nanna and settled that their children should be man and wife; so in that way Bruno was made glad, and no longer jealous of Tony—poor Tony, who had not a single small coin that he could call his own. Yet it was Tony whom Nanna loved— Tony whose wife she wanted to be. But what can a young girl do when the one she loves is poor, and there is another whom her parents have chosen for her who has a little farm promised him by his father the day he shall bring home the wife they would have him marry? Nanna neither resisted nor rebelled; but only went to Tony who was as helpless as herself, and there against his breast wept her heart out.

It was only when Bruno declared that he was going to America to make a great deal of money (saying that the farm was not enough—that when he and Nanna were married he wanted they should be rich) that a ray of hope shone for Tony.

"I, too, will go to America," Tony whispered to Nanna, "and perhaps there I also may find a fortune. Then—when I come back—I may marry thee; may I not, little dear one?"

And for answer, the little Nanna lifted her arms to his neck and her lips to his own.

The night before the two men sailed away to the strange, far-off land, Nanna and Tony walked together under the oaks and ilexes.

"Thou wilt miss me, little one, but thou wilt be true, I know. I shall think of thee all the time—every hour. Thou wilt long for me, as I for thee. Thou wilt miss my kisses; is it not so? But I———! Ah, Nanna! Nanna! Here———" And bowing over her hand he pressed kiss after kiss in the upturned little brown palm, closing her fingers tightly upon them as he raised his head and smiled in her eyes.

"There! These I give thee, sweet one, so that when I am gone it shall be that thy Tony's kisses are with thee, and are thine whenever thou wilt."

All the morrow, when the ship had sailed away, Nanna lay on her cot up in the little whitewashed bedroom under the eaves, and with lips pressed close upon the palm that Tony's lips had touched, sobbed her grief out, till she sank into exhausted slumber.

One year; two years; three, came and went. Tony off in America was making money, and soon he could go home and they would be married in spite of her parents or Bruno. The fourth year he wrote her how the sum had grown—it was almost enough. Then she

The Loom of the Desert

began checking off the months ere he would return to her. Eighteen—sixteen—fourteen—now only twelve months more! A year, and Tony would be with her! Then half that year was gone. Six months, only, to wait! Happy little Nanna! And Tony was not less happy, away off there in his little stone cabin in the mountains, or hauling goods for the miners across the valley. His heart was so full of her that—almost—he forgot to think of the Indians when he was traveling along the road.

"Thou art a fool," said Bruno to him over and over again. "Thou art a fool, indeed. It is more money—this hauling—yes! But some day—ping!— and it is the arrow of an Indian. Then what good is it, the money? Thou art a fool, I say. As for me, I will work here with the many in the mines."

Bruno had just said this to him for the hundredth time, as Tony was yoking his oxen for the long journey up the wide valley to the North. And his answer had been as always, that the saints would protect him. Yet, should he not return the thirteenth day, then indeed might Bruno think all was not well with him, and could send some of the men from the mines to go to him. He was not afraid, though. Had not the saints protected him for nearly five years? He was soon to go back to Italy, and (he whispered to himself) to Nanna! So with a light heart, and a laugh on his lip, he went down the cañon beside the oxen, cracking his whip as he warbled a song he and Nanna had sung together when they had played by the boats and among the fishing nets in the long, long ago.

The wagon jolted and rattled on its way down the rocky road to the plain; and Tony's big, beautiful

St. Bernard dog, Bono, followed in the dust sent skyward by the heavy wheels as they came upon the softer earth of the lowlands.

Everyone was Tony's friend in the little mining town. Therefore everyone was anxious when the thirteenth day came, yet not Tony. With few words (at such times such men do not say much) they selected a dozen from among the town's bravest and best, and with heavy hearts set out on their journey that was to follow Tony's trail till they should find him.

Down into the hot valley—a-quiver under the summer heat, over a road of powdered alkali, along the Humboldt's banks—through mile after mile of sagebrush and greasewood—under the glaring, white sun, they rode two and two. And so riding they spoke seldom.

When they were nearing the place they knew Tony must have reached the third day out (now more than ten days gone) they saw outlined against the blue— high, high in the air—circling spots of black. Dark things that swept with a majesty of motion that was appalling. Round and round, in great curves half a mile wide, they swam through the ether, and dipped and tilted without so much as the quiver of a wing or other motion than that given by their marvelous self-poise; sailing through mid-air as only a vulture can.

They swept and circled over a spot that was awful in its silence under the metallic brightness of the hot August sun. The men looked at each other; looked without speaking—for they understood. So without speech they rode on to the place where the warped irons from the burned wagon lay, and where a gaunt, nearly starved St. Bernard howled over something that had once been his master. He had guarded the dead man through ten hot days—through ten long nights. Bono's wail sounded long and mournful through the narrow pass where the whistling arrows had found them. Tony had never been neglectful before, and the dog could not understand it.

Alas, poor Tony!

When Bruno went back to Italy that fall he told Nanna that Tony was dead. And Nanna who came of a race more or less stoical in time of stress did not cry out, but simply shut her sorrow up close in her heart where the others could not see. It had been their secret—hers and Tony's—and they had guarded it well. Henceforth it would be hers alone. So she gave no sign except such as she might for an old playmate's death.

By and by she married Bruno. What would you? Her father and mother wished it; Bruno loved her; he had money now to provide well for a wife; and there was the little farm that his parents would give him the day when he should bring home his bride. So, after the manner of her kind, she finally yielded to his wooing; and one day they were wed in the little church on the hill where they had both been christened when babies.

She bore him children, and was a good mother—a good wife. She lived to be an old woman, and her hair grew streaked with gray; yet to the last day of her life she had a way of falling asleep with the fingers of her left hand slipped under her cheek, and her lips touching the upturned palm.

It was her one disloyalty to Bruno.

And so it was they found her lying on that morning that she did not waken.

THE VENGEANCE OF LUCAS

THE little adobe house stood flush with the street, halfway between the business houses and the residence portion of the town which turned its back on the sand and sage-covered hills that—breaking into gray waves—far off cast themselves on the beach of blue skyland in great breakers of snow-crested mountains.

At the side of the house was a dooryard—so small!—beaten hard and smooth as a floor, and without a tree or a bush. There was no grass even at the edge of the sturdy little stream that ran across the square enclosure, talking all day to the old-faced baby in its high chair under the shake-covered kitchen porch. All day the stream laughed and chattered noisily to the owl-eyed baby, and chuckled and gurgled as it hurried across the yard and burrowed under the weather-bleached boards of the high fence, to find its way along the edge of the street, and so on to the river a quarter of a mile below. But the wee woman-child, owl-eyed and never complaining, sat through the long sunshine hours without one smile on its little old face, and never heeding the stream.

As the days grew hotter, its little thin hands became thinner, and it ate less and less of the boiled arroz and papas the young mother sometimes brought when she came to dip water.

"Of a truth, there is no niña so good as my 'Stacia; she never, never cries! She is no trouble to me at all," Carmelita would exclaim, and clap her hands at the baby. But the baby only grew rounder eyed as it stared unsmilingly at its mother's pretty plumpness, and laughing red lips, and big black eyes, whenever she stopped to talk to the little one.

Carmelita—pretty, shallow-pated Carmelita—never stayed long with the tiny 'Stacia, for the baby was so good left alone; and there was always Anton or Luciano and Monico to drop in for a laugh with the young wife of stupid old Lucas; or Josefa coming in for a game of "coyote y gallos."

It was Lucas who went out to the porch whenever he could spare the time from earning money that he might buy the needed arroz and papas, or the rose-colored dresses he liked to see her wear.

It was for Lucas she said her first word—the only word she had learned yet—"papa!" And she said it, he thought, as if she knew it was a love in no wise different from a father's love that he gave her, poor little Anastacia, whose father—well, Lucas had never asked Carmelita to tell him. How could he? Poor child, let her keep her secret. Pobre Carmelita! Only sixteen and no mother. And could he—Lucas—see her beaten and abused by that old woman who took the labor of her hands and gave her nothing in return?—could he stand by when he saw the big welts and bruises, and not beg her to let him care for her and the niña?—such a little niña it was, too! Of a verity, he was no longer young; and there was his ugly pock-marked face, to say nothing of the scars the oso had given him that day when he, a youth,

had sent his knife to the hilt in the bear that so
nearly cost him his life. The scars were horrible to
see—horrible! But Carmelita (so young—so pretty!)
did not seem to mind; and when the priest came again
they were married, so that Carmelita had a husband
and the pobrecita a father.

And such a father! How Lucas loved his little
'Stacia! How tender he was with her; how his heart
warmed to the touch of her lips and hands! Why,
he grew almost jealous of the red-breasted robin that
came daily to sit by the edge of her plate and eat
arroz with her! He begrudged the bird its touch of
the little sticky hand covered with grains of rice
which the robin pecked at so fearlessly. And when
the sharp bill hurt the tender flesh, how she would
scold! She was not his 'Stacia then at all—no, some
other baby very different from the solemn little one
he knew. There seemed something unearthly in it,
and Lucas would feel a sinking of his heart and wish
the bird would stay away. It never came when
others were there. Only from the shelter of window
or doorway did he and the others see the little bright
bird-eyes watch—with head aslant—the big black
ones; or hear the baby bird-talk between the two.
Every day throughout the long, hot summer the robin
came to eat from the niña's plate of rice as she sat
in her high chair under the curling shake awning; and
all the while she grew more owl-eyed and thin. A
good niña, she was, and so little trouble!

One day the robin did not come. That night,
through the open windows of the front room,
passers-by could see a table covered with a folded
sheet. A very small table—it did not need to be
large; but the bed had been taken out of the small,
mean room to give space to those who came to look

at the poor, little, pinched face under a square of pink mosquito bar. There were lighted candles at the head and feet. Moths, flying in and out of the wide open window, fluttered about the flames. The rose-colored dress had been exchanged for one that was white and stiffly starched. Above the wee gray face was a wreath of artificial orange blossoms, but the wasted baby-fingers had been closed upon some natural sprays of lovely white hyacinths. The cloying sweetness of the blossoms mingled with the odor of cigarette smoke coming from the farther corners of the room, and the smell of a flaring kerosene lamp which stood near the window. It flickered uncertainly in the breeze, and alternately lighted or threw into shadow the dark faces clustered about the doorway of the second room. Those who in curiosity lingered for a moment outside the little adobe house could hear voices speaking in the soft language of Spain.

To them who peered within with idle interest, it was "only some Mexican woman's baby dead." Tomorrow, in a little white-painted coffin, it would be born down the long street, past the saloons and shops where the idle and the curious would stare at the procession. Over the bridge across the now muddy river they would go to the unfenced graveyard on the bluff, and there the little dead mite of illegitimacy would be lowered into the dust from whence it came. Then each mourner in turn would cast a handful of earth into the open grave, and the clods would rattle dully on the coffin lid. (Ah, pobre, pobre Lucas!) Then they would come away, leaving Carmelita's baby there underground.

Carmelita herself was now sitting apathetically by the coffin. She dully realized what tomorrow was to be; but she could not understand what this meant.

She had cried a little at first, but now her eyes were dry. Still, she was sorry—it had been such a good little baby, and no trouble at all!

"A good niña, and never sick; such a good little 'Stacia!" she murmured. Carmelita felt very sorry for herself.

Outside, in the darkness of the summer night, Lucas sat on the kitchen porch leaning his head against the empty high chair of the pobrecita, and sobbed as if his heart would break.

*　*　*　*　*

That had happened in August. Through September, pretty Carmelita cried whenever she remembered what a good baby the little Anastacia had been. Then Josefa began coming to the house again to play "coyote y gallos" with her, so that she forgot to cry so often.

As for Lucas, he worked harder than ever. Though, to be sure, there were only two now to work for where there had been three. With Anton, and Luciano, and Monico, he had been running in wild horses from the mountains; and among others which had fallen to his share was an old blaze-face roan stallion, unmanageable and full of vicious temper. They had been put—these wild ones—in a little pasture on the other side of the river; a pasture in the rancho of Señor Metcalf, the Americano. And the señor, who laughed much and liked fun, had said he wanted to see the sport when Lucas should come to ride the old roan.

Today, Lucas—on his sleek little cow-horse, Topo— was riding along the river road leading to the rancho; but not today would he rope the old blaze-face. There were others to be broken. Halfway from the bridge he met little Nicolás, who worked

for the señor, and passed him with a pleasant
"Buenos dias!" without stopping. The boy had been
his good amigo since the time he got him away from
the maddened steer that would have gored him to
death. There was nothing 'Colás would not do for
his loved Lucas. But the older man cared not to
stop and talk to him today, as was his custom; for
he was gravely thinking of the little dead 'Stacia,
and rode on. A hundred yards farther, and he heard
the clatter of a horse's hoofs behind him, and Nicolás
calling:

"Lucas! Lucas!"

He turned the rein on Topo's neck, and waited till
the boy came. In the pleasant, warm October sunlight
he waited, while Nicolás told him that which would
always make him shiver and feel cold when afterward
he should remember that half-hour in the stillness and
sunshine of the river road. He waited, even after
Nicolás (frightened at having dared to tell his friend)
had gone.

The señor and Carmelita! It was the truth—
Nicolás would not lie. The truth; for the boy had
listened behind the high fence of weather-beaten
boards, and had heard them talk together. He, and
the little stream that gurgled and laughed all day,
had heard how they—the señor and Carmelita—would
go away to the north when the month should end.
For many months they two had loved—the Señor Metcalf and the wife of Lucas; had loved before Lucas
had made her his wife—ay! even before the little
'Stacia had come. And the little 'Stacia was the
señor's——— Ah, Lucas would not say it of the dead
pobrecita! For she was his—Lucas's—by right of
his love for her. Poor little Anastacia! And but that
the little one would have been a trouble to the

"Their eyes met." — Page 65

Americano, they—the woman and the man—would have gone away together before; but he would not have it so. Now that the little one was no longer to trouble them, he would take the mother and go away to the new rancho he had just bought far over on the other side of the mountains.

"Go!"—said Lucas, when the boy had finished telling all he had overheard—"Go and tell the señor that I go now to the corral to ride the roan stallion. And— 'Colás, give to me thy riata for today."

*   *   *   *   *

Lucas had driven the horses into one of the corrals. Alone there he had lassoed the old blaze-face; and then had driven the others out. Unaided, he had tied the old stallion down. As he lay there viciously biting and trying to strike out with his hind feet, Lucas had fastened a halter on his head and had drawn a riata (sixty feet long, and strong as the thews of a lion) tight about him just back of the forelegs. Twice he had passed it about the heaving girth of the old roan, whose reeking body was muddy with sweat and the grime and dust of the corral. The knots were tied securely and well. The rope would not break. Had he not made it himself from the hide of an old toro? From jaw-piece to jaw-piece of the halter he drew his crimson silk handkerchief, bandaging the eyes that gleamed red under swollen and skinned lids. Then, cautiously, Lucas unbound the four hoofs that had been tied together. The horse did not attempt to move, though he was consumed by a rage against his captor that was fiendish—the fury of a wild beast that has never yet been conquered.

Lucas struck him across the ribs with the end of the rope he was holding. The big roan head was lifted from the ground a second and then let fall, as he squealed savagely. Again the rope made a hollow sound against the heaving sides. Again the maddened horse squealed. When the rope struck the third time, he gathered himself together uncertainly—hesitated —struggled an instant—staggered to his feet, and stood quivering in every muscle of his great body. His legs shook under him; and his head—with the bandaged eyes—moved from side to side unsteadily.

Then Lucas wound the halter-rope—which was heavy and a long one—around the center-post of the corral where they were standing.

As he finished, he heard someone singing; the voice coming nearer and nearer. A man's voice it was, full and rich, caroling a love song, the sound mingling with that of clattering hoofs.

Lucas, stooping, picked up the riata belonging to Nicolás. He was carefully re-coiling it when Guy Metcalf, riding up to the enclosure, looked down into the corral.

"Hello, Lucas! 'Going to have some fun with the old roan,' are you? Well, you're the boy to ride him. 'Haven't got the saddle on yet, hey?' Hold on a minute—— Soon as I tie, I'll be with you!"

Lucas had not spoken, neither had he raised his head. He went to where little Topo was standing. Shaking the noose into place by a turn or two of the wrist, while the long loop dragged at his heels through the dust, he put his foot in the stirrup and swung himself into the saddle. He glanced at the gate— he ran the noose out yet a little more. Then he began to swing it slowly in easy, long sweeps above his head while he waited.

The gate opened and Metcalf came in. He turned and carefully fastened the gate behind him. He was a third of the way across the corral when their eyes met.

Then—with its serpent hiss of warning—the circling riata, snake-like, shot out, fastening its coils about him. And Topo, the little cow-horse trained to such work, wheeled at the touch of the spur as the turns of the rope fastened themselves about the horn of the saddle, and the man—furrowing the hoof-powdered dust of the corral—was dragged to the heels of the wild stallion. Lucas, glancing hastily at the face, earth-scraped and smeared and the full lips that were bleeding under their fringe of gold, saw that—though insensible for a moment from the quick jerk given the rope—the blue eyes of the man were opening. Lucas swung himself out of the saddle—leaving Topo to hold taut the riata. Then he began the work of binding the doomed Americano. When he had done, to the doubled rope of braided rawhide that was about the roan stallion, he made Carmelita's lover fast with the riata he had taken from Nicolás. He removed it slowly from the man's neck (the señor should not have his eyes closed too quickly to the valley through which he would pass!) and he put it about the body, under the arms. Lucas was lingering now over his work like one engaged in some pleasant occupation.

The halter-rope was then unknotted, and the turns unwound from the center-post. Next, he pulled the crimson handkerchief from the horse's eyes— shouted—and shook his hat at him!

Maddened, terrified, and with the dragging thing at his heels, the four-footed fury fought man, and earth, and air about him like the very demon that he was till he came to the gate that Lucas had set wide for him, and he saw again the waves of sage and sand hills (little waves of sweet-scented sage) that rippled away to the mountains he knew. Out there was liberty; out there was the free life of old; and there he could get rid of the thing at his heels that— with all his kicking, and rearing, and plunging— still dragged at the end of the rope.

Out through the wide set gate he passed, mad with an awful rage, and as with the wings of the wind. On, and on he swept; marking a trail through the sand with his burden. Faster and faster, and growing dim to the sight of the man who stood grim and motionless at the gate of the corral. Away! away to those far-lying mountains that are breakers on the beach of blue skyland!

A SHEPHERD OF THE SILENT WASTES

TO be hung. To be hung by the neck until dead.''

Over and over I say it to myself as I sit here in my room in the hotel, trying to think connectedly of the events which have led to the culmination of this awful thing that, in so short a time, is to deprive me of life.

At eleven o'clock I am to die; to go out of the world of sunshine and azure seas, of hills and vales of living green, of the sweet breath of wild flowers and fruit bloom, of light and laughter and the music of Life, to———what? Where? How far does the Soul go? What follows that awful moment of final dissolution?

At eleven o'clock I shall know; for I must die. There is no hope, no help; though my hand has never been raised against mortal man or woman—never have I taken a human life.

At the stroke of the hour a great crowd will stand in the prison yard, and gape at the scaffold, and see the drop fall, and—fascinated and frowning—gaze with straining eyes at the Thing dangling at the end of a hempen rope. A Soul will go out into immeasurable space. A purple mark on my throat will tell the story of death by strangulation. Two bodies will lie stark and dead tonight—his and mine. His will be laid in the pine box that belongs to the dishonored dead; while mine will be housed in rosewood, and satin, and silver.

You do not understand?

Listen, let me tell you! Let me go back to the first time we ever met—he and I.

After college days were over, I left the Atlantic coast and all that Life there meant to me, and came out to the West of the sagebrush, and the whirlwinds, and the little horned toads. And there in the wide wastes where there is nothing but the immensity of space and the everlasting quiet of the desert, I went into business for myself. Business there? Oh, yes! for out there where men go mad or die, cattle and sheep may thrive. I, who loved Life and the association of bright minds, and everything that such companionship gives, invested all I had (and little enough it was!) in a business of which I knew nothing, except that those men who went there with a determination to stick to the work till success should find them, brought away bags full of gold—all they could carry—as they came back into the world they had known before their self-banishment.

So I, too, went there, and bought hundreds of sheep—bleating—blear-eyed, stupid creatures that they are! I, essentially a man of cities and of people, began a strange, new life there, becoming care-taker of the flocks myself.

A lonely life? Yes; but remember there was money to be made in sheep-raising in the gray wastes; and I was willing to forego, for a time, all that civilization could give. So I dulled my recollections of the old life and the things that were dear to me, and went to work with a will in caring for the dusty, bleating, aimlessly-moving sheep. I wanted to be rich. **Not** for the sake of riches, but to be independent of the toil of bread-winning. I longed with all my soul to have money, that I might gratify my old desires for travel away to the far ends of the earth. All my life I had dreamed of the day I was to turn my face to those old lands far away, which would be new lands to me. So I was glad to sacrifice myself for a few years in the monstrous stillness of the gray plains so that I might the sooner be free to go where I would.

Friends tried to dissuade me from the isolated life. They declared I was of a temperament that could not stand the strain of the awful quiet there—the eternal silence broken only by some lone coyote's yelp, or the always "Baa! Baa!" of the sheep. They told me that men before my time had gone stark mad —that I, too, would lose my mind. I laughed at them, and went my way; yet, in truth, there was many a day through the long years I lived there, when I felt myself near to madness as I watched the slow-moving, dust-powdered woolly backs go drifting across the landscape as a gray fog drifts in from the sea. It seemed the desert was the emptier by reason of the sheep being there, for nothing else moved. Never a sign of life but the sheep; never a sound but the everlasting "Baa! Baa! Baa!" Oh! I tell you I was very near to madness then, and many another man in my place would have broken under the tension. But not I. I was strong because I was growing rich. I made money. I took it eastward to the sea, and watched the ships go out. It was a fine thing to see the great waste of waters move, as the desert waste never had. There was the sea, and beyond lay far lands! Still, I said to myself:

"No; not yet will I go. I will wait yet a little longer. I will wait until I hold so much gold in my

A
Shepherd
of
the
Silent
Wastes

hands that I need never return—need never again look upon the desert and its ways.''

So—though I watched the ships sail away to waiting lands beyond—the time was not yet ripe for me to go. Back to the money-making a little longer—back for a while to the stupid, staring-eyed sheep—then a final good-bye to the desert's awful emptiness, and that never-ceasing sound that is worse than silence —the bleating of the flocks!

It was on one of these trips to the Atlantic coast that I saw, for the first time, him of the Half-a-Soul.

The hour was late afternoon of a hot mid-summer day. The sun was red as blood and seemed quadrupled in size where it hung on the horizon with its silent warning of another terrible day on the morrow. Block-pavements and cobbles radiated heat, and the sidewalks burned my feet painfully as I stepped on their scorching surfaces coming out of my friend Burnham's office. The hot air stifled me, and I flinched at the dazzling light. Then I stepped in with the throng, and in a moment more was part of the great surging mass of heat-burdened humanity. Drifting with the pulsating stream, I was for the time listlessly indifferent to what might be coming except that I longed for the night, and for darkness. It might not, probably would not, bring any welcome cool breeze, but at least in the shadows of the night there would be a respite from the torturing white glare that was now reflected from every sun-absorbing brick, or square of granite or stone. I was drifting along the great current of Broadway life when——

There was a sudden clutching at my heart—a tension on the muscles that was an acute pain—a reeling of the brain—and I found myself gazing eagerly into two eyes that as eagerly gazed back into mine. Dark eyes they were, smoldering with evil passions and the light of all things that are bad. The eyes of a man I had never known—had never seen; yet between whom and myself I felt existed a kinship stronger than any tie that my life had hitherto admitted. For one instant I saw those strange black eyes, blazing and baleful, the densely black hair worn rather long, the silky mustache brushed up from the corners of the mouth, the gleam of the sharp white teeth under a lifted lip, the smooth heavy eyebrows slightly curving upward at the outer edges, giving the face the expression we give to the pictures we make of Satan. These I saw. Then he was lost in the crowd.

Where had I seen him before that these details should all seem so familiar? I knew (and my blood chilled as I confessed it to myself) that in all my life I had never seen or known him in the way I had seen and known others. And, more, I knew that we were linked by some strange, unknown, unnamed, unnatural tie. It was as though a hand gloved in steel had clutched my heart in a strangling grip as he moved past. I gasped for breath, staggered, caught myself, and—staggering again—fell forward on the pavement.

"Sunstroke," they said. "Overcome by the heat."

And then——

Long afterward I saw him again.

I was traveling in far lands. Going over from Stamboul to Pera I stood on the Galata bridge watching the great flood of living, pulsing human life—those people of many races.

There was a fresh breeze from the North that day, and it set dancing the caiques and barcas where they threaded their way among the big ferry-boats and ships of many strange sails, and all the craft of summer seas. There was a sparkle on the Bosphorus under the golden sunshine and a gleam on the Golden Horn. A violet-hued haze hung over the wide expanse, and through it one could see the repeated graces of mosque and minaret, the Seven Towers and the rounded whiteness of Santa Sophia. Higher, there was the green of laurel and lime, of rose-tree and shrubbery in profusion—terrace upon terrace—and now and again darker shadows made by the foliage of cypress or pine. All the morning I had reveled in Nature's great color scheme; had feasted eye and sense on the amethyst, and emerald, and sapphire of water, and sky and shore. And then I went to the Galata bridge.

There I stood and watched that medley of races moving by. Arab and Ethiopian, Moslem and Jew; the garb of modern European civilization, and the flowing robes of the East; Kurds, Cossacks and Armenians; the gaudy red fez and the white turban of the Turk; dogs lean and sneaking-eyed; other eyes that looked out from under the folds of a yashmak. And always the babel of voices speaking many tongues. Greeks and Albanians; the flowing mantle of Bedouins and the Tartar in sheepskins. Ebbing and flowing— ebbing and flowing, the restless human tide at the great Gateway of the East.

As I stood looking and listening, there came again without warning that clutching at my heartstrings— that sharp pain in my left side—that same dizzying whirl of thoughts—that sickening fear of something (I knew not what) which I could not control; and out of the flowing tide of faces I saw one not a stranger—he whom I did not know. His eyes held mine again; and in that moment something seemed to tell me that he was my everlasting curse. Through him would come things dread and evil; from him there was no escape. I looked long—my eyes starting in their sockets. I gasped—caught at the air—and lost consciousness.

When I recovered myself I was sitting in a little café whither a young lad had assisted me. I gave him a few piasters and told him to leave me. He took them, said:

"Pek eyi!" and went away.

Left alone at the café table, after motioning the attendant also away, I sat and pondered. Where would this haunting dread end? The basilisk eyes I so loathed had borne me a message which I could not yet translate. Not yet. But he would pass me again some day, and once more his eyes would speak a message. What was it? Something evil, I knew. But what?

So I went away; went away from the Galata bridge; away from Pera and Stamboul.

And then——

Then from the deck of a dahabeeyeh on the Nile!

I was with the Burnhams. We were eight in the party. Lucille Burnham (Joe's sister) and I were betrothed. Betrothed after months and months of playing at love, and the making and unmaking of lovers' quarrels. Each had thought the other meant nothing more than what makes for an idler's pastime, until drifting on the current of old Nilus we read the true love in each other's heart, and the story (old as Egypt is old) was told over again there where it was told centuries before by men and women who loved in the land of the lotus.

Joe and his wife, and the Merrills (brother and sister), Colonel Lamar and his pretty daughter, and my dear girl and I. What a happy, care-free party we were! My most precious dreams were coming true; and now I went up and down the earth's highways as I willed.

Under the awning that day I was lying at Lucille's feet, half-asleep, half-awake and wholly happy. I remember how, just there above Luxor, I noticed two women on the river bank, the dull-blue dress of the one, and the other carrying a water-skin to be filled. A boy, naked and brown-skinned, sprawled in the sand. Moving—slow moving with the current—we came drifting out of that vast land that is old as Time itself reckons age.

Then between my vision and the banks beginning the level which reached far and away to the hills beyond, came the shadow of a lateen sail not our own. A dahabeeyeh was slipping by, going against the current. I raised myself on my elbow, and there—unfathomable, dark as Erebus, and gazing out of deep sockets—were the eyes of a man who drew me to him with a power I was unable to resist; a power fearful as————

The thin, sneering lips seemed to whisper the word "Brother!" and "Brother——" I whispered back.

The sight of that face under the shadow of the lateen sail—like a shadow cast by a carrion bird where it slowly moves above you in the desert—coming, as it did, in the midst of my days of love and new-found joy, left me unnerved and wrecked both mentally and physically.

"Come, come! this won't do," said Joe; "I am afraid you are going to have the fever!"

"It is nothing," I declared, shrinking from his scrutiny, "I ——I have these attacks sometimes."

"Who is he? What is he?" I asked myself the question hourly. And there in the silence of those nights under the stars of the East, while we breathed the soft winds blowing across the sands the Pharaohs had trod, the answer came to me:

He was my other Half-Self—the twin half of my own Soul. This brother of mine—this being for whom I had a loathing deep and intense—was one in whom there lived an incomplete Soul (a half that was evil through and through) and mine was the other half. I was beginning now to understand. We had been sent into this world with but one Soul between us; and to me had been apportioned the good. But evil or good—good and evil—we were henceforth to be inseparable in our fate.

But always I cried out in my helpless, hopeless agony, "Yet why—why—why?" It is the cry of the Soul from the first day of creation.

I turned my back on the far East, and set my face towards America.

Then——

Then I started on a trip through California and old Mexico. My health was broken. My marriage with Lucille was postponed.

On the Nevada desert our train was side-tracked early one morning to allow the passing of the eastbound express which was late. A vast level plain stretched its weary way in every direction. Only the twin lines of steel and the dark-red section house showed that the White Man's footsteps had ever found their way into the stillness of the dreary plains.

We had fifteen minutes to wait. I got out with others and walked up and down the wind-blown track, smoking my cigar and spinning pebbles, which I picked up from the road-bed, at a jack rabbit in the sage-brush across the way. The wind made a mournful sound through the telegraph wires, but a wild canary sang sweetly from the top of a tall greasewood—sang as if to drown the wind's dirge. Dull grays were about us; and we were hemmed in by mountains rugged, and rough, and dull gray, with here and there touches of dull reds and browns. On their very tops patches of snow lay, far—far up on the heights. Miles down the valley we could see the coming train. A few minutes later the conductor called to us "All aboard!" and I swung myself up on the steps of the last sleeping-car as we began to move slowly down toward the western end of the switch.

There was a roar and a clatter—a flash of faces at the windows—a rush of wind and dust whirled up by the whirling wheels—and, as the Eastern Express shot by, I saw (on the rear platform of the last car) him, between whom and myself a Soul was shared.

The conductor stepped up on the platform where I stood, and caught me by the arm as I reeled.

"The high altitude," he said, "makes a good many folks get dizzy. You'd better go inside and sit down."

Then again.
On a ferry-boat crossing the bay from the Oakland

pier to San Francisco.   I had just returned that
morning from a four-months' tour of Mexico.   It was
raining dismally, and everything about the shipping
on the bay was dripping and dreary.   Gray-white sea
gulls circled and screamed; darting and dipping, they
followed our wake, or dropped down into the foam
churned up by the wheels.   Winds—wet and salty,
and fresh from the sea—tugged at our mackintoshes;
and flapped the gowns and wraps of the women where
—huddled together away from the rail—we stood
under shelter.   Sheets of flying fog—dense, dark and
forbidding—went by; gray ghosts of the ocean's
uneasy dead.   And back of the curtain of falling
waters and fog, whistles shrieked shrilly, and the fog
horns uttered their hideous sounds.   Bellowing—moaning; moaning—bellowing; suddenly still.

The city seemed but an endless succession of terraced, water-washed houses under an endless rain.
The storm lashed the waves in the harbor into running ridges of foam, and on the billows the ferry-boat
(falling and rising, rising and falling) pushed her
way through gray skeleton-ships at anchor, and into
her slip at the wharf.   The drivers of wagons and
trucks on the lower deck, wrapped in oilskins yellow
or black and all dripping with wet, drove down the
echoing planks.   Then the people began to descend
the stairways.   With my right hand steadying me, I
had taken three downward steps when the gripping at
my heart told me who was passing at my left (always
at the left, it had been; at the left, always) and he of
the smoldering eyes that burned into mine like live
embers passed me quickly, and went on down the
stairway and into the rain-wetted crowd.

And again————
It happened when, with a guide and some Club

A Shepherd of the Silent Wastes

friends, we went through the Chinatown slums of the city.

It was Saturday night; the night of all others for hovels and evil haunts to disgorge their hives of human bees to swarm through passage and alley, or up and down the dark and wretched stairways.

We had begun at the Joss Houses—gaudy with tinsel, and close and choking from the incense of burning tapers. We had gone to restaurant and theater. At the one, going in through the back way and on through their cooking rooms where they were preparing strange and repulsive looking food; at the other, using the stage entrance and going on the stage with the players. Into opium joints our guide led the way, where the smokers in their utter degradation lay like the dead, as the drug carried the dreamers into a land of untranslatable dreams. We had looked at the pelf in the pawn-shops, and at the painted faces of Chinese courtesans looking out through their lattices.

Then underground we had gone down (three stories) and had seen places and beings hideous in their loathesomeness; loathesome beyond description. To the "Dog Kennel." Up to earth's surface again; to "The Rag Picker's Paradise." Through "Cum Cook Alley"—through "Ross Alley," where within a few feet, within a few years, murder after murder had been committed, and (the murderers escaping through the network of secret passageways and hidden doors) the deaths had gone unavenged. Through the haunts of highbinders, and thugs and assassins we moved; and once I passed a little child—a half-caste—toddling through the alley that was reeking with filth. "Look out, Baby!" I said, as he stumbled

"Again the sirocco passed." — Page 79

and fell. "Look out, Man!" he answered in English, and laughed.

Then, somewhere between high walls that reached to the open air, I found myself alone—left behind by the others. I could see the guide's light burning —a tiny red spark—far ahead in the darkness, but my own candle had gone out. Away up in the narrow slit showing the sky, shone the cold, still stars. Under my feet crunched clinkers and cinders wet with a little stream from some sewer running over the ground.

Then in the dark wall a door opened, and as the light from within lit up the inky blackness without I saw him again. Again the sirocco passed, burning —scorching the life-blood in my veins.

They came back and found me lying in the wet of the noisome alley. For weeks, in the hotel, I lay ill; then, as soon as I was able to walk unassisted, I took passage for Japan, intending to extend my trip to Suez, and through Europe, on home. I said to myself that I would never again set foot in San Francisco. I feared that horrible something, the power of which seemed stronger over me there than elsewhere. Six times we had met and passed. I shrank from the seventh. Each time that we had come face to face—met—passed—drifted apart, I heard a voice saying that my life was being daily drawn closer and closer into his, to be a part of the warp and woof of his own. And the end? It would be————when? Where? In what way? What would be that final meeting of ours? How far off was it? What would that fatal seventh meeting mean for us both?

I fled from the city as one does from the touch of a leper. I dared not stay.

But the third day out on the ocean there suddenly came over me a knowledge that a greater force than my own will would compel me to return. Something bade me go back. I fought with it; I battled with the dread influence the rest of the voyage. It was useless. I was a passenger on the ship when it returned to San Francisco. There I found the whole city talking and horrified, over a murder hideous, foul, revolting. Carmen de la Guerra, a young Spanish woman, had been brutally murdered—butchered by her lover. I was sick—chilled, when I heard. A foreboding of the truth came to me as I listened. I feverishly read the papers; they told of the tragedy in all its frightful details. I went to the public libraries for the back files. Then I went to the jail to look at the face of the fiend who had killed her. I knew whom I should see behind the bars. It was he. And it was the seventh meeting.

His eyes bade me go and get him release.

"Go!" they said, "Call to your aid all the angels of your heaven, and the help of the demons who are one with me in hell, that you may save me from the gallows. My Soul is your Soul; if I die, you also must die with me. Keep the rope from me; for you are fighting for your own life. Go!"

I went out of the chill jail corridors a madman. I raved against the hellish destiny. What use? I must save him, or I must die with him. No one understood. I told no one my secret. Early and late; day and night I worked unceasingly to get him pardoned. God! how I worked to save him. I tried every conceivable means to secure him his life. I exhausted all methods known to the law. I spent money as a mill-wheel runs water.

"You believe him innocent?—this fiend!" my friends cried aghast—amazed at my mad eagerness to get him acquittal.

"No! not that!" I answered in my agony, "but he must not die—shall not hang! Shall not! Do you hear? Innocent or guilty—what do I care? Only he must live, that I shall not die."

But no one understood.

It has been in vain. At eleven o'clock he is to be hung. The death-watch is with him. And the death-watch is here, too, with me. Two are here; and the name of one is Horror, and the other's name is Fear. Down below I hear the rattle of traffic on the streets, and in the hotel corridors I hear the voices of people talking—just now I heard one laugh. They do not know. And Lucille—— Ah, my poor Lucille!

The tide of life is running out, and the end is drawing nigh. I have come to find at last that evil is always stronger than good; and in that way he draws me after him. I cannot hold the half of his Soul back. Closer and closer together we come. A Divided Soul—his and mine. His body has housed the evil half—mine the good. His is all that is vile, and bestial, and bloodthirsty; mine has always striven after the best. Yet because of his sin I, too, must die.

At the hour of eleven he will hang for the murder of Carmen de la Guerra. At eleven I, too, must die. As the sheriff cuts the rope, and the evil Divided Soul swings out eternity-ward from the body which has housed it evilly, so will I die at that instant—death by strangulation. For a Divided Soul may not live when its twin is gone. Death. And then one body in the rosewood casket, and one in its box of pine.

At eleven———

"Baa! Baa!" I hear the sheep——— No; it is———
What is it? I cannot see——— Something is being
pressed down over my eyes, shutting out the light.
My arms—my feet are being tied—I cannot move.
Help! Something is closing on my neck—I cannot
breathe. It is tightening—choking——— I hear the
bleating of the sheep——— God! God! I am strangling! The rope——— It is the rope—and Death.

May God have mercy on my Soul!

BY THE OIL SEEP UNDER THE BLUFF

JON LANDIS turned the bit of black rock over and over in his hand as he held it under the searching Nevada sunlight. The lids of his light blue eyes narrowed as he looked, and he chewed nervously at the corner of his long upper lip under its cropped reddish mustache. Finally, as though wholly satisfied with the close scrutiny he had given it, he nodded his head slowly.

"You think he good? All same like that other kin' you show um me?"

The young Paiute was peering into his palm, too.

"I guess so, Nick," answered Landis; "Anyway, you no tell um 'nother man 'bout this. Savvy?"

The Paiute nodded. It was evident that he "savvied." He had shown Landis a copper ledge off in the mountains, two years before, and Landis had given him a hundred dollars. It was Indian Nick's opinion that Landis was "heap pretty good man;" and he now recognized the value of silence until such a time as Landis would let him speak. Other white men had, before this, got him to show them prospects upon promises, and—without an exception—had cheated him out of his due. But Jon Landis was different. This big, quiet man who talked but little, and never laughed at all—him he would be "partner" with, and

By
the
Oil
Seep
Under
the
Bluff

show him the place down by the river where the black rock sample came from, and the bluffs where—underneath—a queer little spring (that wasn't water) oozed forth, and lost itself a dozen feet away in the muddy current of the greater stream.

Indian Nick didn't know what that stream—a very, very little stream—was; and he didn't care to know. Indians as a rule are not inquisitive. He only knew it looked "heap greasy;" and if the black rock on the sandy mesa above was like the piece that Landis showed him, saying it was from California—then Nick was to have another hundred dollars.

Now that Landis had "guessed" that the rock sample was the same sort, Nick (seeing a hundred dollars easily earned) looked furtively about him as they stood on the railroad track—where the section house and the freight house were sole evidence of a station—to discover if they had been observed talking together. For even a Paiute knows that precaution may prevent a secret from being suspected. No, no one had seen them together. The section foreman was out on the road with his men, and the telegraph operator had not come out of his office in the freight house since he had reported the train that had just brought Landis back to Nevada. No one from the town (as the mining camp up in the foothills was called) had come down to the station that day. The Indian was satisfied; no one would guess that he and Landis were "partners."

"You come now; I show you that place. He not far —can walk."

"How far?"

"Maybe two mile, I think. You see. You come now?"

Landis deliberated. Presently he asked:

"You got a shovel, Nick? Got a pick at your wick-i-up?"

"I got um ol' one—not much good."

"Well, never mind; they'll do for today. You go get 'em, and trot on ahead. Where is it?"

Nick pointed in the direction of the river bluffs; and when Landis had reached the mesa the Paiute—with pick and shovel—was already there.

"The ol' man—my father—asked um me where I go. I no tell um. He ask what for I take pick—take um shovel—what I do. I no say nothin'."

"That's right, Nick! Don't tell anybody. By an' by, when I get the business all fixed, then we'll talk. Savvy?"

And again Nick "savvied."

All about them was the black rock from which Nick had got the sample. Not much of it, but enough to demonstrate the value of what it indicated. It was undoubtedly asphaltum; the indication for oil was good—more than good. Landis was interested. The Paiute was moving off through the stunted greasewood to the bluffs near the river edge, and Landis followed.

The face of the bluffs—eroded and uneven—rose high above the river level; leaving but a narrow foot-way between their base and the stream, here at this point. Across by the other bank, was a growth of rabbit-wood and sage. A twisted, leafless buck-bush stood lonely and alone at the rim of a dry slough. The carcass of a dead horse—victim of some horse-hide hunter—furnished a gruesome feast for a half dozen magpies that fluttered chattering away as the two figures appeared on the top of the bluffs; and a coyote that had been the magpies' companion, slipped away into the thicket of rabbit-wood. The river was deep here, and dirty with the debris brought down by its

By
the
Oil
Seep
Under
the
Bluff

By
the
Oil
Seep
Under
the
Bluff

rising waters. Froth, and broken twigs, and sticks swirled around in the eddies. To Landis, there was something unspeakably depressing about the place, though he was well used to the country in all its phases. Its very stillness seemed today to weigh on him.

The two men began the descent; the Indian slipping quickly down the face of the bluffs, and Landis clambering after.

There—at the foot—in a gully so narrow it would escape any but the keenest eye, a tiny, slow-moving, dark thread of a stream oozed from beneath the bluffs of clay, and following the bottom of the narrow cut that ran at right angles to the river—slipped down into the roily waters that bore it away. Landis squatted down by it for closer inspection. He rubbed it between his fingers. He smelt of it. Yes, it was oil!

"All right, Nick! You'll get your hundred dollars!"

Nick grinned delightedly; but the face of Landis—from the high cheek bones down to the square set jaws that were burned as red as the skin of an Indian is supposed to be—was a mask of immobility. This find meant many thousands of dollars to him, but he only said:

"Here, boy! Pitch in now, and dig out under that bank!" as he pointed out a part of the bluff at the very edge of the gully. And Nick—strong, and young, and keen as himself to know how much of the "greasy" stream was dammed up behind the bluffs that the pick could disclose, swung it with strong strokes that ate into the clay in a way that did Landis good to see.

He had been working but a short time when the pick point caught into something other than lumps of clay; caught at it—clawed at it—and then dragged out (one—two—half a dozen) bones stripped of all flesh.

Nick stopped.

"What are you stopping for?" Landis asked sharply. "Go on! It's only some horse or a cow that's died here." But already he himself had seen the thigh bone of a human being. Nick hesitated; still staring at what lay there.

"Damn you, go on! What's the matter with you?"

The steady strokes recommenced. Little by little there was uncovered and dragged out the skeleton of some one Who Once Was. Nick looked sullen and strange, but he did not falter. He worked steadily on until they lay—an indistinguishable heap—beside the narrow gully. Landis said nothing, and the pick strokes ate farther and farther into the bank.

Suddenly there was a terrible sound—half a shriek and half a gurgle that died away in the throat —which startled them; and swinging around, Landis saw an old Indian tottering along the narrow ledge that bordered the river there. He was stumbling and blindly staggering toward them, waving his arms above his head as he came. A bareheaded, vilely dirty and ragged old man—how old no one might be able to say. As his bleared eyes found the skeleton heap, he shrieked forth in the Indian tongue something (though Landis knew no word of what he might say) that sent a chill over him of prescient knowledge of what was to come. He turned his back on the old man, and addressed himself to Nick.

"What does he say?"

The younger Paiute looked old and gray with a horror that Landis refused to translate.

"My father——"

By
the
Oil
Seep
Under
the
Bluff

"Yes, I know. Your father. What does he say?"

"My father——" Nick's words came slowly, "He say——them——bones——"

"For God's sake, what? Why don't you say what? Can't you talk?"

"Them," Nick's teeth were chattering now, "my ——my——mother."

Landis caught his breath. Then a stinging pain shot through his left arm, and something fell to the ground. He swung around in time to see the old Paiute, with another stone in his raised hand, his face distorted with hate and fury.

"Quit that!" Landis yelled, and strode toward him. But the old man's fury was now turned to fear as he saw this white giant bearing down on him, and the stone fell short of its mark. He started to flee before the strength he feared, but the narrow ledge that lay between the river and the bluff would have been but insecure foothold for steadier steps than his. He tripped—reeled—and then with a cry that Landis will remember so long as he lives—he went backward; and down into the muddy river the eddies sucked him— down and down—and so out of sight.

Then Jon Landis fought with the one who, with raised pick, stood ready to avenge the death of his father, and the desecration of his other dead. The struggle was not long, but they fought as men do who know that but one man shall live when the combat be done. Twice the pick descending almost struck the bared head of the white man; thrice his adversary forced him to the very water's edge. Landis knew he was fighting for his life, and he watched his opportunity. It came. Eluding that rain of death-meant blows, he caught the Indian close to him, and with a quick movement flung the pick far out into the river.

Then they clinched in the final struggle for life that to the white man or the brown man is equally dear. Back and forth, swaying and bending, the hot breath of each in the other's face, they moved over the narrow confine. It was not for long; for—with one mighty final effort—Landis wrenched himself loose, caught at the other, shoved—flung him off, and it was over. Jon Landis stood there alone.

The fleshless skull grinned out at him from the heap of bones. Landis shivered; he felt cold. Overhead, clouds like swansdown were beautiful against the sapphire blue of the afternoon sky. A soft wind blowing down the valley brought him the sound of a locomotive's whistle; and the breeze was sweet with the breath of spring flowers growing upon the banks, away from the bluffs. A little brown bird began to warble from the buck-brush across the river.

It must have been five minutes that Landis stood there without moving. Then he picked up the shovel and walked over to the Indian woman's bones. It did not take him long to dump them into the little gully where the oil ran, and to cover them over with loose earth from the place she had lain for thirty years. Afterward, he scraped the earth about with the broken shovel, to destroy all footprints. Then he dropped it into the stream. He would never come here again; and now there was no evidence that he had ever been there.

Then he climbed the bluffs. Nor did he look back as he walked rapidly away.

By
the
Oil
Seep
Under
the
Bluff

THE BLUE-EYED CHIEF

T sounds a bit melodramatic, in these days of "Carlisle" education for the Indian, and with "Lo" himself on the lecture platform, to tell of a band of one time hostile red men having a white chief —once a captive—who so learned to love his captivity that when freedom was to be had for the taking, he refused it, and still lives among them, voluntarily. Contentedly—happily? Who knows? He says so; and with no proof to the contrary we must needs believe him.

Once in every three years he leaves his home among the mountains of eastern Oregon, and goes for a week to San Francisco by the sea. Once in every three years he may be seen there on the streets, in the parks, at the theaters, on the beach, at the Cliff or the Heights, as strangers are seen daily, and with nothing about him to mark him in any wise different from a thousand others. You might pass him dozens of times without particularly observing him, save that he is always accompanied by a woman so evidently of a different world than that which he has known, that your attention is at once arrested, and your curiosity is whetted to know the story—for story there is, you are sure. And what a story! One does not have to go to fiction for tales of the marvelous; and these two—he, roughened, bearded and browned, clothed as the average American laborer taking a holiday; she, with the bearing of a gentlewoman, and dressed as they do who have found the treasure-trove that lies at the end of the rainbow—these two have a tragic story, all their own, that few know. It is this:

Back in those far days when the Pacific Railroad was undreamed of—before we had so much as ever guessed there might in reality be a stage line between the Missouri and the Sacramento—one noon the wheels of an emigrant wagon were moving down a wide Nevada valley, where the sage gray of the short greasewood was the only thing remotely green; moving so slowly that they seemed not to move at all. It was a family from one of the States of our Middle West, going to California. The man walked beside the slow-moving wagon. Sometimes some of the children walked, too. The woman rode and held in her arms a wee boy whose own arms fought and sturdy legs struggled often to walk with the others—a blue-eyed boy, bonny and beautiful.

Days and days of unblinking sunshine; and always the awful stillness of the plains. There had been weeks of it; and this day when they came down the broad wash that was the drain from the bordering mountain range, a thick heat lay on the land, making welcome the promised noon rest where the greasewood grew tall. All down the length of the now dry wash the brush was more than shoulder high—annually wetted as it was by the full spring creek.

When the greasewood grows so high it may easily hide a foe.

The wagon bumped and ground its wheels over the stones of the road here in the wash toward the row of tall greasewood, a dozen yards away. Over there they would halt for a noon rest. Over there they would eat their noon meal—drink from their scanty water supply—and then resume the dreary journey.

This day was just such an one as all their other desert days had been; the place seemed to them not different in any way from the other miles of endless monotony. As they neared the high brush, one of the children—a fair-haired girl of eight—picking up a bright pebble from the road, held it up that her father might see. The other children walking beside the wagon picked up pebbles, too—pebbles red, and purple, and green, that had come down the bed of the creek when the flood came. In the wagon the woman sat holding the blue-eyed boy in her arms.

Then——

There was a swift, singing sound in the air, and one of the oxen staggered—bellowed—fell!

The sound of an arrow boring the air isn't quite like anything else one may ever hear; and the man knew—before he heard the big steer's roar of pain—that the thing he had feared (but had at last come to believe he had no cause to fear, when weeks passed and it had not happened) had finally come to them.

Dashing out from the greasewood cover, the Indians —half naked and wholly devilish—made quick work of their victims. They did not dally in what they had to do. Back on the plains another wagon—two, three, four, a train!—was coming; they did not dare to stay to meet such numbers. They struck only when sure of their strength. Now they were two to one—nay, ten men to one man! And he, that man, went down with a wife's shrieks and the screaming of children's voices in his ears.

It was the old story of early times and emigrants on the plains. You have heard it time and again.

After the arrow, the knife; and bloody corpses left

by a burning wagon. Things done to turn sick with horror the next lone wayfarers who should reach this gruesome spot. Human flesh and bone for the vultures of the air and the wolves of the desert to feed upon, till—taken from their preying talon and tooth—they might be laid in the shallow graves hollowed by the roadside.

Yet one was spared. The wee bonny laddie wrested from the clinging arms of a dying mother, was held apart to witness a butchery that strained the childish eyes with terror. He lived, but never was he to forget the awful scene of that hour in the desert. And when the brutal work was over, savage arms bore him away to their homes on the heights of near mountains gashed by many a cañon.

There, for years upon years—growing from babyhood to boyhood—from boyhood to youth—he lived among them; and so became as one of their tribe. They were a small tribe—these—of renegade Bannocks; shifting their camps further and further into the North, and away from the White Man's approach as civilization began to force them back. Northward; and at last into Oregon.

The sturdy little frame remained sturdy. Some children there are who persist in thriving under the most adverse conditions. And he was one of these. Yet, it must be admitted, his captors were kind; for the Indian—savage though he may be—deals gently, always, with his children; and this boy had become to them as their own.

The baby words of the White Man's tongue were soon forgotten, and Indian gutterals took their place. The little feet were moccasined with deerskin, and the round cheeks daubed with paint. The little body was kept warm in a rabbitskin robe. Their food was his food—grass seeds ground into paste, and game; and his friends were themselves. To all intents and purposes he had become an Indian.

When, at length, he reached early manhood he took to himself an Indian bride. Then the tribe made him their chief.

*   *   *   *

Mines in the mountains had brought an army of prospectors into the once wild country. The mines prospered, and camps—permanent ones—multiplied. The Red Men saw their enemy growing in numbers beyond their strength to battle, so the depredations became fewer and fewer, and finally ceased altogether. "Lo" is something of a philosopher, and he generally accepts defeat with a better grace than his white brother. These knew they were beaten, so they were willing to accept peace; and began to mix, by degrees, with the Whites. They adopted the White Man's dress—some learned his speech. The blue-eyed chief, too, whose position among them was never quite clear to the miners, again learned the language that seemed as one he had never known.

It was a long time before he came to realize that his chains of captivity had dropped away—rusted apart by time and circumstances—and that he might now, if he so chose, go back to the people of his own blood. He thought of it dully, indifferently, at first—then deeply. The way was open for him! He could go! But he came to know that down in the depths of his heart an affection had grown up for these people who had made him their own, that no other people could lay claim to, ever. That for all the days of his life his lot was here.

The awful events of that long gone day in the desert were too deeply branded into his recollection ever to

be forgotten (young child though he was at the time);
but the years had dimmed its horrors, and the associations of a lifetime had dulled his sensibilities.

No! he would remain among them. As he had been,
he would still be—one of them. He had lost all desire
to go. How many years had come and gone since the
longing for liberty left him? He could not remember.
This was his home—these were his people—he would
stay.

And there he is today. There, a dozen years ago, a
San Franciscan, drawn by the mines, found him; and
during a summer's companionship, gaining his confidence, learned from his lips his story.

Months later, this thrice strange tale served to
entertain half a score of people who met together in
his parlors on his return. They gathered around the
story teller—close listeners—intent on every syllable;
but one there was who went white as she heard. And
when she could see him apart and unnoted, she said:

"He is my brother! I saw them take him away. I
was hid behind a greasewood bush—I do not know how
they overlooked me. I saw it all—everything! Then,
those in an emigrant train behind ours, came and took
me with them. I was a little child then—only eight;
and he—my brother—was younger. I thought they
had taken him away and killed him—I never guessed
he lived. I know—I am sure this is he. Tell me all
you can; for I must go and find him."

What that meeting was, no one can say. She found
him there surrounded by those who were his nearest
and dearest—a brown-skinned wife and little bronze
bairns—his! She stood face to face with him—she
clasped hands with him; yet a lifetime and all the
world lay between. Children of the loins of one

father—born of the same mother—these two had nothing in common between them—nothing—save the yearning for a something that was always to lie just beyond.

He yielded to her persuasions and went home with her to see the city by the sea of which he had heard much, but knew nothing. It was a visit of but a few days; yet in that time no hour struck for each alike. Try as each would for a feeling of kinship, the other was ever a stranger.

She showed him the sights of the city, but he was more and more bewildered by what he saw. At the beach it was better; he seemed to understand the ocean best, though seeing it for the first time. She sought to awaken in him an interest in the things of her world. And to his credit be it said, he honestly tried to respond in the way she would have him.

But up and away to the Northeast was all he had interest in or heart for; and so at the end of a week he went back. Going, he pledged himself to come to her every third year for a week's stay; for "blood is thicker than water," and though they might never strike the same chord, yet, after all, she was his sister.

The years wax and wane. Every third one brings in fulfillment of the promise, the very commonplace-looking brother who is something of a mystery to her metropolitan friends. Time has brought brother and sister a little more closely together, but it will never bridge the chasm. Always there is a restraint, a reserve, which comes from a common knowledge that there are things in his past life he may not tell—yet, which she guesses with an unspoken, unnamed fear.

Once (when the bronze brown woman was dead), he tried to accept civilized life as a finality. The month had not rounded out to fullness when each saw the futility of the attempt.

Back on the rough Oregon mountains were sons and daughters, "flesh of his flesh, bone of his bone," brown skinned though they were; and he turned his back on the White Man and his unfamiliar ways, and set his face toward those whom he knew best and loved.

Somehow, you like and respect the man for going, as you couldn't had he stayed.

The story reads like fiction, doesn't it? But the pity of it is that it is true.

The
Blue-
Eyed
Chief

ACCORDING TO ONE'S STANDPOINT

THERE were three people in the group on the station platform at Humboldt. The two who were standing were a white man and a white woman.

The man was tall, with breadth in his shoulders, five-and-thirty, and rather good looking. His dress evidenced prosperity, and his manner betokened long residence in a city—one of the cities east of the Mississippi.

The woman also was tall; and graceful, and very pretty, and not over twenty-five years of age. She was, without doubt, a bride, and—equally without doubt—a fit mate for the man. She carried her chin high (a trick common to those wearing eye-glasses) and moved with an air of being quite sure of her social position. She was inconspicuously dressed, but her gown, when she walked, rustled in the way that speaks of silken linings. She looked like a woman whose boots were always made to order, and who, each night, had an hour spent upon brushing her hair.

The third person in the group was an Indian. A Paiute fifty years old, but who looked twenty years older. Old George. His little withered brown face was puckered into a whimsical smile as with head aslant he looked up from where he sat on the bench that was built round a tree-box. This was his frequent seat when the trains came in, and here he came daily to answer the inquisitive questions of people who deem themselves well bred.

He was old, and much dirtier than even the others of his race. But he afforded entertainment for the travelers whose pleasure it was to put questions.

"Yep, me old. 'Forty?' I guess so. 'One hundred?' Maybe so; I no know." He chuckled. It was the same thing over and over again that they—on the trains—asked him every day. Not a whit cared he what they asked, nor was it worth while telling the truth. When they asked he answered; saying the things they wanted to hear. And sometimes they gave him nickels. That was all there was about it.

"Where did he live?" "What did he eat?" "Did he work?" his inquisitors queried. "Was he married?" and "Had he any children?" "Had he ever killed any white men?" Then they would note his maimed, misshapen limbs. "How long ago had his leg been broken?" "In what way had he crippled his hands?" But to all there were the same replies:

"I no know. Maybe so. I guess so."

What did it matter? They were satisfied. And meddlers they were. Yet——generally he got the waited-for nickel.

So today he answered even as they questioned. Then the woman (pretty, and with an unmistakable air of good breeding) nodded and said: "Good by!" and the man (well-mannered, well-groomed and self-compla-cent) gave him a silver quarter as he went back to the "Pullman."

"Henry, dear," she asked, after they had settled themselves comfortably again in their compartment of the sleeping-car, "how do such creatures exist?

Do they work, or only sit idly in the sun waiting for some one to give them one or two nickels?''

"Oh, he is a confirmed beggar, one can see! They never work—these Paiutes. Mere animals are they, eating, drinking and sleeping as animals,'' her husband replied. "So degenerate have they become since the days when they were a wild tribe and warriors that they go through life now in docile stupidity, without anything rousing them to what we would call a live interest in their surroundings. I doubt very much if, in the life of any one of them, there ever occurs any stirring event. Perhaps it is just as well, for at least it gives them a peaceful old age, and they can have no harassing recollections.

"And no happy ones, either,'' the woman said. "Think what it must be to live out one's allotted time of physical existence without ever experiencing the faintest romance—without even a gleam of what love means! I presume that the sense of attachment is unknown to them; such affection as——''

"As ours?'' he interrupted laughingly. "Well, rather unknown I should say.''

The man looked with fond eyes into the eyes of the woman; then, as the train pulled out of the station, they saw the old Indian limping away toward his camp.

Are the individual histories of Indians—even Paiutes—even the "degenerate tribes''—uneventful or wholly devoid of human interest? Let us see.

Old George can tell you a different story, it may be. From his point of view there is perhaps love; perhaps even romance. Much depends upon the standpoint one takes. The hills that look high from the valley, seem low looking down from the mountain.

When I first knew George (he was "Young George" then), he was married and had children. Four; two boys and two girls. More than other Indians, he aped the Whites in their ways, and was reckoned (for a Paiute) a decent fellow. His camp was the best, his food the most plentiful, and his children the best kept and cleanest. The mother sewed well, and neither she nor the children ever went ragged. Among Indians they were as the hard-working, temperate laborer's family is among the white men who work—work with their hands for a living.

According-
ing
to
One's
Stand-
point

George had money laid by—joint earnings of his own and of Susan, his wife. He worked at the settlers' wood-piles in winter, chopping wood; and in summer he worked in the hay fields. She washed and ironed for the white families. Wage was high in those days, and George and Susan prospered. That was a contented little camp built there in the tall sagebrush, and they were happy as needs be.

And then——

There happened that which is not always confined to the camp of the red man. It was the old story—another woman. Well, has not the world seen such things before? There are women—even those without the dower of beauty—of whose strange power no explanation can be given save that they can, and do, "charm men." And in no less measure was this brown-skinned woman a charmer. She had already parted more than one husband and wife—had destroyed the peace and quiet of more than one home, when she and George stood where the ways met.

If this had happened some three thousand years ago, and she had lived on the banks of the Nile, and if you were a poet, or a recorder of history, no doubt you would have written her down a siren—a dark-eyed charmer of men—a sorceress of Egypt; but she lived on the Humboldt river instead, and all this happened within the last four decades, and she was only a squaw of one of our North American tribes. Neither was she a pretty squaw judged by our canons of beauty. Yet are not such things matters of geography governed by traditions? And when a man is bewitched by a man, brown-skinned or white, he is very apt to see charms where another cannot discover them.

Sophy, the siren, came into the camp, and with her coming fled peace. Poor Susan, unloved and deserted, sat apart and cried her heart out—as many a white woman has done before her, and since—when powerless to prevent, or right the wrong that was done her. So, bewitched and befooled, George gave himself up to the madness that was his undoing. The money which had been laid by went like water held in the hand. The camp was neglected; the stores were wasted. The children, from whom the mother had been banished, went ragged and oftentimes hungry.

It took George a long time to awake from his delirium, but he did awaken finally—after many months. All things come—some day—to the writing of "finis." And no joy falls so soon and so completely as the joy built on an unsound foundation. One day George came to his senses. Then he cast the woman out; cast her out, and forever. He brought back to his home the mother of his children, and she foregave him. Well, what would you?—she was his wife, and a woman forgives much for the sake of the children she has held to her breast. So the camp was made tidy again and the children cared for as of old, and there were new stores gathered, and money was again saved.

Now George—being an Indian, being a Paiute—had never heard of Colley Cibber, else he might have been reminded that "we shall find no fiend in hell can match the fury of a disappointed woman—scorned! slighted! dismissed without a parting pang." Neither did George —being a Paiute Indian—know the meaning of the word "Nemesis."

Accord-
ing
to
One's
Stand-
point

That was more than twenty years ago; and for more than twenty years the woman, Sophy, made his life a series of persecutions. If he builded aught at the camp, it was torn down; what he raised in his garden was destroyed; what he bought, was quickly broken. Horses were driven far astray; and his favorite dogs were poisoned. Then, when she had exhausted all her ingenuity in these and a hundred other ways of making his life a torment, she turned her wiles on Doctor Jim, one of the great medicine men of the tribe, married to Susan's mother, and an inmate of George's camp. Doctor Jim's long residence in the house had given to George a certain enviable status among the Indians, and this prestige the woman now meant to destroy. On Doctor Jim were bestowed her blandishments, and—like George before him—he was fain to follow whither she led. With the medicine man's going, departed the glory of the house. And it left, in the person of the deserted wife, another mouth for George to feed; while at the same time the assisting support which Doctor Jim had given the household was taken away.

Troubles came thick and fast to Old George. He had begun to be called "Old" George now. One day while he was handling a cartridge it accidentally exploded and tore away part of his hand. This hampered him in what work he got to do; and sometimes because of it he was refused employment. Then the evil fate that had chosen him for a plaything, threw him from a train running at full speed, and left him lying on the track with broken legs, and pitifully crippled. He got well after many weary months while Susan nursed him, and between whiles of nursing earned the living for the dwellers within the camp. When Spring came, Susan died.

On George fell the care of the four children. It was harder for him to work now, and there was less to be earned; yet he worked the harder for his four. Another year; and there were but two for him to shelter and to feed. The great White Plague stops not at the camps of the White man, but has hunted out the Red man in his wick-i-up, and is fast decreasing the number of the tribe; so two—the older two—of the children had gone to answer its call, and George was alone with the two that were hardly more than babies. Mourning for his dead, he must yet work for the living.

We give our sympathy to the woman left widowed who has little children looking to her for support. But she seldom fails in her trust, for the world is usually kind to a woman and ready to lend her aid. Rather give of your pity to the father who has babes to provide for when there is no woman to take up the burden with him. He must care for the home, and must go out in the world, as well, to work. Remember the burden is no less hard for him to bear even so be he is an Indian. It may not seem so to you, a white man, but you must recollect that the Indian takes a different point of view.

Long, long after his children were grown, and the old grandmother was dead, and George was living in his camp with grandchildren about him, the woman came again—she, Sophy, came to him—trying to win him back now that the woman he cared most for was dead. Sophy at last had tired of her revenge, had tired of jealousy and strife; had tired of everything in life but the one man who had once cast her off. Doctor Jim was dead—had died many years before. And so she came to the one she cared for still—as even she had cared most for. For George she cared always; so she came and stood at his door. Many snows had come and gone since his blood had moved at her will; and now it was too late for her influence to weigh with him. He was old; and when he sat before the camp-fire and saw a woman's face move to and fro in the the smoke wreaths, it was the face of the woman who best loved him, always—not the face of the one he had loved for a time—that he saw.

So she went away, and at last there was peace between them. She died the other day. But George—Old George—lives still, and alone. He goes to the station day after day, as is his habit, and watches the trains as they come in, and answers the questions of the inquisitive travelers.

If my characters were white you might call this a love story with a bit of romance threaded in. Perhaps you will, anyway. For it all depends upon how you look at it. It is just a little story of what is happening all the while everywhere in the world. Love and jealousy; hatred and revenge. It does not very much matter whether they live on the water side of Beacon street (as they do who stood talking to Old George yesterday); or whether it is in the wick-i-ups of the sagebrush out on the great Nevada plains. These things come into the lives of all races alike.

George paid for the folly of his youth, as the transgressor usually does have to pay. If you live by the sea in the East, you will perhaps call this a punishment for George laid upon him as a rebuke by the "hand of

According to One's Standpoint

divine Providence.'' But if your home is by the Western sea, and you have knocked about a bit on the rough trails in the West, you will mayhap see in it only the workings of "natural law."

That is all. It is a little story, but quite true. It might very easily have been made a White man's story; but it isn't, it is only the true story of a Paiute.

George is an Indian; but one in a whole tribe—each having his own story. And the tribe is but one of the race. And the race——

Are we not brothers?

For, the world over, under white skin or skin of bronze-brown, the human heart throbs the same; for we are brothers—ay! brothers all.

Yet, even so, there is still the point of view.

WHERE THE BURROS BROWSED.

ELLO, Dick!"

"Hello, Reddy!"

Seven little gray burros—browsing upon the dust-covered chamiso— lifted their heads at the words; and turned seven mealy noses and seven pairs of inquisitive ears toward the speakers in indolent curiosity.

The two men who met upon the mesa had been drawing slowly together on the long white road winding up toward the mountain a dozen miles away. The dust, raised by the shuffling feet of their horses, floated—a long streamer of white—down toward the muddy, crooked river in the valley far below. The dust had whitened, too, the slouch hats and worn blue overalls they wore; and their faces were marked with furrows, burned deep by the harsh, relentless sun of the plains. It was pouring its rays down now with the fierce malignance of some demon bent on destroying every vestige of plant-life that had the temerity to put forth its young shoots; and save for the scant bunch-grass, and the sage, and the greasewood, and a few distant and scattering junipers that grew dark upon the mountains beyond, no growth of vegetation was to be seen. It was within an hour of noon, and the scorching rays descended upon the blistered earth through a sil-

ver-gray haze that—reaching across the valley—quiv-
ered over the scene like the heat that comes through an
open furnace-door.

Little gray lizards with black, shining eyes; little
horned toads with prickly backs, lay with palpitating
bodies in the scant shade. The saucy Paiute squirrels
which earlier in the day darted in and out of their bur-
rows, had now disappeared into subterranean darkness.
Jack-rabbits, with limp ears lying back, crouched under the edges of the greasewood. The three horses stood
with listless, drooping heads; the two men sat with
listless, drooping bodies—one leaning forward to rest
his crossed arms on the horn of the Mexican saddle he
bestrode; the other, with loosely held reins between
his fingers, leaned with his elbows on his knees.

After the brief Western greeting, the one on the
buckskin horse asked carelessly:

"Been in with some hides, Reddy?"

"Yep."

"What luck you been havin'?"

"Poor. Tell you what 'tis, Dick, I ain't seen more 'n
fifty head o' horses sence we been a-campin' at Big
Deer Spring; an' the're so wild you can't git to within
a mile of 'em. Tommy an' me are goin' to move.
They're waterin' over to them deep springs north."

"Yaas," drawled the other, "they've been shot among
so much they're gittin' scarry. Me an' my pardner are
campin' over at the mine with them Dagos there; but
we don't see many bunches of horses around, nohow.
Guess we'll skin out next week, an' go over to The
Cedars. I don't s'pose———" he moved his horse
nearer to the wagon, and bent a contemplative gaze
upon one of the front wheels—"I don't s'pose Austin
an' the Kid'll kick if we do crowd over on their lay-
out a little; for there must be near a thousand head

o' mustangs over 'round them Cedars that ain't never heard a gun yit. So't there'd be good shootin' for all of us, an' plenty o' horses to go 'round. Hey?''

The other nodded his head affirmatively.

"But that Austin's a queer sort of a feller! Wanted him to come in with my pardner an' me (he's an all-fired good shot—good as I am myself; an' I c'n shoot all I c'n skin in a day), an' I thought him an' me could do the shootin', an' my pardner an' the Kid could do the skinnin.' But, no sir-ee; he wouldn't have it! Just said the Kid couldn't come; an' 't two was enough in a camp, anyway. He's about as stand-offish as anybody I ever see. I ain't sorry now 't he didn't take up with my offer; for the boys say that the Kid wouldn't be no 'count along anyway. He can't shoot; and he just nat'rally won't skin 'em—too squeamish an' ladylike. Aw!''

"I know. He just tags 'round after Austin all day; an' don't never seem to want to git more'n a hunderd yards from him. An' Austin's just about as bad stuck on the Kid,'' said Reddy.

"Yaas, I know it; an' that's what beats me. I don't see what they're stuck so on each other for,'' said Dick, as he leaned back in the saddle and rammed a hand into the depths of a pocket of his overalls. As he drew forth a section of "star plug'' he tapped the buckskin's flanks with his heels to urge the sorry specimen of horseflesh closer to the wagon.

"Chaw?''

The smaller man accepted. Turning the square over and giving each side a cursory glance, he picked off the tin tag—a tiny star—and set his jaws into an inviting corner, bending it back and forth in his endeavor to wrench off a generous mouthful. Passing it in silence back to the owner (who regaled himself also with a like quantity before returning it to his pocket), and having—with the aid of thumbnail and forefinger—snapped the shining little star at a big horse-fly that was industriously sucking blood from the roan's back, he remarked:

"Hides is gone up."

"That so?" exclaimed Dick, with animation; "what they worth now?"

"Dollar an' a quarter, to a dollar an' six bits; and three dollars for extra big ones. Manes is worth two bits a pound. What you comin' in for?"

"Ca'tridges. Shot mine all away."

"I c'n let you have some till you git your'n, if you want. What's your gun—forty-five eighty-five Marlin?" asked Reddy.

"Nope—won't do," answered Dick; "mine's Remington forty-ninety. Much 'bliged, though."

"Say, Dick!" exclaimed Reddy, "them Mexicans down on the river are comin' out to run mustangs. I saw that Black Joaquin an' his brother yist'day, an' told 'em if they wanted to run 'em anywheres out on our lay-out, that we wouldn't make no kick if they'd let us in for a share. See? They think they c'n run in about a hunderd an' fifty head, anyway. An' they'll furnish the manada, an' the saddle horses, an' all, for the whole crowd. So, I told 'em. 'All right! go ahead, as far as me an' my pardner are concerned.' He says Austin's agreed. How are you an' Johnny? Willin'?"

"Oh, yes; I'm willin'," answered Dick, as he jerked at the bridle-rein, disturbing the buckskin's doze. "Well, good luck to you! See you again!"

"Same to yourself. So long!" answered Reddy.

The saddle-horse fell into a jog trot again to the pricking of the spur; and the sorry span started the wagon groaning and rattling on its way up the road whose furrows were cut deep by the great teams that hauled sulphur and borax from the furthest mountains down to the railroad in the valley.

The creaking and rattling of the wagon had only just recommenced, when Reddy stopped his team to call back.

"Oh, Dick!"

"Hello!"

The little burros that had returned to nibbling on the brush, again lifted their heads at this second interruption.

"Say! Austin ast me to git him a San Fr'ncisco paper so as he could see what hides is quoted at; an' I plum clean forgot it. Wisht you'd bring out one to him when you come!"

"All right! So long!"

"So long!"

The men moved on again. And the two streamers of white dust grew farther and farther apart, till they had faded out of sight in the hazy distance.

The burros were left in undisturbed possession of the mesa the rest of the stifling hot day, while they browsed along on the greasewood. Late in the afternoon their little hoofs turned into a wild horse trail which led them, single-file, down to the river where the mealy muzzles were plunged into the swift, muddy current for a drink.

But while they had been munching the uninviting brush and sage, and flicking the flies away with their absurd paint-brush tails, Harvey Austin, over on the foothills near the Cedars, sat in the tent which was now the only home he knew; and with his hat fanned the face of the one whom the horse-hunters had named "The Kid."

The boy, who had been ailing, was asleep now; but

the flushed cheeks, and parched lips that were always calling for water, were cause enough for the fear that came over Austin as he sat there. What if this were but the beginning of a long fever? Suppose there should be a serious illness for him?

Again Austin asked himself the same questions that he was putting to himself daily. What had the future in store for them? From here, where were they to go? To stay through the long winter, with the mercury below zero, and the wild blasts of wind about their tent—perhaps to be buried in deep snow—all these things were not to be considered for a moment. Before the coming of winter they must go. But where? Only away from civilization were they safe.

He had come to see, at last, that they had both made a horrible mistake of life. In the beginning of this, it had not seemed so; things looked differently—at first. But, at times, of late there had come a feeling of repulsion over him for which he could not account. Was it the aftermath of wrong-doing? Well, he must make the best of it; it was too late to undo all that had been done. He must bear it—the larger share—as best he could. He said to himself that, thank God! at least he was enough of a man to hide from the "little one" what he himself was beginning to feel.

It is the great immutable law that the fruits of pleasure, plucked by the hands of sin, shall turn to bitterness between the lips. For sin, there is suffering; and for wrong-doing, regret. None escape the great law of compensation. Justice must have payment for the defiance of her laws.

Austin drew his breath in sharply. Oh, merciful God! how long was this way of living to last? Why, he might live on thirty—forty—fifty years yet! Penniless, what was their future to be? To return to that world which, through their past years, had surrounded them with all those things that make life worth living, would be to tempt a worse fate than awaited them here. The desolation which spread around them in the foothills of the bare, lonely mountains was as naught to the humiliation of returning to the peopled places where most would know them, yet few would choose to recognize.

It had not seemed that the price they would have to pay would be so dear when first he had faced the possible results of their rash act. Was it only a twelve-month ago? Why, it might have been twelve times twelve, so long ago did it seem since he was walking among men holding his head up, and looking fearlessly into the eyes of honest fellows who greeted him with warm hand-clasps.

His face had a strained look as he let his eyes fall on the unconscious figure beside him; and a strange expression—almost one of aversion—swept across his features. But he drew himself up quickly, tossing his head back with a movement as though—by the act—he could cast off something which might, perhaps, master him. For some time he sat there, his sensitive, refined face rigid and set, fixing his eyes on vacancy. Then he sank back, sighing wearily.

Before him was memory's moving panorama of a splendid past. Out of the many pictures—plainer than all the rest—rose the face of the man who had befriended him; the one to whom he owed all he had ever been, or enjoyed. The one but for whom he would have been left, when a boy, to the chill charity of strangers. From that generous hand he had received an education befitting the heir to great wealth, and that noble heart had given such love and care as few sons receive from a parent. He could now, in recollection, see the austere

face of his guardian softening into affectionate smiles
as his tender gaze fell on his two wards—himself, and
the pretty, willful Mildred.   Only they whom he so
fondly loved knew the great depths of tenderness and
gentleness in his nature.   It stung Austin now to think
of it; it shamed him as well.

And was he—this coward hiding in the mountains
of the West, leading a hateful existence hunting wild
horses for the few dollars that the hides would bring,
that he might be able to buy the necessaries of life,
since he had failed to get work in any other calling—
was he the one whom John Morton had once loved and
trusted?   He shuddered with disgust; no man could
feel a greater contempt for him, than he felt for himself.

He rose abruptly and walked to the opening of the
tent, looking out on the sweep of sagebrush-covered
foothills about him.   It was useless to think of the past,
or to give way to remorse or idle regrets.   What was
done could not be undone.   He must arrange, as best
he could, for the future years, and provide for the needs
of the present.   He must do his best in caring for and
protecting the one for whom this life was harder—
far harder—than for himself.

He turned his back on the dreary landscape before
him, and came back into the tent, busying himself about
camp duties till the other awoke.   And the young eyes
—wistful and sad—that kept seeking Austin's, saw no
trace of the heartache and remorse he was bravely
trying to bury.

When the sun had gone down behind their mountain,
and a welcome coolness had settled itself over the
burning ground, they went to sit by the spring that

bubbled out of the hillside. All through the twilight
they sat without speaking, their thoughts far away.
Then darkness came and hid the barren hills, merci-
fully shutting from their sight the pitiful poverty of
the life that was now theirs. A soft west wind sprung
up; and the balmy night air, cool and dry, seemed to
have driven away much of the illness the boy had felt
through the day. They sat in a silence unbroken only
by the crickets' perpetual shrilling, the hoot of a
ground owl, and a coyote yelping to its mate across
the cañon. When the first prolonged cry pierced the
air, the slight form had nestled instinctively closer to
Austin. Then the mournful wail of the little gray
ghost of the plains grew fainter and fainter, and finally
ceased altogether, as he trotted away over the ridge, in
quest of a freshly-skinned carcass where some unfortunate horse had fallen a victim to the sure aim of some
horse hunter.

They sat for nearly an hour in the silence of night
in the mountains, Austin wondering if the time would
ever come when the "little one" would guess how mis-
erably tired of it he had become in less than a year. He
hoped—prayed, the other would never know. And
(worse still) would a sickening disgust ever find its
way into that other heart, as it had into his own? With
all his soul he silently prayed it might never be so.

"Come, little one," he said, gently, "we must go in.
It is late."

The other made no response.

"Don't you want to go yet? Are you not sleepy—
and a little bit tired, poor child?"

Still no answer, though Austin knew he was heard.
He waited. Then——

"Harvey,"—the voice was almost a whisper—"we
have seen some happy days—sometimes—and you have

always been good to me; but, do you——— I mean, when you remember what we have lost, and what we are and must always remain, do you find in this life we are living, compensation enough for all that we suffer? Do you? Tell me!''

So! it had come to the other one, too.

A day of fast, hard riding had drawn to its close. Reddy and Dick, and their ''pardners,'' and Black Joaquin and his brother, together with two or three others had made their first day's run of wild mustangs. Three or four ''bunches'' of native wild horses had been surrounded and driven with a rush, in a whirl of alkali dust, into a juniper corral far down in the cañon. Then the circling riatas had brought them— bucking and kicking—down to the earth; and biting and striking at their captors, they fought for their liberty till exhausted and dripping with sweat—their heads and knees skinned and mouths bleeding—they found themselves conquered, necked to gentler horses, or else hoppled.

At early morning Dick had come to Austin's camp, bringing the newspaper; and the two had ridden away together. And now that each man had made his selection in the division of the day's spoils, Austin turned his pony's head toward the far-off tent—a little white speck in the light of the sunset on one of the distant foothills.

''Well, good-night, boys! I'll join you again in the morning.'' He loped away to the place where the ''little one'' was awaiting him.

The morrow's sun shone blood-red—an enormous ruby disc, in the east through the smoky haze that hung over the valley still. By eight o'clock the air was stifling, and the men standing about camp ready for the second day's run were impatient to be off. It was easier to endure the heat when in the saddle and in action, than to be idling here at the corral. They were wondering at Austin's delay. And most of them had been swearing. Finally, Black Joaquin was told to go across to the white speck on the foothills, and "hustle him up;" for they were short of men to do the work, if he did not come. So the Mexican threw himself across the saddle, and digging his spurs into the flanks of the ugly-looking sorrel, loped over the hill to Austin's camp.

Where the Burros Browsed

Half an hour later he came back at racing speed to tell a story which made the men look at each other with startled glances, and even with suspicion at himself (so surely are evil deeds laid at the door of one with an evil reputation); but when they rode over to where the stilled forms lay beside the rifle whose aim had been true, they saw it had not been Black Joaquin.

Who, then? Too plainly, they saw. But why?

The newspaper Dick had brought lay folded open at an article that told the pitiful story of their love, and their sin, and their shame. It was Johnny, Dick's partner, who saw it, and read:

"Living among Horse Hunters—An Erring Couple Traced to Nevada—Harvey Ashton and Mrs. John Q. Morton Seen—The Woman in Male Attire.

"The public no doubt remembers press dispatches of a year ago from Boston, regarding the sensational elopement of Harvey Ashton and the young and beautiful wife of John Q. Morton, a prominent and wealthy commission merchant of that city. All parties concerned moved in the most exclusive circles of society.

"Young Ashton had returned home from a prolonged

tour of Europe to find that Morton (who, though not related to him, has always assumed the part of an indulgent father) had just wedded his ward, Miss Mildred Walters, a handsome young woman many years his junior; and whose play-fellow he—Ashton—had been when a boy, but whom she had not seen for a number of years. She had matured into a beautiful, attractive woman, and Ashton soon fell a willing victim to her charms. Soon after, society of the Hub was startled and shocked to hear of the elopement of Harvey Ashton with his benefactor's wife.

"Subseqeuntly they were discovered to have been in San Francisco, where all traces of them, for the time, were lost. Nothing was heard of them again till, some two months ago, when they were seen in Reno, Nevada, by an old acquaintance who cannot be mistaken in their identity.

"He states he had come down from Virginia City, and was waiting to take the train for the East, when he saw Ashton pass by the station once or twice, in company with what was apparently a small, slightly-built young man, but who, he is positive, is none other than Mrs. Morton in male attire. He purposely avoided the couple, but inquiries elicited the facts that Ashton was passing under the name of Austin, and had stated that his companion was a young brother. It was also learned that they were practically without means, and were leaving Reno for the interior part of the State. Later reports locate them in a range of mountains a short distance from the railroad, where they are with a number of cowboys and sheep-herders who are out of work, and who are at present engaged in shooting wild horses, furnishing hides for the San Francisco market.

"The friend who recognized the couple at once communicated with the deserted husband, who, it is reported, is on his way West in quest of the erring pair.''

This was their story, then! The story waiting in the newspaper for Austin when he got back to the ''little one'' the evening before.

The afternoon's shadows were slanting down the valley when the seven little burros saw Reddy's wagon come down the long, dusty road leading toward the river. From where they browsed they could see it go over the bridge and the alkali flats, on its way to the railroad station in the hazy valley. The big sheet of canvas, taken from Dick's bed, covered something that lay in the bottom of the wagon. Two somethings there were—side by side, rigid and cold—sharply outlined under the folds of white canvas.

The wagon creaked, and rattled, and groaned on its way. The afternoon sun parched and burned the earth, as it had done for weeks. Rabbits hid under the edges of the greasewood on the side where the greater shadows fell. The burros still flicked with their absurd tails at the sand-flies. Buzzing above the canvas were some big green flies that followed the wagon till after the sun went down. A buzzard circled overhead; and a lean coyote trotted behind the wagon on the mesa for a mile or more.

The burros, too, crossed the bridge that night, and morning found them browsing along the foothills nestling against the mountains across the valley, where feed was better. Near the base of the mountain, and not far from the little railroad station, was a graveyard. Treeless, flowerless, unfenced. There were no headstones, 'tis true; but the graves were well banked with broken rock, to keep the hungry coyotes and badgers from digging up the dead.

At the station Black Joaquin had helped lift the new pine boxes into the wagon. As he watched them start on their ride to the place of rock-covered mounds near the foothills, he said to the men gathered about:

"Por Dios! Not so muchos hombres to shoot mostang now!"

And his brother Domingo, who had been drinking, answered with more freedom:

" 'Sta 'ueno! Not so muchos hombres; more mostang por me. 'Sta 'ueno; si, 'sta muy 'ueno!"

He laughed slyly. Then he went over to the saloon, followed by the other men.

The little gray burros watched the wagon for a long time, as it went rattle—rattle—rattle over the stony road. By and by it stopped. Then they began nibbling again on the scant bunch-grass and white sage.

AT THE WILL OF THE WATERS.

BLOCKHEAD! idiot! ass! 'Tenderfoot' isn't adequate for such a fool as I have been!'' he exclaimed bitterly.

He tried not to care; even he tried to forget that the good-looking, successful mining engineer had given him a title which had made him wince: "the deckle-edged tenderfoot!'' But it stung, nevertheless. Perhaps the reason that it hurt, was because of its fitness. And what hurt more, was the fact Cadwallader had taken pains that Evaleen Blaine should hear it said—Cadwallader, who seemed so well fitted to take his place in the rough Western way of battling with life, where he himself did but blunder and stumble, and earn the name of "the deckle-edged tenderfoot!'' That Teamster Bill had christened him "this yer gentlemanly burro frum Bost'n,'' cut far less keenly. But then, Bill wasn't trying to move heaven and earth to get Miss Blaine. Whereas Elwyn Cadwallader was.

However, on all sides opinion was the same, if differently expressed. The fact of his being a gentleman had not prevented him from becoming a fool— chiefest of fools—else he never would have trusted so implicitly in old Zeke Runkle's misrepresentations of the group of mining claims in those foothills that lay just below the Monarch group. The Monarch was the talk of the camp for its richness. If there was a fortune in the one group (he argued to himself), then why not also in those so nearly adjoining. At any rate, it seemed to him it was his one chance to find a fortune by a short cut; so, paying for them with all ,he had, save a few hundreds that afterwards went for useless development work, the mines became his. The camp welcomed him into its midst, and winked, and grinned when he wasn't looking; and (to a man) voted him "an easy thing!"

His eyes not having been focused for fraud, he never doubted but that the rich samples shown him had come from the mines represented; nor ever suspected that, under his very eyes, the tests he himself made had been tampered with.

Old Zeke Runkle's annual swindles had been a camp joke for a score of years; but Sherwood—being an inexperienced stranger—saw only in him an honest (if usually drunken) prospector. A kindly, if simple, old man, too; for Zeke had generously made him a gift of an entire mining claim which had not been included in the original number—one quite distinct from the original group. True, it seemed to be but an undeveloped claim—its one tunnel only running in ten or fifteen feet. And the gift had been tendered him at the suggestion of Cadwallader, from whom Sherwood was surprised to receive evidence of a kindly feeling which had not been previously displayed. That this unusual interest in him had surprised old Zeke, too, was plain; for he seemed puzzled at first, as though it were not possible for him to comprehend Cadwallader's meaning. After a few whispered words from the younger man, however, Zeke's face had brightened with understanding, and he turned to Sherwood insisting he must accept it. The unexpected part Cadwallader had taken, and the old man's unselfish attitude, showed to Sherwood such a fine glimpse of Western good-fellowship that he warmed to the place and the people as he had done at no time before. It turned the scale and the bargain was closed.

So he became sole owner of the seven mines on the sagebrush-covered hills, that comprised the Golden Eagle group; and of the one isolated claim in the foot of the bluffs that rose abruptly at the edge of an old-time ruined mining camp which had been deserted for more than thirty years.

It lay there in a cañon where once men came in search of precious metals; and in that cleft of the mountains they built their homes. Along the cañon sides, from end to end, there trailed a double line of houses, now all in ruins—fallen walls of adobe or stone. Roofless and floorless, with empty casements and doorways, the houses stood mute witnesses of the false hopes which once led men to squander money, and youth, and strength of purpose there in the long-ago, when the State was new.

Almost a double score of years had gone since the place knew human voice or human movement, save when some lone prospector passed along the brush-grown street that crept upward with the cañon's slope. The dead town's very stillness and desolation were full of charm, albeit tempered with that sadness a ruin always has for the beholder. For through the empty doorways came the whisperings of those who were gone; and looking through the sashless windows as you rode by, you saw wraithlike figures pass and repass within. It might have been only the wind's breath as it rustled the dark leaves of branches overhanging the crumbling walls, and the ghosts, mayhap, were but the waving boughs which tremulously

At the Will of the Waters

moved over the gray adobes; but when you were there
—in that stillness and amid all that mystery—you felt
it was true. You hushed your quickening breath to listen for the breath of some other. You moved through
the silence with wide-lidded eyes looking for—you
knew not what. You felt yourself out of place there
—an alien. Only the lizards on the decaying walls,
and the little brown birds that pecked at berries growing on the bushes along the creek, and the cottontails
that scurried away to hide in the brush, seemed to
have honest claim there.

On a level with the dead camp's one street, the
short tunnel of the Spencer mine ran into the cliff which
pushed itself forward from the cañon's general contour
—the mouth itself being all but hidden by the falling
walls of what had once been an adobe dwelling, its
rear wall but a few feet from the limestone bluffs. To
it, old Zeke brought Sherwood and showed him the tunnel below and the croppings of white quartz on the
cliff top. It looked barren and worthless; but an assay
certificate, in which the values were marked in four
figures, held before Sherwood's astonished eyes, sent
his hopes up to fever mark, and left him eager to begin
the work whereby he might reach the precious stuff
hidden well away within the dull-colored bluffs. If the
croppings promised such wealth, what might not the
mine itself yield when he extended the tunnel, and
had tapped the ledge at a greater depth? He felt
his heart beating the faster for his dreams. A fortune! His, and—hers! All that was needed to bring
it about were pick strokes, powder and patience. It all
seemed very simple to Hume Sherwood. Without doubt
he was a "tenderfoot."

So the Summer found him putting every pulse-throb
into his labor. Was it not for her that he wanted it?

For what other end was he working, than to win the
maid who had come into this land of enchantment?
To him, it was as Paradise—these great broad levels
of alkali, and sand (blotches of white on a blur of gray)
and the sagebrush and greasewood-covered foothills
that lay, fold upon fold, against the base of grim mountains—prickly with splintered and uncovered rocks.

Each day he blessed the fate which had called her
from her home by the Western sea and placed her under
the same roof that sheltered him in the rough little Nevada camp that called itself a town since a railroad
had found it, and given it a name.

Here Judge Blaine and his daughter settled themselves for the Summer. That is, an array of suit-cases
and handbags, great and small, and a trunk or two,
proclaimed the hotel their headquarters. That was
all. Every day saw the Judge up near the top of the
mountain, getting the Monarch's new machinery into
running order; while trails, and roads—old and new
—and even the jack-rabbit paths that lay like a network over the land, saw more of the young woman in
khaki than ever the hotel did, so long as daylight
lasted—the light which she grudged to have go.

It was Evaleen herself who had suggested coming
to Nevada with her father, instead of spending the
season in the usual way with Mrs. Blaine and the
other girls at whatsoever place fashion might dictate
as the Summer's especial (and expensive) favorite for
the time.

"Daddy, dear," she had said, standing behind his
chair, with both arms tight clasped around his neck,
"I've made up my mind to do something that is going
to surprise you. Listen; I'm not going with Mamma
and the girls when she shuts up the house for the Summer. But, I—am—going—with—you! Oh, yes, I am!

No, no! Not a word! I've always wanted to know
what a mining camp was like; and this is my golden
opportunity. You know you do want me there. Say
so! While you are putting up the new works, I can go
roaming over the country in old clothes. Listen to that,
Daddy—old clothes! A lovely Summer; and not a cent
spent on gowns!''

Ways and means at just that time being matters of
difficult solution with the Judge, her argument had
force and bore fruit. Midsummer found them where
the alkali plains stretched away to distant ranges, and
the duns and drabs of valleys reached across to the
blended purples and blues. Such distances! And such
silence! She had never dreamed of their like before.

On the levels or on the heights, she was day by day
finding life a new and a beautiful thing. It was all
so good; so fresh, and sweet, and strong! How easily
she had fitted into her new surroundings and the new
order of things—crude though they were, beyond any
of her preconceived ideas. And now how far away
seemed all the other Summers she had ever known.
She felt that, after all, this was the real life. The
other (that which Jean and Lili had their part in) was
to her, now, as something known only in a dream. She
was learning a grander, fuller sense of living since all
that other world was shut away. So (companioned by
her would-be lovers, Hume Sherwood and Elwyn Cadwallader, through a Summer of glad, free, full indrawn breaths) she rode the days away, while under
the campaign hat she wore her face was being browned
by the desert winds. Hot winds. But, oh, how she
had learned to love their ardent touch! No sun was
ever too hot, nor road too rough or long, to keep
her back from this life in the open; and in the saddle

she had come to know the valleys and mountains as one born to them.

The cañon which held the ruined walls had for her an especial charm, and toward it she often turned her horse's head. It lay but a short distance from the road leading to her father's mines. So, turning aside, she often took this short cut through the deserted town. There, one day she heard from Cadwallader the story of Crazy Dan, whose home had once been within the walls that hid the entrance to the tunnel of the Spencer—the mine which had been a gift to Sherwood.

Daniel Spencer—Crazy Dan (for whom old Zeke named the claim he had given away, because on the very ground there Dan had made his home) had worked in the creek for placer gold during all the long gone years when others worked the higher ground for silver lodes. An ill-featured, ill-natured old man, having no friends, and seeking none; he had burrowed the cañon's length for gold as persistently as a gopher does the ground for roots, and—as all had prophesied—with as little showing of the yellow metal. Only a crazy man, they said, would ever have prospected that cañon for gold. It was a cañon for ledges, not placers; for silver, not gold. So the miserly, morose old man followed a phantom to the last; working alone from day-dawn till dusk with rocker and pan, in ground that pitying neighbors vainly tried to lead him away from. Admitting he had never found gold, yet working day after day, Crazy Dan could be seen there for twelve long years. Twelve years of toil that showed no reward for his labor. Then he died. One morning they saw there was no smoke issuing from the cabin chimney; and guessing what they would find, they pushed the door open.

Death had come when he was alone; there had been

none to close the staring eyes. He had been near to starvation; there was scarcely any food within the cabin; there were no comforts. Years of toiling for something that was always just beyond; and a lonely death at the end—that was the story.

As she heard, Miss Blaine was stirred with a profound pity. When Cadwallader ceased speaking, her thoughts went straying to those far days, in wonder of the man who made up the sum of the town's life. Dead, or scattered to the four corners of the earth. Crazy Dan's death was no more pathetic, perhaps, than that of many another of their number. She rode on in silence, saddened by the recital.

Suddenly Cadwallader's ringing laugh startled her. But as quickly he checked himself, saying:

"I beg of you, Miss Blaine, don't misjudge me. I wasn't thinking then of poor old Dan's tragic death, or more than tragic life. I happened to remember the sequel to this story; and which, I'm sure, you've never heard. Let me tell you——" He hesitated. "Or, no; you've heard enough for today, and its humor would jar now on what you've just heard. I'll tell you some other time."

Nothing more was said about it by either; but she felt confident it related in some way to Hume Sherwood and the Spencer mine.

The latter had kept men continuously at work on his newly acquired property since coming into possession of them; but the faith that was his in the beginning, grew fainter with the waning of Summer. Autumn brought decided doubt. With the coming of Winter came a certainty of their worthlessness, he knew he had been befooled by a sharp trickster, but how far his ignorance had been played upon he did not yet know. Nevertheless, he felt he had well earned the titles the camp had bestowed on him, for the claims, he found, were but relocations that had been abandoned years before as utterly worthless. He had simply thrown his dollars into the deep sea.

If only that had been all!

Evaleen Blaine and her father, contrary to all their earlier plans for a return to San Francisco at the beginning of Autumn, were still in Nevada, and there Winter found them, though the machinery was all placed and the big reservoir and dam completed. But an offer to buy the Monarch property—mines, mill, and all that went with them—had come from a New York syndicate, and the Judge was now detained by their agents. He must stay yet a few days more—then home to "mother and the girls." Nor would Evaleen leave without him; so for the first time in all his married life he was to be away from home on Christmas. Thus matters stood when the greater half of December had gone.

A storm was brewing. There had been scarcely any rain or snow thus far, but a damp wind from the south had shut away the mountain behind dark and threatening clouds. The Judge found he was needed at the mine that morning, but had promised Evaleen he would be back the next night, to make Christmas eve as merry as possible for them both—separated from the others. By staying one night at the mine he could, without doubt, return on the morrow. He had kissed her good-bye and left her looking out of the window in the gloom of the early day. Fifteen minutes later she heard his heavy tread again on the stairs, and he stormed into the room.

"See here, daughter!" he panted in indignation, "I've just heard of the —— —— (I beg your pardon, child); I mean the shameful trick that that cur of a Zeke Runkle played on young Sherwood. Sherwood has just told me—just heard of it himself. Have you heard anything about it? No? Well, I thought not—I thought not! It seems everybody around the place, though, has known of it all along—but us. Why didn't anybody tell me? Hey? What? Yes; but why didn't anybody tell me, I want to know! Ah, they knew better. I'd have told Sherwood that he'd been played for a sucker! Yes, sir!" (forgetting his audience again) "and a —————— shame it is, too! There I go again—but I don't know when anything has so worked me up!"

"But, Daddy, what is it?" faltered Evaleen. "What has happened? I don't understand."

"What has happened?" shouted the Judge. "Everything has happened—everything. Of course, you don't understand. I don't, myself—all of it. Somebody (I haven't found out yet who, but I will!) put up that miserable old rascal—that drunken thief of a Zeke Runkle—to palming off on Sherwood as a bona fide mine, the worst fake I ever heard of. Hey? What? Why! a dug-out, I tell you—a hole in the cliff—a tunnel-like cellar-above-ground, if you want, that Crazy Dan, it seems, used to store away bacon, and flour, and potatoes in, more than thirty years ago. Just an old store-room, nothing else. That's what! Made him a present of it (the foxy old rascal) so the law couldn't touch him. Oh, he's a clever swindler! I'm sorry for Sherwood—mighty sorry for him. I like the fellow; there's good stuff in him. It's a —————— A—hum! But, for the life of me I can't see old Zeke's object; for he made nothing by it. Somebody must have put him up to it

—mark my words. And I'd like to know who."

Who had done it? Evaleen was again hearing Cadwallader's laugh, and the words, "An amusing sequel to the story." And "I'll tell you some day." He need not tell her now. She knew; and she knew why.

All that day she stayed within her room. She felt she couldn't see Sherwood in his humiliation; and Cadwallader she wouldn't see.

That evening when she went down to dinner she was purposely late that she might avoid both men. Elwyn Cadwallader was out of town, she learned, called away unexpectedly on business. Hume Sherwood, after having been with her father all day, up on the mountain, had just returned—going directly to his room. He had declined dinner.

Almost any man can bear censure, but it takes a giant to brave ridicule.

When Miss Blaine went back to her room she found two letters awaiting her. She read the first with the angry blood mounting to her forehead, and lips tightened into a straight, hard line. It was from Cadwallader. He closed by saying:

"Give me the one thing I most want in all the world! I will go to you Christmas morning for it—for your 'yes!'"

Miss Blaine's face was very stern as with quick, firm steps she walked across the floor to the stove in which a fire was burning cheerily. She opened the door and flung the letter into the flames.

The letter from her father was hurriedly scrawled, "so that Sherwood can take it down to you," it said. There were but a dozen brief sentences: He couldn't be with her, after all, on Christmas eve—he had about closed the deal with Akerman, and there was much business to settle up. She was to pack their suit-cases and trunks at once; to be ready to start home any day. He hoped (didn't know—but hoped) to leave the evening of Christmas day, etc. There was a postscript: "Akerman (acting on my advice) bought Sherwood's little group today for seven hundred and fifty dollars; which is just seven hundred and fifty dollars more than they are worth—as mining claims. But Akerman wants the ground for other purposes, and will use it in connection with his other property. I'm glad for the boy's sake he got it, for I guess Sherwood needed the money. Of course he hasn't said so (he's too much of a thoroughbred to whimper) but I don't believe he has a nickel left."

Evaleen Blaine laid the letter down with a tender smile on her face. "Dear old Daddy!" she murmured. She understood the sympathetic heart which had been the factor in bringing about the sale of Sherwood's claims. "Oh, Daddy, you're good—good! I love you!"

Four or five hours after, she had finished packing and got up from where she had been kneeling, and looked about the room. Everything was folded away in place and awaiting the turning of the key, except the khaki suit and the wide brimmed hat. She would soon be miles and miles away from Nevada and its joys. A very sober face looked out at her from the mirror, making her force her thoughts into other channels.

"Not spend Christmas eve with you, Daddy? 'Deed, an' I will! I'll just astonish you tomorrow morning!"

She laughed to herself in anticipation of his surprise. Then her face sobered, remembering that—for the first time—she would make the trip alone. She knew every inch of the way. She wasn't afraid; there was nothing to harm her. And by taking her coffee and toast by lamplight, she would be with him by nine o'clock. As she fell asleep that night she was wishing some good fortune might come to Hume Sherwood, making his Christmas eve less lonely.

When day broke, though as yet no rain was falling, a storm was already gathering itself for the onslaught. Fine dust filled the air, and the wind was racing up the valley with the swiftness of a prairie fire, where, on the alkali flats, great breakers of white dust rose from the sea of dry storm that ran ahead of the rain. Dead branches of greasewood, tumble-weeds light as sea-spume on the waves of the wind, rabbit-brush wrenched from the roots—these (the drift-wood of desert seas), were swept on and away!

In the gray early dawn Miss Blaine's horse had been saddled under protest.

"We're a-goin' to hev a Nevady zephyr, I'm a-thinkin', an' th' house is a mighty good place f'r wimmin-folks 'bout now!" were the words she heard through the whistling wind as she mounted.

There was something electric in the strange storm that drew her into its midst—some kinship that called her away! She was sure she could reach shelter before the rain reached her. "Then, hurrah for the ring of the bridle-rein—away, brave steed, away!"

Mountain Boy snuffed at the dust-laden air and broke into the long stride that soon carried them into the foothills. At times the wind nearly swept her from the saddle, but she loped on and on. Then she gained the high ground; and the dust that had smarted her eyes and nostrils lay far below. It was misty, and the wind came in strong buffetings. Up, and still up they climbed. The rain-clouds were surely keeping their burden back for her! But, nay! she had almost reached the mill—was almost under shelter, when the storm swept down upon her and the waters fell in a flood. Drenched and disheveled she reached the mill. Disappointment and consternation awaited her—her father was not there! Nearly two hours before—just the time she was leaving the valley—the Judge, with Mr. Akerman, had driven away by the north road to take the morning express from the station above, and were now at the county seat thirty miles away, if they had met with no mishap.

Evaleen was aghast! What to do? Her father believed her to be at the hotel, to which place she must return at once—there was nothing else for her to do. Back through the wind and the wet! She heard the foreman's voice in warning and entreaty swept away by the gale as she turned; but—shaking her head—she plunged down the road and back into the storm. Away and away! The road ran with many a curve and turn —easy grades, made for wagon use—; so, though steep it was for such riding, she loped down the mountain, while the wind, and the rain, and the roar of the storm shut the world away.

A feeling of numbness came over her, a something that was neither terror nor awe, yet which held something of each. As time went on she seemed to have been riding hours innumerable—it seemed days since she had seen a human face. Down, farther down must she go. She was becoming exhausted, and the sleet was chilling her to the very center of her being. It was terrible—terrible! To reach the valley and shelter! There on the mountain the wind shrieked and howled about her; the air was filled with voices that were deafening, dizzying, frightful. The horse himself was half mad with fright. Twice he had almost thrown her as thunder claps and flashes of lightning had seemed to surround them on all sides. Three miles yet to shelter! Could she stand it? But where

—where was there nearer relief? Ah! the Spencer tunnel—— There would be safety there till the worst of the storm was over. A turn of the rein, and Mountain Boy was running straight for the old tunnel under the cliffs.

Hark! What was that? There came to her ears a great roaring that was neither the howling of the wind, nor the rush of the rain, nor the mingled awful sounds of the storm as she tore along the cañon. She could see nothing of the thing she heard, for the wet slap of the rain blinded her. Closer and closer it came! As she slipped from the saddle at the tunnel's mouth, the horse—terrified at the roaring which rose above the voice of the storm, and which was coming nearer—broke from her, and was off and away, with a ten-foot wall of water racing at his heels. The overtaxed dam had bursted its bounds, and the flood was cutting a waterway down the center of the cañon, but below the level of the old tunnel! She was safe! But ——alone, and her horse was gone!

When, more than two hours afterward, Hume Sherwood found her, it seemed the most natural thing in the world that he should take her in his arms, and her head should lie on his breast, while she told him how it had happened. Without question he claimed her as his own; without a word she gave him her troth.

"I knew you would come, Hume—I knew you would find me," she said, softly.

"Dear!"

So simply were they plighted to one another; so easily does a great danger sweep away all disguises.

When the riderless bay had come into camp, Sher-

(right margin) At the Will of the Waters

wood (half mad with an awful fear) had hurried away to the hills, lashing his span without mercy over the storm-washed road—or out through the open country where the road was gullied out. When in the up-piled drift where the flood had left it—he found the gray campaign hat he knew so well, a sickening fear fell upon him as though he had already looked upon the face of the dead. At length he thought of the tunnel, after fruitless search elsewhere; and there—in the dug-out that had been palmed off on him as a joke on his credulity, he found his heart's desire. After all, Spencer's old store-room—his cellar-above-ground—was worth a king's ransom—when valued by this man and this maid.

The waters had gone down, but left the tunnel entrance flooded; for the fallen walls of the old adobe created a small dam which the flood overflowed. To get past this—without wading knee-deep in the mud—was a problem. The whirling waters had eaten away the earth which formed the front part of the tunnel—wider now by two feet—and in the place where the earth had melted away stood a small box. Sherwood put his foot against it, to pry it out of the mud.

"I'll get this out for you to stand on, dear; then you can jump across I think, with my help."

But, deep settled into the mud and debris, it resisted him. He went back in the tunnel and got a pick from among the tools he had used in extending the "cellar" to strike the ledge that wasn't there; for the "croppings" that had been shown him had been hauled there—salted, to deceive the "tenderfoot."

The box refused to move, even when Sherwood's pick—used as a lever—was applied; so, swinging it over his head, he brought the pick down into the box, shattering the lid into pieces. It was more than half filled with small rusty tin cans, bearing soiled and torn labels, on which were the printed words in colors still bright: "Preston & Merrill's Yeast Powder." A case of baking powder of a sort popular five-and-thirty years before. Strange!

Sherwood laughed. "We've found some of Crazy Dan's stores!" and attempted to take one of the little cans. It lifted like lead. He stopped—afraid to put it to the test—and looked at Evaleen queerly; and she (remembering the story she had heard of Dan's persistence in working the cañon for placer gold) gave a little cry as he started to open it. It seemed too much to dare to believe—to hope for—— Yet——.

He lifted the lid. Gold! The gold dust that Crazy Dan (ay! Miser Dan) had, back in the dead years, hoarded away in the safest place he knew; adding to it month after month, as he delved, and died with his secret still his own.

The Judge was at the County Seat—at the station buying his ticket to go back to his "little girl"—when the train from the West came in. In the dusk he caught a glimpse of a tailor-made suit which seemed familiar to his eye, and that made him look twice at the wearer.

"Why! Bless my soul, child—and Sherwood, too! Well! Well! What are you doing here? I wrote to you about it. Didn't you get my message, Evy?"

"Yes, Daddy, dear; you said: 'Be at the station to-night ready to go home—I start from here.' But as everything was packed I thought I'd come up and join you, and we could both start from here."

"And," added Sherwood, after they had gone into

the now empty waiting-room, "I wanted to see you, sir, before you left."

"Why, of course! Glad you came to see me off, Sherwood. You must come down to see us, you know; and meet mother and the girls. We'll—— Eh! What's that? * * * What! * * * Evy—my little girl?"

The Judge stuttered and stammered, bewildered at the suddenness of the attack.

Sherwood talked long and earnestly; and the Judge's eyes wandered to the daughter who had, until now, never seemed other than his "little girl." But she had "grown up" under his unseeing eyes; and now somebody wanted to take her from him. Sherwood—— Well, Sherwood was a fine fellow; he would make his way in the world in spite of the luck that was against him now.

"My boy," (and the Judge laid his hands affectionately on the young man's shoulders as they stood facing each other) "I know you to be a gentleman, and I believe you to be every inch a manly man. I want my child to marry not what a man has made, but what he is made of. You will win in the world's rough and tumble of money-making, if you're only given a chance; and I've been going to tell you that there's a place waiting for you in our San Francisco office when you are ready for it. And now I'll add, there's a place in my family, whenever Evy says so.

"As to your not having much more than the proverbial shilling just now, that cuts no figure with me. Why not? Let me tell you."

He put his arm around Evaleen, drawing her to him.

"This child's mother took me 'for better or worse' twenty-five years ago this very night, when I hadn't a dollar in the world that I could call my own—married me on an hour's notice, and without any wedding guests or wedding gowns. She trusted me and loved me well enough to take me as I was, and to trust to the future (God bless her!) and neither of us have ever had cause to regret it.''

To have this assurance from the Judge before he knew of the wonderful story Sherwood had to tell of the secret of Crazy Dan's tunnel, added to the joy of the young people who now felt they were beloved of the gods.

The Judge's jcy over the finding of the treasure box was even greater than Sherwood's; for the older man had lived long enough to realize (as a younger generation could not) that this wealth would put many possibilities for happiness within their reach that otherwise might not be theirs. To them—the lovers in the rose-dawn of youth, with love so new—love itself seemed enough; save perhaps that the money would make marriage a nearer possibility.

''Darling''—and a new thought, a new hope rang through Sherwood's earnest tones—''do you believe you love me as well as she—your mother—loved him?''

''Oh, Hume!'' was all she said, but the reproach in her eyes answered him.

''Then marry me now, as she did your father, at an hour's notice. Here—this evening, before the train comes. Judge, why can not this be so? What is there to prevent our being married at once, without all the fussing and nonsense that will be necessary if we wait till she gets home? Let us be married here, and now, and all go away together.''

''Why, bless my soul! This takes my breath away.

You young people—what whirlwinds you are! You—
Yes, yes, but——— Hey? What's that? I did?
I know; but——— What? I should rather think it
would be a surprise to mother and the girls to bring a
son home to Christmas dinner. Oh, yes, I know;
but——— What's that you say? Her mother did——!
Yes, yes, I know .... Well, well, my lad, I don't know
but you're right. Her mother——— Love is the one
thing—the rest doesn't matter. Evy, child, it is for you
to say.''

And remembering that girl of the long-ago who
twenty-five years before had gone to a penniless lover
with such a beautiful love and trust Evaleen Blaine,
putting her hand with a like trust into her lover's,
walked with him across to the little parsonage, and
there became Hume Sherwood's wife.

    *   *   *   *   *   *   *   *

When Cadwallader got back to the camp the next
morning, he heard much he was unprepared for; for
news travels fast where happenings are few. What
he heard did not tend to make his Christmas a merry
one.

Evaleen Blaine and Hume Sherwood were now man
and wife! He did not want to believe it, yet he felt it
was true. And Sherwood had sent to the mint (from
the "Spencer" mine, too,) the largest shipment of bullion that had ever gone out of the county! Neither
did he want to believe this—and did not. There must
be some mistake.

He went over to the express office through the snow
and the cold; for the rain had turned to snow and the
Nevada winter had begun. It would be a cheerless
yule-tide for him. It was true as he had heard—
true in all particulars, except that the consignment to
the mint had been in gold-dust, not in bullion.

Elwyn Cadwallader knew mines. Therefore he knew ledges do not produce gold dust; and Sherwood had owned no placers. Whatever suspicion he had of the truth he kept to himself. It was enough for him to know that all he had done to make Hume Sherwood the butt of the camp, that he might all the more surely part him from Evaleen Blaine, had been but the means of aiding him in winning her; and that the richest joke of the camp had proved to be rich indeed, in that it had placed a great fortune in the hands of "the deckel-edged tenderfoot."

At
the
Will
of
the
Waters

And here ends "The Loom of the Desert,"
as written by Idah Meacham Strobridge,
with cover design and illustrations made
by L. Maynard Dixon, and published by
the Artemisia Bindery, which is in Los
Angeles, California, at the Sign of the
Sagebrush; and completed on the Twelfth
day of December, One thousand nine hundred and seven.

THE LAND OF PURPLE SHADOWS

"Chasms where the sun comes late, and leaves while yet it is early afternoon."—Page 2.

The Land of Purple Shadows

by

Idah Meacham Strobridge

THE ARTEMISIA BINDERY
Los Angeles
MCMIX

To

YOU

**Who were born in the West--who
live in the West--who love the West.**

CONTENTS

FOREWORD

At various times—in various places; in many moods, and in different mediums, are the studies and sketches made, which the painter brings back to his studio after his working-vacation is over. Mere suggestions and rough outlines are they—the first impressions of what he saw; what he felt; what he lived. Not for the galleries did he make them, nor for the critics, nor the careless. But the portfolio is opened to those who will understand; those who—in the incomplete sketch, the half-finished study—see The Truth.

Even as the painter shows you such, so, too, are put before you these studies of the West—this land of golden sunlight and purple shadows.

IN QUIET CANONS.

IF YOU are a mountain lover, and live here in Sunset-Land, you count the clefts and chasms of the Coast Range and the Sierras, as among old friends—such friends as one well loves, and loves long.

They are dark and beautiful with pine, and tamarack, and fir; but far back from the sea, on the eastern slopes, are some which do not have the rich blue-green coloring. What of these, and other cañons that lie in purple mountains far to the eastward, where gray foothills go down to meet the leprous white of the great plains? Do you know these quiet cañons; or, are they only strangers to you?

Yet they are ours, even as the others are. Not to the desert States only must you go to find them.

Nor is it in cañons teeming with active life, where mills are grinding ores all day—all night—amid the deafening roar of tireless machinery; nor where the houses hang like swallows' nests against the cañon's terraced sides, and men and mines fill the busy day with noisy work, that one feels the complete fascination of these Western mountains. Not where human life and human interests are found; but in the little known, passed by and forgotten cañons of the States that lie west and away from the Missouri's flood, and east of the Sierra's eternal battlements, where they lift above the line of pine-tree, and tamarack, and fir.

The mountains are furrowed and gashed by ravine and gorge—chasms where the sun comes late and leaves while yet it is early afternoon. And their sides are hollowed, too, into sunny hiding places of repose and calm for those who love the heights. Here, in these quiet cañons, one goes hand in hand with Nature in all her charm of waywardness when unrestrained by meddling man.

In Spring-time they are fair to look upon, as all things are fair which are fresh and sweet with budding youth; but it is in the Autumn, when they take on all the gorgeousness of changing leaf and vine, when every shade of the colors of fire and blood is seen, that one finds them in their fullest beauty and at their best.

Some there are, it is true, that are bare of that luxuriance of color in which the others revel; and you may turn your horse's head up one of these, upon some Autumn day of mountain climbing, and only find scattered clumps of buck-brush and willow growing in a hollow between two hills. Beneath them are hidden springs—springs which have no water to spare now to turn a rivulet loose that it may dance and sparkle down the way to meet you, but which keep the sparce shade green throughout the hot Summer, and the roots moist and growing.

Grass grows here—a patch of wild rye, browned now by the suns of the long Summer. Rabbit-brush is everywhere; the nettles and hoarhound are brown and dead. White butterflies are fluttering above weeds that are a-bloom with blossoms of gold.

How still the world is! The only sounds are your horse's hoof-falls, his labored breathing as he climbs the heights through the rarefied air, and the creaking of your saddle-leathers.

You startle a mountain quail into flight, catching but a flash of her red-brown wing as she sweeps across your sight.

In Quiet Cañons

The thistles and Mariposa lilies, which earlier in the year grew white and purple up and down the cañon's length, have dry seed-pods now.

You turn your bridle-rein across your horse's neck to guide him over the ridge into the next ravine, and as he begins the steeper ascent your fingers twist themselves into his mane, to aid you in keeping your place in the saddle. Higher and higher you climb. Up, and still up, at last to reach the dividing ridge, where you can give your sweating horse a breathing spell. As he stands panting and trembling there, your eyes go up to the summit's rugged peaks that—with all your climbing—seem as far away as ever. How grandly beautiful they are! How pure and restful the mountain tops seem, capped with their eternal snows! How far, and how fair!

How you long to climb till you reach their inviting peace and quiet, to be there alone in the awful stillness of those heights where God speaks to one through the silence.

But it is too far for you to climb today; the sun is slanting to the west. You descend into the cañon beneath you, into a gorge so deep that the sun's rays only find its granite-gravelled floor at mid-day. There you come across a mill-dam, resting from its useful work of years gone by. The waters overflow its stony rim in a series of trickling, creamy little rills, and—falling on the boulders down below—come tumbling down in a thousand fantastic forms of glittering, sparkling spray. The water drips from the neglected flume that a dozen years ago gave power to a mill a mile or two further down the cañon, where it stands through the changing seasons, silent and at rest.

The creek is bordered with rose-thickets, and thickets of wild plum. It is walled with tall cliffs that in the early afternoon begin to throw long, purple-black shadows across the cañon to rest upon the sheer walls of other cliffs that face them.

The coral-red upon that bush which catches on your clothing as you ride by is the seed-buds of wild sweet-brier which, earlier in the year, made the creek banks lovely with a mass of pink and fragrant bloom. Rose-bushes, and the bushes of the wild gooseberry, are turning red and yellow as New England's Autumn woods.

A pair of turtle doves are busily picking at some tall, brown weeds which rattle as you pass. The doves, from the higher ground where they have flown, are darting their pretty heads back and forth in fright at the unwonted presence of man.

Oh, the charm of these Western cañons!

But, some day, you may come across others burned bare of all their beauty; cañons which lie between high and rolling hills, and where there are neither cliffs nor chasms. Fire has swept out every tree and shrub to make a pathway through the tangle of brier bushes that have plucked at the fleece of the passing flocks which graze on these mountains in summer.

The cañon is burned and bare. Your horse's hoofs beat up the dust in blackened puffs of burned brush; and in the air is a smell of charred wood at which your nostrils revolt, while your eyes rove in pity over the desecrated spot. Fire and flame have here destroyed some of the choicest pictures that Nature has hung in the royal art galleries of the West. From the head of the ravine down to its mouth, not one growing thing remains. Though with another year the bunch-grass will spring up for nibbling mouths to munch, now you look only on desolation. The trail of the sheepherder is over it all. And where this year you find the burned and blackened earth, the next will show you a spot made white with the countless small, snowy stars of the wild tobacco-plant—the deer's daintiest morsel. To burn the brush in one of these cañons, is to invite the star-like, blossoming weed to grow. And wherever it grows you may be reasonably sure to find a deer's track in the trails.

In
Quiet
Cañons

And the birds! They are everywhere. Go where you will in these cañons, the birds are there. Though the trail of fire has passed through here, yet a meadow lark flies away as you approach, and you catch the glint of yellow on his breast. You frighten little Paiute squirrels and a hare by your tread. There are caves in the limestone cliffs where impudent wood-rats build their nests.

The cliffs are carved and hewn into arch and archi-trave by the elements in the hand of Time. Higher, you see where an avalanche of rocks has fallen and left an arch so wide, so high, that a great patch of the deep blue sky shines through. Three chariots abreast might pass beneath its span at once.

You cross half a dozen cañons that are but shallow ravines; where no stream flows except early in the year. The wash is parching in the sun; but under the willow clumps little springs give forth enough water to quench the thirst of the mountain's birds and beasts that come this way. Cowslips and brookmint are here.

Here, too, in the dust of the wild-horse trail which leads down to water, you see the pads of coyote and wild-cat; and near the spring, oozing from ground moist and spongy under the cover of water-cress and weeds, is a track which—fresh and sharp-cut in the damp earth—tells you that a deer has just been down to drink. Involuntarily you raise your eyes to the clump of willows higher on the hillside where the spring is dry. Is he hiding there? Are his soft eyes watching you through the leafy screen of green and silver-gray? You look intently for perhaps a full minute; but you see nothing. Then your gaze goes to the higher hills up at the sky-line, far, far above. So high they are, they seem to touch the thin crescent moon where it rides the blue depths of the infinite sky like a skeleton ship on the sea.

"When the moon is up, deer are feeding." As you repeat to yourself the saying of an old hunter, you feel sure that there is no sleek, dun-coated animal hidden away down in the cañon. He is feeding on the heights; and safe, at least, today. But, though you carried a gun across your arm this quiet afternoon, I doubt if you could have it in your heart to disturb the perfect peace of the place and the hour with the startling sound of a rifle shot.

How silent it all is! You stop and listen; and you hear the beating of your own heart.

Down the cañon you ride, and come upon a grove of aspens where there is always a whispering sound going through their shivering leaves, as they stand in the midst of the circling silence. It is not the soughing of the wind as you have heard it through the trees in a pine forest; but a gossiping, whispering little wind which says things of you—not to you—as you pass them by.

Down the cañon you ride, and come to a place all green with wire-grass and moss, still keeping its Summer freshness while other things are turning brown. A spring is there. In the wet places, late columbines are growing, and marsh-mallows not yet gone to seed. Yellow evening primroses—fading and pink-tinted at the edges—hang wilted on their stalks. A hundred yards away, half an acre of wild poppies—the thistle-poppy of the desert country—have tossed their thin white petals to breezes which have carried them afar. You dismount, and slip the bridle from your horse's head that he may drink. Then, when he begins to nibble at the grass growing there, you throw yourself down beside him, and—with hat drawn low over your eyes—in the hushed solitude, with the afternoon shadows purpling in the cañon, you drift into reverie. So, with narrowed eyelids, you fall to studying the tints and tones of these, Nature's etchings and water colors.

In
Quiet
~
Cañons

There are pictures all about you; pictures to delight the artistic sense which is in each one of us who loves these mountains and their ravines. How their beauty thrills one! How their loveliness enters like wine into the veins to set the blood aglow! Pictures—pictures everywhere!

Fine feathery grasses are growing at the base of a great granite boulder where, lying against it, is a dead, bare-of-leaf bush whose skeleton branches show as delicate as a bit of sea-moss from the coral isles of the Pacific. Across the boulder runs a clinging vine with stems of claret-red. Seams and crevices are touched with gray and brown mosses and lichens. Gnarled, rough-twisted, and devoid of all bark, pearly-tinted and shading into darker tones of gray, part of a dead juniper riven from its parent trunk lies where it fell against the boulder, just as it has lain ever since it came tumbling down into the ravine. When? How long ago? Who shall say?

Higher, the cañon's side is slashed with a deep and rugged cut where once a cloud-burst struck on the crest of the ridge, and the water came plowing a furrow down the mountain, washing away everything in its course. Boulders have been carried along by the force of the flood. In the wake of destruction you see that weeds and brushwood were bent downward and half buried in the soil; and there, where a jutting ledge caught them as they came with the freshet, are two uprooted trees.

The magpie which flew up from the spring with a hoarse "Cheep!" when you frightened him away, sits tilting backward and forward on a branch of the dead juniper, regarding you with evident suspicion. A chipmunk—brown-striped and bonny—on the highest point of the granite boulder, is saying "Tst—tst—tst —tst" in a nervous flutter of excitement at your proximity. Lower, on the rock's vertical side, a little glossy black lizard clings motionless; his head turned toward where you are lying. He is ready to dart out of sight if you but move a finger. A big, black-shelled beetle—tip-tilted, with its nose to the ground—is going back and forth in desperation at the bottom of a deep and dusty hoof-print just beyond the spring. Back and forth, round and round, it goes in a frantic and fruitless endeavor to find a way out of its prison.

The moments pass, and you have forgotten to reckon time. Is it an hour you have been here, or only five minutes? Through half-closed eyelids you have been gazing, but they are falling even lower and lower. The air is so soft, so soothing (for you are a bit tired after the hours you have been in the saddle), that you are carried almost to the gates of slumber.

Hark! What was that? What made that pebble come rolling down the hillside just over there? Listen!—! With bated breath you strain your ears, but you hear nothing. You sit up and look intently at the spot whence came the small rolling stone. There is nothing moving there, that your eyes can detect. From top to bottom of the cañon's sloping sides, you see only the gray of granite rocks, and bushes of stunted sage. For a full minute and more—alert and intent—you watch in silence. Then, to yourself, you softly say:

"No, there is nothing there. Strange, though, what started that stone rolling down!"

Again you lie back, still keeping your eyes, however, on the spot where instinctively you feel there is something which is watching you—something which notes your every movement, though you can not see it, whatever it may be. Nothing breaks the uniform gray of the long slope. And again you are dominated by the supreme stillness of this quiet cañon. For a long time you lie so, and slumber comes creeping back, and almost lays her gentle touch upon your eyelids, when—

There! What is that? Ah! something is moving there, after all! Something that a moment ago your eyes rested lightly upon, as you glanced along the sagebrush of the hillside; but now you see it is moving—coming down (oh! so carefully) to the spring. Larger than a barnyard fowl, and not quite twenty feet away, now you see the sage-hen which your searching eyes could not hitherto discover. A dozen times in the past ten minutes you looked directly at her, but you thought it only a bush of gray sage. In her speckled dress, so like the bushes of these hills that she seems to be one of them, she comes cautiously, carefully, slowly down the slope. How slowly she picks her way that her approach may be noiseless! See how carefully she lifts her foot at each step she takes! Observe her head turned sidewise as she cautiously looks in your direction to see if she dare venture for her afternoon drink! See how she avoids coming out into the open places, but directs her course so that there is always a bunch of grass, or a rock, or a bush between you and herself, as she moves toward her goal! ˙She has seen you, you know, but she keeps

bravely on to the spring. How near she is! You are
sure you could hit her with one of the bits of stone at
your elbow, were you to try. The hunter's instinct
stirs within you; but as you carefully raise yourself
on your arm, half tempted to test the accuracy of your
aim, there is a whir of wings— She has sailed straight
away over the ridge, without an instant's warning, and
your opportunity is gone.

Whir!—! Whir!—! There go two others! Where
did they start from? You saw them not. You did
not even guess others were there. You had forgotten
how you might stand within three feet of one of these
wary sage hens, and—lest it move—you would pass on
without knowing its presence. Only sharp and well-
trained eyes may discover these clever, gray-robed
birds of the hills.

As you spring to your feet, trying to follow their
flight with your eyes, a dozen others take wing—then
two, then a single bird, then half a dozen more—and
the whole flock of a score sweeps over the ridge into
the next ravine, straight as the arrow shot from a bow.

All these cañons will somewhere show you quartz.
Sometimes of little worth; but silver and gold, copper
and lead, are in the ledges that crop out everywhere.
There are gorges walled with granite and porphyry,
and the walls are streaked with ledges of white quartz.
Night comes soon in these deep-cleft cañons, yet in
their depths are creeks where riotous sweet-brier
blushes and blooms when the melting snows of the
early months of the year feed the streams, filling them
bank-full with sparkling, crystalline waters.

Riding through these mountains, some day you will
come unexpectedly upon the ruins of a long-forgotten
town, relic of dead mining days. Adobes and stones
which made the walls of the houses more than a quarter of a century ago, are now crumbling—tumbling

down. All around you are inclines, and tunnels, and shafts; their entrances choked by the slipping, sliding earth which Winter brings down each year to hide the work of those men who put into useless labor, heart and soul, and the best efforts of a long-gone youth. Time is obliterating their work, and little silvery lizards, wearing vermilion collars, hold possession.

Here is an old orchard of trees which no longer bear the apples and peaches or the pears and plums that the one who planted in youth's hopeful season saw hanging on the limbs. Nature is taking back her own; the cañon is returning to its wild tangle of brush and vine.

You see that once, in the long ago past, some one planted locust seeds which grew, and had their seasons of blossom and of seedtime, in turn to scatter their own seeds broadcast, and a little grove of locust trees has sprung up in what was once the town's public thoroughfare.

The pallid bloom on the dead-ripe fruit of the elders catches your eye as you ride by. Great bunches of berries, that soon will be drying, weigh the boughs down till they rest upon the growth of lower bushes underneath.

On the thorny boughs of the wild gooseberry little brown birds are pecking at some of the purple fruit which has withered in the Autumn air.

Choke-cherries grow here; black and shining, though dried, on limbs which bend so low you bow your head as you ride under their shade. Beneath their thick screen it is cool and dark. They grow tall and strong, and at last bar your way. Turning aside, you follow a trail along the hillside to where, ahead, you see an opening in the grove. Down through the elders, and red willows, and quaking asps you go. The leaves are turning; spots of brown and russet shine out from

In Quiet Cañons

the background of cool, dark green. Orange and palest yellow, crimson and vermilion are here.

And here, in a group, stand a dozen dead trees. Naked of leaf, and bleaching, their white boles and bare boughs show with the delicacy of an etching against the darkness of the shadowed growth beyond. An empty nest—an oriole's—swings from a barren limb. Higher, are sticks and ragged stems woven together in a crotch of the tree where a hawk has builded.

Below the dead grove, is a living one, though the leaves are yellow—a sulphur yellow—now. The topmost boughs of many of the trees are caught together in a tangle of wild ivy. Long shadows slant across the road, and through the waving branches of the cotton-woods rays of sunshine fall to dance along your path.

There comes into your mind a line from a loved author: ''Through the shimmering leaves the sunshine drips in weightless showers of gold.'' Ah, he who wrote the words is one who lives close to the heart of Nature! He writes from an overflowing soul; and you, in reading, are thrilled to your heart's core as it beats in unison with the heart of the world under the influence of his genius. It was such a day as this, you are sure, when he saw the dripping yellow of the sun, and told you of it in words whose memory is a strain of golden melody raining down on you as you ride.

Ahead of you a cottontail scurries down the roadway. A breeze comes comes up the cañon and plays about you; but so delicate and light a thing is it, nothing else is stirred by it but the tendrils of hair which grow about your forehead, and which the little wind lifts and lets fall—over and over again—as if hiding tender, little kisses underneath. Soft as a baby's hand on your face is its touch on your eyelids and your cheek. You look about you and find that no other thing is being moved by it; no spear of grass, or leaf of bush or tree is trembling in the silent atmosphere. It is only here by you—for you. To you alone are whispered the secrets which your willing ears are listening to; on your face only fall the lingering, clinging caresses. When you ride forward, it goes with you; when you stop—made glad by its touch—it encircles you as if it were some creature of sentient life. Then, as you ride on down the trail, it goes with you, following you to the end.

Presently you hear the roar of water rushing over the rocks down in the gorge. Guided by the sound, your eye finds a succession of laughing, tumbling, rollicking cascades, and leaping, plunging waterfalls. But another roaring comes up the cañon, not from the wind or the waters. Up from the valley it comes, bearing to your ears a sound that—increasing in volume each moment—is like that of the mighty storm-driven winds of the mountain as they sweep down from the snow heights in Winter. Away down—so far—perhaps half a dozen miles beneath you and away to the plains, a freight-train is creeping along the twin threads of shining steel that are the bands binding the West to the East.

You are so close to the civilized world, and yet so remote! How good a thing it seems to be away from the petty meannesses of the daily routine of your life in a bickering, bartering, bullying world of mankind and money-making!

When you dismount to examine a seam of quartz running down the face of a porphyry cliff, and before turning away, stand there a moment in the shadow of its great height, with your cheek laid close to its cool surface, you seem to hear it saying to you:

"Why go away? Stay, and I will tell you secrets

In Quiet Cañons

of what is hidden hundreds of feet down where the quartz seam goes. Do you want to know how it will be in a thousand years? Do you wonder if the delightful solitude of my cañons will still be unbroken, or if in the world's transformation they will have been changed with all else in a world made of changes? Do not go. Be wise, and stay in the mountains. Why go back to the places where men toil and drudge, and moil and slave just for the few short years which they can call their own? How they labor and weep! How they work and worry! And for what? Stay, let me teach you the lesson of life. Let me show you how to read its teachings aright. Take no heed of that world where busy men fret their days out in trying to solve the problem of how they should live, and—ere the lesson is learned—return to the dust from whence they came. I am here through all the fretting and fuming of puny man; fire and flood, war and pestilence may come and go, yet I endure—impassive—immutable— eternal. Ah, if you but turn to me to learn how to live a life of perfect calm and peace I would lead you to those places where in the clefts and chasms Nature stands ready to fold round you that shelter and quiet which enwrap one as with a garment.''

The place and the hour have so strongly influenced your mental being that it is with an effort you now rouse yourself and move on. Even as you ride away from this cañon into another you are still musing on the wonderful ways of the wise old world when these mountains lay under glacial ice aeons ago—in ages of which we know nothing. Thinking and thinking, the hours slide by without your ken, and the day is almost done. Katydids and crickets fill the late afternoon with their shrilling. Dry grasses in the trail are beginning to shiver in the evening wind. Daylight has vanished so swiftly that darkness encompasses you ere you are aware.

From far up in the topmost branches of a half-dead tree comes a sharp noise—the sudden snapping of dry twigs. Startled at the sound, your horse springs quickly aside from the trail, and your own heart is set to throbbing violently in your throat. As you chirrup to him to urge him to faster speed, an owl flies forth with slow-flapping wings, disappearing in the gathering darkness.

You raise your eyes aloft and look into the measureless deep of the Heavens. Faint stars are coming in the twilight sky.

In
Quiet
Cañons

THE QUAIL'S CANON.

RISTLING with rocky cliffs and deep ravines—its face is furrowed and scarred where cloudbursts have warred their way; but all softly beautiful in its blending of violet-blues and shadowy purples as you view it from afar, is this rugged mountain where—in the long ago—miners and prospectors burrowed its sides full of holes, as the badgers burrow the plains away down below, making their tunnels and inclines and shafts in the quest for silver. For these things of which I tell you, happened in the days when silver, not gold, was the metal men went a-seeking.

Ledges were there in every cliff; and in a sunny cañon lying to the west they built their cabins, setting them in two long rows at the sides of the creek that came down in rowdy fashion (making much noise, and taking up much room) after it left the sky-line where it was born under the melting edges of the snow-banks.

The mining camp nestled happily between two uneven ridges; and there it grew lustily, and the miners called it a "city," and great things were expected of it. A busy, hopeful little community it was which had gathered there in those old days of honest endeavor and steadfast work; and all signs pointed (they would tell you) to the time that it would become a great silver camp. But "all signs fail in dry weather"; and although it was indeed a dry land, and although there came seasons of unprecedented wet, and snow, and cold, as in other lands, one could not tell if it was in spite of the signs, or because of them, that none of the good things prophesied and hoped-for ever came true.

The mountain was a network of ledges, and in them silver was found in abundance. Willing hands were ready to do the work—the hands of men who were young and brave and strong as they must be who go to blaze the way through a new country. But a score of unforeseen difficulties leagued against them, and as they saw their chances for success diminish, their numbers decreased—they drifted away, one after another, going back to the old homes in the cities from whence they came.

First one cabin, then another, became tenantless— each owner taking with him all that was possible for him to carry. Down along the home road to the sea, they would find purchasers for all which they had no use for; so windows, and doors, and roofing were taken away, to be sold to other miners in other cañons farther toward the West. Lumber was priceless in a land which had neither railways nor water transportation.

Far away, across a continent, a civil war was rending our country, but the meager news which came to the miners in the isolated cañon seemed but as a story. Letters and newspapers must journey many a week ere ships, and ponies could bring them to their destination. "The world forgetting, and by the world forgot," the few who were left there numbered but two score when the Winter of the Great Snow descended on them.

Their supplies—cached in abandoned tunnels—had

been growing less and less, with no immediate means of being renewed. Each man was looking forward to the Spring when he, too, would return to the Coast. There would be enough to carry them through the Winter months, if the season were short, and nothing unforeseen occurred. They had ammunition in camp—not much, but what seemed to be enough for their needs; and rabbits were to be had for the shooting, while powder and shot lasted. Other fresh meat, there was none. They now saw, only too well, how great a mistake it had been for them to remain behind the others. It was too late in the season for them to start back on the long trail toward the sea. They must wait for Spring to open. Winter would be upon them soon.

Winter came—came cruelly, that year. What man among them ever forgot it while he lived!

The sun went out of the sky, and darker and darker grew the heavens. There was no wind. Nothing but a leaden stillness. Then the heavy skies began to sift soft flakes of snow earthward. At first, they came fine as the grains of alkali dust that had been whirled up by the Summer winds down on the dreary plains. Larger, and larger they grew as they hurried onward toward the little colony in the cañon. From big flakes, they grew into great snow-feathers; and these came so fast and so thick, that the sky which had been darkened was now white from the flakes, and shut out the leaden-colored roof of their little world.

Under the snow-drifts, where the wild rose-bushes and willows made a shelter for the stream, the creek shouted and laughed at their dismay and dread, and went babbling on down to the desert where the road was snowed under, and where no living thing moved across the shoreless, silent, ghostly sea.

There were nights when the storm roused itself to a fury that brought winds down from the heights roaring like wild beasts roaming through the cañon. The storm in its frenzy would beat against the rocks as though to rend them from their very foundations; and then would go shrieking over the ridge, and away. Morning would come, and the storm-fury would have spent itself; but not the snow. Always, and always it snowed. Each day dawned upon down-drifting flakes which fell upon a world of unearthly silence.

There was no work done among the men. Who could climb the mountain-sides to the tunnels and inclines? For more than three weeks they had been without tea, or coffee, or flour, bacon, or beans, or any of the things they most needed to ward off starvation. For a man may starve, even with food to eat, if it be not the right sort. There were yet a few articles of food—though little else than sugar and dried "jerky." Not many of the men had ever been without wholesome food before—most of them were from the East, from the cities. The hard life began to tell on them. They grew thin; grew weak—very weak. Some among them sickened, and lay down too ill to care what the end might be.

Then the first one died. Not much more than a boy, and unused to hardships—unable to stand the rough fare, he died for the lack of nourishing food. It was two hundred and fifty miles to Virginia City, where there were both food and medicine to be had; but who could make the trip in the face of the relentless storm which daily piled higher and higher the white barriers between them and that distant help!

So Gilbert Bend died—died just as the storm, wearied of its weeks of warring, ceased. The flakes at last stopped floating earthward—stopped suddenly one day; and there was the sun! But oh! what a world it showed. A vast, trackless waste of dazzling white, unrelieved by even a solitary touch of any color or shading. Snowed in.

In the center of the town, among the deserted stores, was a saloon, also deserted. It was the one building there having a floor. This, they tore up; and making a rude box from the boards thus obtained, they laid in it the body of their dead comrade. Then, taking it on their shoulders, the six strongest men among them bore it down to the top of the mesa where others—ere the storm had fallen—had been buried before. Plowing their way through the soft drifts of blinding whiteness, under the warmth of the dazzling noon-day sun, they came at last to the rocky point amid the foothills. Two, who had broken a trail there before them, had the shallow grave ready; and there they laid him away—one of the unknown Trail-Makers of the West —while, together, they sang a hymn that most of them knew, and had sung in the old days "back home." Then one—his partner—tried to speak of the dead, but sobbing turned away; and so they slowly tramped back through the heavy drifts to their cabins.

When the first rider made his way into the cañon, after the suns of many days had made the roads passable, the men whom he found were very near to starvation; and some who had been among the number when the first flakes of the great snow had fallen, were no longer there. Again—and again had the old saloon-floor gone to the making of the rough boxes, which the few who were left had carried down to the lonely mesa where they left their dead comrades to sleep in an unkind land. So the trail grew wider, and the drifts were beaten down by the feet that passed on the way.

Years came and went; yet never again did the snow fall as it fell that year; the year that (far away) Lee had marched "horse and foot into Fredericktown." To the East, they counted time by the great battles;

here—in the West—events were dated from the "Winter of the Great Snow." Now, time dulls the sharp edges of history, and finally there were those (they were new-comers in the country) who said it was but a fanciful story—that no such heavy snows had ever fallen. But the old men of the old days, shook their gray heads, knowing better.

Colonists had come into the country since that time, and had made their homes. A railroad cut across the flat valley. Other cañons now held other camps; but this one still remained deserted. The last man had gone, long before. Not a roof was left; only the melting adobe walls showed, where the houses had been, or the fallen stones marked the site of a miner's cabin.

The last to go was the first to build in the valley. Down there, in the midst of green fields and orchards which he planted, was the home of one of the pioneers. He plowed and planted; and he prospered. And he was content in the home he had made; and was happy. A grove grew up of trees that were his planting; and birds came to the trees, as birds come whenever and wherever trees are made to grow in desert-land. Birds in numbers came, and of many kinds. Yet what the man wanted to see were quail—the mountain and valley quail he had known long before, in his life among the poppies and pines of California. Try as he would, he could never quite forget those days when he had carried a gun across his shoulder along the Contra Costa foothills. He was lonely for quail!

Back in the old days they had been the oftenest-seen birds about him—those speckled black and steel fellows of the field, trig and trim; with cousins on the uplands, that flash a ruddy-brown wing past your sight as they take flight. There were larks, and robins, and doves here in the cañons; and on the heights were great flocks of sage-chickens; and water-fowl of many kinds

were down on the river, but he longed for the sound of
the quail-call, and the sight of their whirring flight—
the quail of the valleys and mountains of California!

Persistent were the recollections that haunted him of
old hunting days; and he spent many hours thinking,
and thinking. Finally he said to himself, that there
was but one thing to be done—to fetch them over the
Sierras, from the fields and foothills beyond, and then
wait until their numbers multiplied.

So crate after crate of trapped birds came over in
that first season when the trans-continental railroad
was an established fact. Valley quail, and mountain
quail, both. Crate after crate, and still more and
more. And all were taken up to the cañons where
there was plenty of water, and the wild grasses which
yielded seeds; and there they were turned loose—
scattering over the ridges or scurrying into the brush.
There in the old deserted "city" they were freed; and
among the tall, blossoming weeds, and the spicy junipers on the hillsides.

The little emigrants took very kindly to the change;
and another year saw several flocks far from the range
where they had been given their freedom.

Most Indians have as great a sense of honor as have
some white men in respecting the rights of others
when not protected by law, and the Paiutes—when
they came to understand the purpose of bringing the
stranger birds—were as zealous as the white man in
their joint guardianship of the new bird-colony. No
one seemed to have any thought of hunting them—
they had become a sort of public charge. They multiplied amazingly. On the hills they were as numerous
as were the jackrabbits down along the valley. Away
off in other ranges—in cañons miles and miles away
—across the valleys that lay between, and where on
the mountain-sides green spots marked springs and

shade, one could always find flocks coming in to water. They were everywhere!

At last they were plentiful enough that the sportsman might be allowed to hunt them; and for one short, sport-full season (when everyone went gunning) did the hunters have their will. Only one.

Then, with no foreshadowing of that which was to come, there fell upon the land a Winter more terrible in its bitter chill than that other one, more than five-and-twenty years before, when the little handful of early prospectors in the snowbound cañon waited through the long, white silence for the coming of the Spring. Earlier—much earlier than had ever been its wont, did the storms begin. Nor was it rain that came, as in the other years. Rains softened the brush, and swelled the seeds among the dried grasses and weeds on the mesas where the sheep and cattle grazed. Rain was good. Here, too, had the quail thrived, even as they had in their home on the other side of the high Sierras. But with deep snows overlying the land—! What were the little emigrants to do in their struggle to live if the wild elements waged battle against them? How were their small hearts to keep on beating throughout the chill Winter, and until the warmth of the Spring suns should set all the little creeks and rills running down the rugged old mountain's cañons and crevasses, to bring the grasses again? On mountain and plain were the wild things—helpless furred and feathered creatures, who would find death in the storms if they were many or long.

So the days went by; and on the plains the snow fell so deep that the chill layers of ghostly white hid the brush and sage as completely as though they had been sucked down and swallowed by these quicksands of the Winter.

Along the foothills where the valley quail had loved

to run, the drifts filled the shallow ravines; on the higher elevations—where among the rocks and stunted junipers the mountain quail had lived and found life good—now the sharp outlines were smoothed out under the rounded whiteness. Farther down, in the valley, the river ranches were blotted out. Snowflakes—like grains of icy sand—fell thickly, steadily, gently; with that soft insistence which is harder to do battle against than fire or flood. Then winds—cruelly cold, and dealing death where they touched animal life—would come and whirl the sharp grains (fine and dry as sand) into high drifts which—in turn—were buried under the stinging flakes that were ever falling—falling—falling, until it was once again a vast, unsounded level.

From the high lands where they grazed, the storm drove the stock into the valleys where it followed them, and where they died. Sheep dropped by the thousands at its icy touch; cattle weakened—staggered —fell. The birds and the four-footed wild things came down out of the mountains, no longer afraid, and too weak to flee. They, too, like the sheep and the cattle, died as though a pestilence had swept over the land. So they died everywhere, and each day the number grew.

There were times when a sickly sun tried to shine from out the sky, only to be beaten back by the storm. Colder and colder grew the days; lower and lower fell the mercury. Five below zero. Ten. Then eighteen—twenty—thirty—thirty-six! The stoves were kept (nine of them) choked with the hardwood crowded in; and all day the fires roared up the chimneys, and red-hot patches glowed on their iron sides. More than half the night the fires burned; but by and by they would die down, and in those early hours of the new day, one could hear the crack and creak of the timbers as the house grew colder.

Morning brought increased labors to keep alive the suffering animals that turned to man in their extremity. Life resolved itself into a monotonous repetition of those duties that were most necessary for the present hour. No one looked ahead; no one dared. It would be time enough for the cattle-owner to count the fearful cost when Spring should come, and he rode the range and reckoned up his losses. Now he must see that his men hauled feed to the cattle that were too weak to get on their feet; that the ice was cut in the river so that horses and cattle might drink; that snow enough was melted for household needs (for the water-pipes had long ago frozen and burst); that the wood-boxes were heaped high with split logs; that the bread, and meat, and milk was thawed—freed from the flakes of ice that they gathered.

Up the valley where the railroad ran, the tracks were under the snow. Over them had no wheel passed for seventeen long days. Blockaded. The great, monstrous machinery of man's making, with its noise and its grime, was silenced—its strength and power crushed out by this soft, white, silent thing that never missed one day out of the twenty-seven in falling.

When the frost, and the cold, and the drifting snow were gone, and the sun came back, it shone on a crystal world. We looked out over a wide, trackless, shipless, chartless sea of eye-tiring snow-fields. But it stormed no more.

And the quail?

Poor little emigrants into an unkind country! For more than five years thereafter no one ever saw any quail. We looked for them whenever we rode through cañons, or over the mesas. It was always the same—never a one did we see. And we mourned for them, as we do for things that have eaten out of our hand;

for had we not guarded them as something that was our very own? They had all perished, we said, the cold had been too severe for the strangers-to-snow.

Then, one day riding up through a wash all filled with tall rabbit-brush, and wild plum-bushes, I saw a touch of red-brown on a wing that flashed across my sight, and my heart gave a great bound. A quail! Then a long time went by before I saw another. Then others saw them, too. Sometimes a pair; then a small flock. Then another—a larger one; and another one —and another.

And now? The quail have come again! We say "come again" because we hate to think of those that met the chill of that awful Winter, and with the horses and cattle, and sheep on the ranges, died by the hundreds—thousands. Hunters, we, and we have no compunction in going forth with dog and gun, and filling the game-bag. But one would be less than human to think unmovedly of the slow death by starvation and cold that came to so many birds and beasts that Winter of 'eighty-eight and 'nine. So we would rather persuade ourselves that the quail which are now in the mountains, are the same bonny little feathered friends that took up their habitation there so long ago. Once again they are everywhere. Once again the flocks have increased sufficiently to permit one shooting them without fear of extermination. Once again they are on every mountain, and on the low-lying foothills. There are fewer of the valley quail, however, than there are of their little relatives.

Yes; they have "come back again." But the greatest numbers have gone to that cañon where the miners lived the Winter of the first great snow. It was the quail's first home; for there it was that they were loosed in the year they were brought from beyond the snow mountains.

Chinese placer miners working in the creek found gold—much gold; but the silver ledges still lie on the hillsides undisturbed, the tunnel entrances choked with thistles and briar bushes. No longer do men go a-search for silver. Only gold—in the ledges up above, or down on the bed-rock of the water course—lures them in their quests. The little yellow-skinned men of the Orient came, and went, and came again. They made their dug-outs in the banks back from the gray and crumbling walls which were built by miners of old. Up and down the creek bed they move so noiselessly, working with pick and pan, that one can very easily fancy them but gray ghosts haunting the quiet cañons, even as the shadowy wraiths of the dead years linger about the unroofed walls and weed-grown trails. Silently they go about their work, leaving the quail to go their ways.

If you go among the old adobes and fallen stone walls in the ruined town, you will see them scurrying by twos and threes out of the tumble-down, crumbling cabins, to find hiding places in the tall rabbit-wood or sage-brush; or—flushing by flocks—to sail straight away to the hillsides. It is the quail's cañon. Once again they claim the solitude of the place as their own. Before they went away they were less shy than now; for they are beginning to know the fear of man. A while back, in the peace of the tumbling walls, there came no more disturbing sound to the cañon than the rumble of the train down on the desert, or the far-away shriek of its whistle. But they have learned a new sound, and with it has come fear.

The sunlight lies warm on the hillsides; and the soft West winds come to rattle the pods of dried weeds, shaking the seeds in showers to the ground. The quail run hither and thither, undisturbed by the seasons or the little yellow men working among the gravel and boulders in the bottom of the creek; but away up on the slope where the brush and bunch-grass does not grow so thick, you hear the crack of a breech-loader where some hunter has gone hunting. It is the sound the quail have learned to fear.

HAWKS.

YOUR heart-throbs are quickened at the sight of a beautiful painting? Your blood bounds when you look on a magnificent picture? Yes? Then come with me to a rough stone cabin I know —built away up on the side of a great mountain, yet walled about by still greater heights, and set upon a shelf of rock overhanging a gorge where winds and waters make music all day and all night —and there, standing before the east window, I will show you that which (for the brief little hour you may stay) shall delight you; even as, day after day, I, too, am made glad through its exquisite charm.

You love color, and form, and sound when—fresh from Nature's touch—they have not yet been marred by the clumsy handling of Man? Then shall you revel in the beauties of this picture—a picture I have framed only with the unpainted pine casing about the window sash; where the ledge is littered with matches and candles, cards and cartridges, and numerous specimens of gold quartz.

You do not see these things, though; you look beyond. Here! let me slide back the window in its grooves, that there shall be no glass, even, between you and the picture's perfection.

Pouff—ff! The winds come in with a rush; and there is a tempestuous sweeping of loose letters from the bare table, and these go sliding over the plank floor; while it sets papers and magazine leaves a-fluttering noisily where they lie. The winds surge and swell through the cañon. Within, they have madly invaded our calm, and in an instant the supreme quiet which was erst ours is changed to movement and sound. What mightily magnificent winds these are! Gods of Olympus! did you ever know their like on your heights! I doubt if you ever felt about you such winds as these. Ah! but their rough tug and tussle is good to feel! And we stand here in their boisterous company, looking out of the wide-set window through which they entered, and behold the picture I have brought you to see.

A Picture of Hawks!

Porphyry that counts its height in feet which measure hundreds, reaching from the thicket-hidden creek to the sapphire sky, is the background. But such a wall! Sheer; yet of splintered facing which holds a thousand varying forms, as light and shadow move across it. Rent and riven; battered by Time and broken by the elements, it is a wealth of shading and form to the picture lover. The ruddy-brown surface is splotched with lichens—yellow as sulphur, gray as dead ashes, velvety-black as soot. All up and down its perpendicular face—in the crevices—have roots of a little stiff-leaved plant found place to hold; the dark-green, short-stemmed foliage growing in matted patches, indifferent to the buffetings of the wind. This is the Home of the Wind. Daily it comes with the first afternoon slant of the purple shadows, to die away before dusk. It roars and rushes through the cañon wildly enough now; but it will go down with the down-going of the sun, and only the faintest breeze

—soft and murmurous—will linger on these heights through the star-lit night.

Two-thirds up the way of the great cliff is a little shelf—not more than a double hand-span in width—where a hawk has built her nest. The gorge, deep as it is, is narrow, very narrow; the sunlight only finding its way to the bottom hours after its yellow shine has brightened all the valley and outer slopes. So little is the space between wall and wall, that you and I here in my eyrie can look across into the hawk's eyrie over the way, and see there the two baby birds on the nest's edge—defiantly fearless above the sheer descent. So narrow is the gorge, we hear their young cry as clearly as does the mother-hawk circling just above.

Watch her! What wonderful sweep of mighty sinewed wing is there! What marvellous poise! Then, a tilt, and she drops—cutting the crystal-clear air with a grace no other living creature may ever surpass. A breath—and she rises. Skimming the heights with a majesty of motion defying all description, she wheels and circles over the gorge on a level with your eyes—your eyes that look, and look, and still follow her flight when she mounts higher—higher, till you have to lean far out of the casement to see into the vivid ocean-blue of the heavens, hidden else by the overhanging eaves. A speck—two! Up there, they go drifting across space. And you come back to the cliff and the young ones in the nest. My small neighbors over the way!

Do you hear them—hear the cry of their hungry mouths? Like the exaggerated peeping of young chicks, they are lifting up a perpetual plaint for food. "Peep—peep—peep! . . . Peep!" If they perch on the nest edge, slowly turning around in a pivotal way, with now and then a clumsy lifting and limbering of their young wings, they may be silent for a

Hawks

while; but the lull is only temporary. Again you will hear the vociferous demand for meat-food which the small beaks are so eager to tear. When they have turned about to their satisfaction a number of times, and have done much flapping of the young wings, they re-commence their pitiful plaint of "Peep! peep!" Come, mother-bird, your hawklings are calling you! "Peep! peep!"

Now lift your eyes, friend, again to the infinite blue space where she found such grand scope for her flight. Gone! The far specks are no longer there; nothing is moving through the ether between you and that perfect sky.

And the rock walls? Across the gorge these mighty cliffs rise—cliffs worthy of such a roofing. And flanking the central wall, what wonderful cleft domes the rocks are fashioned into! What slender spires reach heavenward from their tops! What architecture is there! How good—oh, how good it is to look at! How more than good it is not only to be able to see, but to feel the beauty of it all! You could never tire of looking at this cathedral-like cliff built up from the very earth's foundations—this noble achievement of the Master Architect! Did ever stained glass window, set within the temples of Man, hold more gorgeous coloring than you see here, where the blue and purple stains of the rock, just there at the right, have mixed with emerald patches of moss, and the splotchings of lichen-tufts in all the shades of yellow—of velvety-black—of grayish-white! And mingled with this is the red-brown of the great rock itself. Oh! it is beautiful—wondrous beautiful, wet with the rain that fell early this morning, and which the sun has not yet dried —for this sheer cliff has just crawled out of its half day of shadow.

Hark! Above the shrill cry of the hawks, you hear

the anthem sung by the cañon winds, mingled with the waters' chanting. You hold your breath as you listen, and the swelling volume of sound which comes up between the gorge-walls stirs you with deeper feeling than you have known this many a day. Surely, God's own music is here.

Down, down—far down below the hawk's nest—is the creek, rushing noisily over boulders hidden by brush and willows. And now a vagrant wave of wind paints a silvery path along the place where the gray willows grow! How lovely that was—that shiver of light that ran along on the yellow leaves and tender branches!

Something sweeps past the cabin window. See! The old hawk has carried a mouse over to her young. Ah! but they made short work of it; and are now clamoring louder than ever, as the mother again goes forth in quest of yet other rodents that live in the rocks.

Not long, and a day will come when (as young beaks and talons fasten onto some dainty bit brought them when they have been left long without food and are ravenously hungry) she will not yield it as now; but —keeping her own clutch on it the while—she will suddenly dip from the shelf of rock and, outspreading her wings, will sail away over the chasm, dragging a youngster out of the nest as she takes flight. Then—!

There will be a tumble into space; a clutching at the vanished nest—at the bare cliff—at the empty air! But instantly will follow the instinctive spreading of young wings. The mother-hawk, in alarm and apprehension, will shrill a new note; not the hawk-scream of every day, but a sound like unto a seagull's cry. The cañon will be filled with the noise of her perturbed clamoring, as—dipping and darting under her young one—she will bear its weight for one brief instant, to give the assistance and assurance of safety which is needed to encourage the frightened small body, that it may find some friendly and near projection of rock. Not only her mate will join in the shrill lamentations, but alien little birds, disturbed by the unwonted noise, will add their cries to the general clamoring. Such a din as there will be! And all the while will be the sweep of wide wings circling close about a frightened young thing, to whom the big world is unknown, untried space.

Then the other wee hawk will be dragged from the nest in like wise; and the mother's alarm-cry, mingled with the chatterings of little perturbed birds, will be repeated. Then will come a week or two of bewildered baby-bird life—the young ones protesting against the new regime—a week or two of crying for the mother-care. But self-reliance will come with the new days, and then they will know themselves young hawks. Babies no more.

No longer fledglings, you will have to fight your world for a living then; but oh! you will find compensation in just the joy of life! No longer fed by the mother-beak, you will have to go far a-search for food, little ones, when that time comes, lest hunger hunt you down!

But is it not worth it, to go all the length and breadth of the land, while you follow your work-ways, just for the sake of the great things one meets the while? Hawk-flight and hawk-life—oh, you will know then what that means! The storms and the snow that will here seek you out in the rough Winter months will be well worth battling with when they call forth all your powers of resistance. Life is worth while when one meets the things which tests one's fighting ability —one's capacity to overcome difficulties!

Not long, and all this will become yours to be and to

do. But, oh! I will miss my hawk-babies when there
is an empty nest over the way.

You are here today, though, little ones; and above,
is the mother, watchful for your well-being. Circling
and circling, she hovers over that jutting bench further
down the cañon; yet not so far away but that we can
see the turn of her head as the keen eyes are bent upon
every foot of ground she passes over. She is searching now where chaparral is growing among the loose
fragments of a rock slide, below the palisades. Cease
your clamoring, you noisy wee ones! Never fear but
that those penetrating eyes will discover what you
want, and she will fetch you other rare morsels, if you
will but have patience. The small talons are grasping
the side of the nest (the rough nest of sticks and twigs
which I watched so long, in the past weeks, waiting to
see the first fuzzy head rise above its rim), and the
shrill cries grow louder.

You, friend, like myself, have grown an affectionate
interest in the little fellows in the hawk's nest, and
you laugh, and call to them—imitating their own cry.
A wee head slowly turns toward you—then another;
and the lamenting ceases for a moment, while the four
eyes stare toward where you stand. Verily, we are
becoming friends, you and I, with our little neighbors
over the way!

And so the day, here on the heights, wears on; and
in like wise it is repeated in other days which are good
to know. Full days.

It is a beautiful world. It is good to live.

Days there are of cloudless skies of sapphire-blue;
other days clouds of white wool drift overhead, chas-
ing the shadows that run over the rocks underneath.
Rock swallows dip and skim over the great cleft in
the cañon. The hawk's cry comes down from the
heights and the linnet lifts its lilt from below,

"And O! and O! between the two,
  Go the wonderful winds of God"—
outsinging the songs of birds!

Not a human footstep to jar its perfection. The place is all one's own. The din of the working-day world is too far away to reach one's ears. The cry of the hawks by day; the owl's hooting in the darkness —that is all. And the mingled melody of chanting winds and waters! They are always here.

And always, too, is the picture framed by the un-painted casing of pine wood, before which I sit so very often—a picture that lives! Whether it be seen beneath the sun, or by the stars' light, it is a master-piece, and one to take to your heart of hearts—this, my Picture of Hawks!

SUBDUING A LITTLE SAVAGE.

TRANGEST of all gifts ever bestowed upon any member of my family was the little seven-year-old wild Indian which a friend—an army officer—sent to my mother when I was a child. We were living in an isolated cañon of the West. For more than a year we had seen no white woman; and only a very few squaws belonging to the tribe of friendly Paiutes living about us.

If you depend upon people for your pleasures, a more lonely existence than such as ours cannot be imagined. But my mother was a woman of infinite resource and entertainment, and she not only made us see a duty in the things to be done, but to find a pleasure in the doing, as well. So our months of self-imposed exile went by, not altogether unhappily for any of us, and for one small girl not at all. Yet the nearest city of any size to the westward was far off in the Sacramento valley, more than three hundred miles away. Neither toward the East were there any cities nearer. Between, lay only scattering little mining camps. Hostile Paiutes were committing depredations all around us, and the killing of the whites became more and more frequent. These Paiutes, together with the still more murderous Shoshones and Bannocks and the offshoots

of those tribes, caused the settlers to live in hourly
dread of the issue of each morrow.

The Indians that year had been unusually trouble-
some—one little band of renegade Bannocks to the
Northeast, in particular, had especially alarmed the
people. A detachment of troops under command of
Lieutenant Hosmer from the military post at Dun Glen
started out with the avowed intention of exterminating
them. They were but a small band, these mongrel
Bannocks, at most but two or three score, but they were
notoriously desperate, as well as keen and shrewd in
their maneuvering. It was therefore deemed best to
have the aid of some of the friendly Paiutes in effect-
ing the plan of action as laid out by the soldiers. So
Cap Sue, selecting twenty picked men of his tribe, volunteered their services, and one midwinter day we saw
them ride out of our cañon to join the soldiers and
hunt down the hostiles in cañons far away.

The story of the many days of trailing them through
the snow, and how they had all but given up the quest
when Cap Sue pointed out the blue spiral of the
enemy's distant campfire, has passed into history. It
is not for me to tell it here, or how they fought them
to the death, so that when daybreak came there was
but one of all the hostile camp that lived. It is only
of him—the little enemy, the one small boy of an alien
people—I shall have aught to tell now. It was this
little fellow—brown of skin, bright of eye; with un-
Indian features, and white teeth (such beautiful teeth
as he had!) yet withal terrified and trembling—who
was sent by the Lieutenant to my mother, when my
father was returning, several weeks later, from a trip
to Dun Glen.

It was late in the afternoon of an April day when
we saw him drive up the one long street of the deserted
mining camp, where the tide of fortune had cast us

ashore with the rest of the wreckage left there when the hopes of the early silver miners went down. Though we had not been of them, we were, at that time, with them, and had been caught in the maelstrom.

In those uncertain days, the temporary absence of any member of the family was fraught with grave fears of danger (a messenger coming to us when one of the household was away, would send a chill to the heart until we were assured all was well), and a safe return was the cause of double rejoicing and welcome; but my astonishment at the sight of the quaint-looking little fellow, who had climbed down from the wagon-seat and now stood looking at us in timid bewilderment, took such complete possession of me that I quite forgot to rush into my father's arms with my usual welcome.

Such a little fellow! What an odd-looking being he was that day, to be sure! When, in answer to my mother's puzzled questioning, I heard father laughingly tell her that it being the seventh of April, he had brought the boy to her for a birthday present, it seemed almost too good to be true that he was to be "truly ours for keeps." I experienced such a succession of emotions as would be difficult for me to describe; but I remember that the first thought was that, at last, I was to have a real playmate like other children. Then succeeded the fear that—as he was such a very dirty little boy—it was doubtful if, after all, my mother would let me play with him. It occurred to me, later, that—as he was wild, really a wild Indian —he might any day go on the war-path and take my scalp; but that was something of minor importance. Children live in the present, only; and I did not dwell on what might be, after all, only a remote possibility. I was to have a playmate! A real live playmate! Nothing else mattered.

The Land of Purple Shadows

Therefore, the principal thing to do was to lend my aid in getting him into the condition of cleanliness necessary to win my mother's approval of an Indian boy as a playfellow; and such a siege as it was to get him into that particular condition—poor, dirty, miserable little wretch that he was! The soldiers, having found him in a state of semi-nudity, felt they had made a distinct advance in dressing him when they put him into a pair of old soldier-trousers cut off far above the knees that their length might conform the better to his short little legs. A very much worn blue blouse, whose sleeves were lopped off far above the elbows, really did duty for all other apparel, and made quite unnecessary and extravagant the wearing of trousers, as it reached easily to the floor, even dragging a little. An old fatigue cap completed the outfit. I smile as I write this, in recollection of the absurd figure he cut; but there was no smile on my face then—nor on his own, poor little survivor of a wild band!

He stood looking from one to another with watchful, frightened eyes; and it was not until long afterward, when he had learned our tongue, that I came to know how the small stranger had thought he had been sent to us that we might put him to death. The White Man had killed his father and mother; all his family; all his friends; all his wild clan. How was he to know that we intended him no harm?

The plate of food put down for him at that first meal he received from our hands, was partaken of at first cautiously—suspiciously; for he believed we wanted to poison him. When hunger asserted itself, he ate ravenously, tearing his food apart with tooth and nail like some wild animal. As I watched my possible playmate, shocked at his ignorance of good table manners, I am afraid he fell many degrees in my estimation. After he had eaten his fill—literally, as the

Indian does eat—by signs and motions he was directed toward the pile of wood just beyond the back door; there, when he was seated on a big juniper log, he was shorn of the thick and long black hair, which was ornamented with buckskin strings strung with bits of carved bone. Long, long afterward he told me how, when he saw the scissors, and the axe at the woodpile, he thought he was to be killed with these strange kind of knives (as he deemed the scissors to be), or struck down with the sharp blade of the axe. He had never bathed otherwise than in the Indian's "sweathouse," and when a tub of soapsuds was prepared for a cleansing of the small body according to our methods, he saw in us only enemies who would drown him therein. When the dirty, discarded clothing, together with the matted black locks, went into the flames of a bonfire, the little stoic made no sign of what he believed was in store for him—the burning alive of himself, as he had seen his people burn their enemies—even as he had once seen his father burn a white man. In our every movement he saw something significant of torture or death being prepared for him, horrible things that were only being delayed in their execution, but which would surely come in time. Yet he gave no sign.

After he had been barbered and bathed, and was ready for clean clothing, the question arose—where was the clothing to come from? There were no stores within many hundreds of miles, neither was there a boy anywhere on our side of the mountain. Clothes he must have, of some sort, however, and at once. A search was made among our own rather meagre wardrobes. It was not a time to consider his sex when it came to dressing him, and it would have been a problem to tell whether the comical-looking little Indian was boy or girl, when we had done. How we laughed at the figure he cut—laughing the louder the longer we looked! But he stood there—an unsmiling, unemotional, unmoving small savage—with hatred in his heart of which we had no thought. Nor did the hot fires die down for many and many a moon. All this, and more, we did not come to know until years had passed, and he and we were friends.

The soldiers, when he was leaving the fort, had given to my father a full suit of the soldier-blue such as they, themselves, wore. These, my mother reconstructed (after I had "ripped them up carefully, and picked all the stitches out") on a less generous plan, fitting them nicely to the sturdy, well-built little body. They were reserved for Sunday use, and some state occasion; and when he donned the suit with its shining brass buttons, he felt himself every inch a soldier, and carried himself as one. The children of the friendly Paiutes living near, could get no recognition from him then. It was only when dressed in the suit which was made for every day use, and he no longer represented the great American army (which all Indians—little and big alike—were beginning to respect, as they began to realize its strength) that he descended from his pedestal, and relaxing from military dignity, deigned to notice them. Even then, it was but a haughty recognition he accorded them. He would rather be my slave than their chief, even in childish plays; and this remained so to the end.

When he came to us he knew no word of English, and by signs only could we, at first, communicate with him; but I have never known anyone to learn a language so rapidly as he—with an intuition that was little short of the miraculous. His intelligence was that of any child of his age among our own people. What he was ignorant of, was by reason of his past environment, not through lack of a fine mental endowment.

Each day, after my own lessons were repeated to my mother, I took the teacher's seat and taught Frank. And no preceptor was ever prouder of pupil than I, when the time came that perfect lessons, signed "Frank Bannock," were handed in for my examination, and there was seldom a criticism to make. Would there were more Frank Bannocks in the world!

Subduing a Little Savage

Naturally studious, he was equally eager to gain knowledge and apply it to some practical use; seeming to feel it would be unworthy of one to simply acquire knowledge and hoard it—that it was its application to anything worth while which created its value. And the lessons he learned caused him to ask questions beyond my power to answer! He told me how unsatisfactory to him were the Indian theories of light and darkness; one of the first questions he asked us when he could express himself clearly being: "Where dark go when light come?" He wanted to know what were the moon, and the sun, and the stars—what caused seasons, or colors—of what was beyond the mountains; of what was beyond the grave? What was the mystery of life? and why was death here? Whence? whither? why? Indian that he was, and even Indian child that he was, he asked the questions we all come to ask sooner or later. And I—knowing no more than he—tried to teach what little I knew; and before my halting explanations would be made, he would ever grasp the unuttered thought back of the spoken word; and together we would go to my mother to straighten for us the tangle. When we got beyond our depth in theology, she would give us leave to take down what we would from the book shelves, the books that had many engravings, and among the pictures we got away from problems too big for us. "Shakespeare," "Byron's Poems," "Godey's Lady's Book—1850"! I can remember now, these many decades later, how he loved the picture of Mazeppa bound to the back of the wild stallion, in the red morocco volume of Byron! I wish that the children of today were as careful in handling books, as was this little wild Indian of the far-away, little-known mountains.

And of those mountains where he was born—where he was one of a savage tribe—where no white man might go, and live to return, he would tell me stories of his people and their ways, that was the strangest entertainment a small girl-child ever listened to! He and I used to go up the steep side of the cañon, above our house, where we could watch the sun go down on the mountains that hid his one-time home, and there he would relate to me the things that were in that wild life of his, far away across the river and the purple range of mountains, and a still farther range to the northwest. No tale of Grimm's could hold such complete fascination for a child as did the terrible recountings of massacres along the old emigrant road, and the burning of wagons by the way; of the scalps his kinsfolk brought home from battles where the soldiers had been driven back; of raids upon small settlements, and killing of white men that they might bring back horses, and cattle—for "jerky." Strange tales for a child to hear; still stranger for another to tell! I knew they were true; but they never seemed real. He was my playmate, and shared all my games; how could I connect him with the things I heard from his lips? No, the tales were possessed of a horrible fascination, and when he would tell such things to me (which was not often—he would rather play—to live in the present—to be one of us) the interest I felt was not born of conviction. They were to me as the fairy-stories of genii and dragon; never of what was about me—everywhere —through those years of my childhood. Could I have felt the truth, I would have better understood what lay back of the calm, expressionless little face the day he was brought to our home—when he expected to receive as his portion what his people had meted out to the invading whites.

The wonder is that he ever freed himself from the terror he had of us when he came. It was weeks before he was reassured; months before he began to evince any confidence in us. But with the years came affection—an affection which we returned in like measure. What a marvel it was; the opening of the doorway of that savage mind! The opening of the doorway of his lonely little heart! I understand you now, Frank, as I did not then. Dear little playmate of the dead and gone years!

When he was not telling me wonderful tales, he would show me no less wonderful things. I learned how to catch rabbits with a noose on the end of a green willow sapling set in the ground—to be sprung by the rabbit as he loped down the rabbit-trails. I learned, as the Indian children learn, to twist cords out of vegetable fiber. He showed me how to make bone and wooden fish-hooks; and how to set them in a row along the twisted fish-line. Then I learned a way of making a spring out of my left thumb and two forefingers so that a small pebble could be sent spinning out of sight.

(The other evening, when some of us had climbed to the top of the highest point in Los Angeles to watch a crimson and purple sunset, I picked up some pebbles, and with the others began sending them as far as I could down into the shadow-filled cañons. Suddenly there came back to me the recollection of my childhood days up on the lonely mountain, and I forgot those who were with me. It was little Frank who was beside me as I placed the pebble against the lower joint of my left fore-finger, and with my right finger and other thumb sent the bit of stone far and away, out of sight.

I had not forgotten the trick learned from the wild little Bannock years and years ago.)

He taught me in those dim years how to string a bow; and how to tip an arrow with flint sharpened against the ball of the thumb with another stone; and how to turn the feather right, on the shaft of the arrow.

I learned more of the signs of the big out-of-doors while he and I played together those years there, than throughout all the rest of my life. Woodcraft and stonecraft were pleasant studying, and every day brought some new knowledge. It has served me good turns in the time since, more than once.

Most wonderful of all, he could rub a greasewood stick so fast between his palms that the point of it placed in a hollow of a bit of dry wood, with a pinch of dry (very, very dry) dust, would presently blaze into a little flame and ignite the dry shredded bark put there to catch the spark. It was marvellous! And what was more marvellous still was the fact that he never failed to make it burn; while I never succeeded in all the time I was with him, no matter how hard I tried. I did precisely as he showed me. It would smoke—oh! so encouragingly—but to blaze, and burn, it refused absolutely and always. It was just the same with the "gorkies" (the Indian's wild onion) that he taught me to find. Whenever I dug down for them the root and stem would separate an inch or two from the surface of the ground, and then the succulent little bulb would be lost. Not so with Frank. He never failed to get them out without severing the slender little root. Then, with the splendid generosity which was so marked a characteristic of his nature, he would pour his whole store of "gorkies" into my lap, while he would dig others for himself—or, if the day was late, go without. It was his will always to give me the best of his spoils of the cañon, whether it was of ber-

ries, or flowers, nests with speckled eggs, or bits of
bright and pretty rock, where every cliff held a
"ledge." What halcyon days those were!

Looking back to that time, it now seems to me that
he was frequently less playmate than slave. Slave to
my imperious whims; but it was a self-imposed bond-
age. I fancy at times I must have made of him a
veritable little beast of burden. All the tasks I dis-
liked to perform he would willingly undertake, in the
household duties which my mother had assigned to
each of us impartially. In my childish games and
plays he submitted to my dictatorial management with
a willingness of which I always took full advantage. I
ordered; he obeyed. Whether it was to drag me about
all day on a sled, or to haul many hundreds of heavy
rocks to build a stone wall around my playhouse (and
which—not finding to my liking—I had him tear down,
and take away), or to dam the creek to fish for min-
nows, it was always the same—I was the ruler, he the
slave.

How unselfish he was! I have a memory of the day
when, in gathering great branches of sweetbrier along
the creek's edge, as I slashed at the thorny shoots with
a sharp knife brought from the house, my eyes on the
pink blossoms, I did not see the little brown hand
reaching out to help me, and the blade struck the end
of his finger—taking away the tip and a portion of the
fingernail. Frightened at what I had done, the knife
fell into the stream, and I burst into tears. When my
mother came—attracted by my frantic wails of grief
—she found Frank trying to dry my tears and comfort-
ing me by saying: "Don't cry—please don't cry! It
don't matter; it—it don't hurt me a bit. Don't cry
any more. I'm sorry!" He was; was sorry for me—
and with no thought for himself. He had no thought

of his own pain while he beheld my remorse. Unselfish little Frank!

How his gaze followed mother as she moved about the room where he lay sick—so very, very sick—with typhoid fever! She had nursed him through weary weeks of an illness that wasted his small body to but little more than a skeleton; but he lived, and her nursing it was that saved him. This he knew without the telling; and in those days after the delirium had passed he would watch her with the look of devotion one sometimes sees in the eyes of a faithful dog.

So, it came to pass that we were unprepared for the change in him that time wrought. In justice to him I must say that he did not alter until there were changed conditions in the country. The first transcontinental railway came through the valley at the foot of the mountain, and it brought white people in great numbers; and these he came to know—the bad with the good. And somehow the bad influenced him most. The inherent traits of a savage race had not been so easily eradicated, after all. Idleness and slovenly ways took the place of the former ways of neatness and industry. The eager desire for knowledge gave place to sullen indifference. He had been gentle and courteous when alone with us; now—led by those who set an unfortunate example—he was cruel and insolent. The glib lie took the place of absolute truth; and where there had been honesty of purpose and action, now was deceit and artifice. He would go away; and returning, beg forgiveness, and that he might begin again with us as before. But it was not to be. By-and-by he went, and did not come home again—ever. He disappeared as completely as though he had gone out of the world; and all our inquiries of white people and Indians alike, through the years which followed, never

The Land of Purple Shadows

brought us any knowledge of him. Finally we gave him up for dead; and—as we do of the dead—we forgave him much that he had done.

Almost thirty years afterward—after he had gone out of our home and our lives—on a blue-and-gold day during one Summer that I spent in the arid country long after I had gone away to live where white people were, I was riding with an Indian woman along the ridge between two cañons, where we could look down into one and see the fallen walls of buildings which had been, for a time, my childhood's home. For a long time I sat on my horse, looking down at the silent and broken adobes, as memories came trooping back.

Then I said: "Come!" and we rode down into the deserted and dead mining camp of the forgotten years. We loosened the cinchas, and took off the bridles that the horses might rest, too; and on a moss-bank where wild violets grew we sat down in the golden sunlight, under that wonderful sapphire sky. The creek—that was fed all the year by the melting snows up—up—up at the peaks above—sang, and laughed, and danced its way to the dry sands of the valley. And birds that builded here sang too. Yet, somehow, I heard only minor notes in all the song!

Back, and back went memory to those days when, a child, I played through the sun or the snow with my little Indian playfellow.

The Indian by me was as silent as the gray adobes; for they are a people who respect your silence when you would be still. So she, too, was silent as I; and, like me, perhaps, was living in days now dead. Once again I was a small girl in gingham apron and stout shoes, building stone forts at the creek-edge, from which we rode forth to kill off whole tribes of hostile Indians. Then (but this as a concession to him and his race, and for which I expected him to be properly grateful) we would be the wild Indians, and the porphyry walls of the cañon would resound to our war cries, as we fell upon an emigrant train going to California. (What a little savage I was!) Then, when the lure of the chase was upon us, we would shoot the antelope, and deer, and mountain-sheep which our imagination created out of the white sage on the hillside, and drag our game to the campoodie of our family. (And I remembered how I had used a hair-ribbon for this purpose, and vainly tried to restore its ruined lustre afterward, lest it invoke maternal reprimand!)

Right there it was, in the rocks, that I lost my first penknife, and never found it. Such a beautiful knife it was—pearl-handled, and with four blades that would cut anything! Mr. Clark from the river had given it to me, saying I must not lose it; and then—I lost it, and neither Frank nor I could ever find it. Strange, how long one remembers!

And there is the place where he and I buried my kitten—under the wild rose, where the brookmint grows still. Or, he buried it; and I stayed home and mourned and mourned, and would not be comforted. Why does one remember such foolish things for three times ten years?

So the afternoon wore on, and in dreams and memories I lived again where I had lived in the days of gingham aprons and stout shoes. The stream and the bird sang on, while I thought of my childhood's strange setting, and the strange playmate of those years.

By and by I came back to the present, and to the Paiute woman beside me I told the story of the little boy of an alien tribe—of his baby days as I had heard of them from him; of his boyhood days as I had known them to be. Of his youth—his manhood, I knew nothing; he had come, and been of us, and gone. That was all I knew. When I had done, I said:

"I think Frank is dead."

In Indian-way she sat still—looking down at the broad levels of the valley below us. After we had seen the shadows lengthen, and lie against the walls of the cañon back of the adobes, she rose, and put the bridle on her horse, and tightened the cincha for the ride forward into the warm glow of the dying sunlight. When I, too, had re-set my saddle, and mounted, we came away from the old ruined mining camp and its haunting shadows of the past. Out on the mesa, loping slowly down, I was thinking of other things when the Indian woman spoke.

"I know that Frank. He no dead."

"Not dead! You know him?"

She was of another tribe; I could not credit it, for no Paiute had ever told us aught of him.

"Maybe some other Frank; are you sure?"

She nodded. "He live close up by that place call 'm Austin. Plenty times I see him. Every time he ask 'bout all you. He work plenty for white people. He good man. Everybody like 'm. He never git married. He never go back to Bannock country. He stay here all time—'bout one hun'ed miles up there. He never forget 'bout you family; he heap like 'm all you."

So he was living, and lived near that part of the country in which we had been much through the long years; and yet never a sign had he made that we might know of him! Yet he had not forgotten us, else he never would have asked of us whenever he met those Paiutes whom he knew. She said he "liked us—heap liked us." And she would not have said it, had it not been true. But he had never once in all the thirty years given one sign!

It is the way of the Indian.

(margin note: Subduing a Little Savage)

THE WONDER OF SUI SEEN FAH.

Y HORSE shied as the lightning flashed in our faces. There was a heavy crash of pealing thunder, and before the last reverberation had died away the big rain-drops began to come down on my riding-habit, while I urged him to still faster pace on the steep and rugged trail leading down the cañon.

A great rush of wind swept up through the gorge, bringing with it the slap of driving sleet. Nowhere was the footing safe beyond a fast walk; and my horse was already doing his best in making as rapid a descent as possible down the slipping, sliding rocks which were brightening their tints in the fast falling rain. Tall, dry grasses, and the brushwood on the banks of the creek, bent and swayed with the winds sweeping through the deep-cleft cañon. Birds with tip-tilted wings were buffeted hither and thither by the strength of the storm, as they fought their way to shelter.

It was one of those sudden storms which one may encounter up on the heights of a mountain ragged with shattered rocks, and cut into cliff and gorge; storms that may not last over an hour, at most, but which—while they do last—rage with a fury that makes them something not to be braved. So I looked anxiously

"There stood a cabin under the lee of the sheer wall."—Page 53

about me for some cover under which I might hide, and an overhanging wall where my horse could find shelter from the brunt of the beating rain-sheets.

Lowering my head to the storm, and looking out eagerly from beneath the brim of my hat, I saw nothing—absolutely nothing—offering the protection I so desired. I had about resigned myself to what seemed to be the inevitable, when a sudden turn in the cañon's winding trail disclosed to me the roof of a habitable building. Made of the jagged, unevenly broken rocks that littered the mountain's western slope, the chinks cemented with a rough plastering of mud, there stood a cabin under the lee of the sheer wall which rose from almost the very edge of the trail.

Riding quickly up to the cabin, I slipped from my saddle to the ground. As I did so, the rude door swung open, disclosing a little, lean, yellow-skinned son of the Orient, who seemed rather startled by my unexpected appearance.

"May I come in, John," I asked, "until it stops raining?"

"Certainly. You go inside. I tie your horse," was the reply, in better English than one usually hears from Chinamen.

While he was securing my poor, dripping, shivering beast, and fastening a rice mat over the saddle in an effort to protect it from further dampness, I entered the one-room dwelling, and found there two other coolies sitting before a stove radiating a generous warmth.

Both nodded pleasantly as they looked up, and one of them offered me a three-legged stool, asking me in broken English to be seated. This I declined, preferring to stand by the fire until I had dried my water-soaked clothing.

My eyes roved over the strangely assorted objects filling the low-ceiled room. A typical "China camp" of the West! Dozens of domestic utensils were lying about, ingeniously contrived from what must have been a meagre supply of manufacturing material. Surely the little yellow man has a wonderful ingenuity! A collection—vast, varied, and chaotic—of ill-looking bags and boxes were stuffed with articles whose uses were, mainly, unguessed by me. Odds and ends of clothing, American-made and of Chinese make, were tossed about. Foul-smelling fish, dried, and surely from China, hung from the rafters. Boxes of tea, mats of rice, vegetables smelling of earth and decay, together with the flotsam and jetsam of a placer camp, littered the mud floor. Bunks built against the stone walls of the room were strewn with blankets and quilts which had—strange to say—the appearance of cleanliness; while curled upon one of the beds was a cross-looking dog that eyed me evilly, without, however, raising his head. Chinese bowls and cups, with grotesque figures in gray and blue, were scattered about on the table. Like the beds they bespoke cleanliness. Standing on the table was an earthen jar of Chinese brandy and a pot of preserved ginger. An opium "kit" was in full view; and the air was filled with the mingled odors of opium, tobacco, dried fish, stove-smoke, and the heavy tuberose-like fragrance which exhaled from a great bowl of exquisitely beautiful Chinese lilies set upon a small shelf near the one window of the squalid room.

White as snow is white, with a center all yellow as gold; sweet as orange flowers, and altogether lovely, they seemed strangely out of place in the dingy, dusky stone cabin under the cliffs. It was as though a feather from some passing angel's wing had fluttered down to fall in the mud and mire of a sty.

My eyes went burrowing among the strange, shadowed corners of this habitation of creatures who seemed to me scarcely human. There was something wonderfully interesting in studying their environment.

With what squalor were they surrounded! And what barrenness of perceptions was theirs! They lived a life wholly limited to victuals and drink, sleep and rude shelter, totally devoid of Nature's poetry, or the beautiful in the world that is lent us by Art—the things that glorify even the meanest surroundings.

"Poor, ignorant, starved wretches!" I said to myself. "Life has never in the remotest degree—even once—touched their days with the finger of graceful thought, nor has the Creator given them the faculty of wandering through lands of delightful fancy. Hard realities, unredeemed by a single quality of poetic imagery (such as, consciously or unconsciously, we are ever adorning our daily lives with), make the sum total of their degraded existence. Animals all—miserable, soulless animals." I declared, "And yet we call them human beings!" And I sighed impatiently.

One of the little yellow men had been busying himself about the stove, and now proffered me a bowl of steaming, fragrant tea; for who can brew the bowl equal to a Chinaman?

"I makee you some tea," he said, pleasantly. "You dlink it, you no catchee cold, I thlink. You gettee plitty wet now; maybe you no dlink, you catchee sick. More better you dlink. You savvy?"

I "savvyed," and smiling an acceptance, drank the delicious beverage.

The third Chinaman nodded and smiled at me in the most friendly way; but evidently he spoke no English. The first one I had met now re-entered the cabin, and a moment later engaged himself in adding fresh water to the bowl holding the lily bulbs that were bedded in bits of sugar-white quartz rock. I noted how his slim, brown, tapering fingers touched with tender care—and almost lovingly—the tall shoots loaded with their clusters of sweet, white flowers. It was the month in which the greatest celebration of their year occurred, "Chinese New Year," and I knew that the blossoming of the lily, as it might be prolific or blighted in bloom, augured well or ill for the luck of the ensuing year to its owner. I commented upon the perfection and profusion of its blossoms, in acknowledgement of the pretty superstition. He looked up with a quick, appreciative smile.

"Yes, I think I have very much good luck this year. I guess I find plenty gold in the creek (I got placer claims here in Black Cañon), so that I get very rich and can go back to China and give my mother nice things. I be very glad, then."

He called my attention to a half-tone portrait of Li Hung Chang, evidently torn from the pages of some magazine, and which was now tacked to the wall above the lilies, and near the shrine-like shelf where a great number of burning punks and gaudy red paper slips gave evidence of an unashamed devotion to the religious observances of a people who shame our own in their infrequent prayers.

As I stepped nearer the picture to look closer at the peculiar face, so unlike anyone of my own race, I saw that part of the text of the article for which the print had been used as an illustration, was there; and my eyes caught the line: "Li has always been something of a mystic, a dreamer, a poet." (My lip curled derisively. A Chinaman! One of the same race as these little oblique-eyed men here? I smiled disdainfully.) "Dr. Bedloe thus translates one of his stanzas;" I read,

"Dragon, who rul'st the shoreless sea of death,
  When I lie dreaming on my loved one's lip,
And thou dost come to steal away her breath,
  O, take me with her on thy phantom ship!"

I stared. It was indeed poetry! Could it be possible that such a gem had fallen from the pen—a pointed brush rolled in India ink, and held by the long-nailed fingers of—a Chinaman? Had the four lines really found birth in the brain of a tip-eyed, be-queued, shaven-headed Celestial?—even the great Li—for a great statesman I must needs admit his being. But a poet—he, a Chinaman! Why, the sentiment—the music of the quatrain were something any man, white-skinned or yellow, might be proud to father. I was confounded—amazed! Ah, but then (I said to myself) his was an exceptional mind! He was not to be classed with ordinary coolies. His public life had shown of what unusual material the great dictator was made. I granted that—foreign as the idea had been to my mind before—he might possess the grace of poetic thought. He was a great statesman—therefore he might be, also, a great poet. But these men here in the mountain cabin—half dug-out, half hovel—they were of his race, but not of his kind; they were mere opium-smoking animals.

"You like that?" A voice broke in upon my musing. The little Mongolian was watching me with interest. "I can read some English," he said, "And I think that very good kind reading." He pointed to the verse. "But, not so good in English as in China." His lips moved as he whispered the Chinese words softly to himself. "Sound very pretty read that kind in China book."

I was mute. The little man, after all, could appreciate that which the great man had written; and I had but just said in my ignorance that these coolies did not know the charm of the beautiful! I turned away to the window, shamed into silence, and watched the drip, drip, drip of the rain from the casing outside where it ran in trickling streams against the glass.

Heaven was shedding a flood of tears in ceaseless weeping; weeping as though never, since the birth of time, had it known aught to grieve over until now, and was giving way to sorrow with the abandon of some young heart hitherto untouched by woe; wailing and weeping as if to wash the wicked old earth free from all its sins, and make it once more pure and clean as when it came fresh from the hand of its creator.

A cheap nickel clock, hanging against the wall, noisily ticked away the moments. Five minutes—ten —a quarter of an hour! Rain—rain—rain; and no promise of cessation. I came back and seated myself near the lilies of China, lifting my face to inhale their fragrance. How lovely they were! A cup of ivory with a heart of gold.

And then—? Then—! How it came about—how the story began, I do not know, nor how long it took for the telling; but, sitting there in that squalid cabin of Chinese miners, I heard for the first time the Legend of the Chinese Lily.

I do not know if he meant to relate the story to me, or if he was simply repeating to himself the lovely legend, as one repeats over and over that which is pleasant to the ear; nor do I remember the exact words he used in the telling of the tale. I only know that there—circled by strange surroundings, with the storm raging through the cañon and beating its water-wings against the window-pane—it fell to my lot, that afternoon on the heights of a great Western mountain, to listen to a fanciful story out of fairyland, and which

held me fascinated, and forgetful of all else in the
world as I heard.

And this was the story:

Long ago—so long that the world, and all in it, was
new; even as all now is old, very old—there dwelt in
that oldest of all lands, China, a man great, and good,
and with money and possessions too plentiful to be
counted. And he had wives—two, three, or four, as a
rich man may. But only the children of the first two
wives have to do with this story. Each wife bore a
son. And the first-born—he that was the son of the
first wife—was the father's favorite. But the second
son it was who loved the father best. This the sire did
not know, for the boy hid his great love; yet ever
obeying to the most minute particular each request
asked of him. For goodness, and honor, and duty, and
truth, for loyalty, and for love this son was one man
among ten thousand times ten thousand. But the
father went about with an invisible fold of cloth, bound
across his eyes by an evil spirit, which blinded him to
this noble son's worthiness. And the evil spirit removed the bandage whenever the father looked on the
elder son, and put, instead, before his eyes a magic
glass which made that son's vices seem as virtues, and
his treachery as loyalty, and his lies as truth, and his
deceitful bearing as love. So the father was ever deceived, and lived out the measure of long life believing
that good was evil, and that that which was evil was
good.

Then when the measure of his days was done, he
died; and the people mourned. For he had been well
beloved for his many virtues, and honored for his
greatness and his riches.

Now, when his father died the elder son fell to
lamenting; and he lamented loudly and long the first

day, and lamented less loud the second day, and the third day lamented not at all. For his heart was bad; and in secret he rejoiced that his sire was dead, for now all these great possessions would be his own. Money, and hills where the tea plants grew, and houses in the village, and rice swamps, and riches of many kinds—much of all—were his own. All that his father had left was his. All but one small bit of waste land far up on the side of a great mountain. A barren tract up there in a hollow of the heights was deemed of no worth; for it had never grown tea-tree, nor rice, nor grass, nor flower, nor weed. So this was the father's bequest to the younger son. For the law was that to every son a man had, must be given a portion—little or great—of his lands when he died; and to this son, to whom he wished to leave nothing, he could give no less.

To the elder and favorite went all else; but to the younger, who was worthier than any other child of China, was given but this tract covered with fine bits of broken rock, where no green thing had ever grown, and where the ground was dry and forbidding.

Yet against the unjust division this noble son rebelled not; but only mourned the father that was dead. Mourned sincerely—mourned without ceasing, and without comfort—that the beloved and honorable being was gone beyond the reach of his gaze.

Of the injustice done him—of the smallness of his portion of the inheritance—he thought little. His father was dead; his father whom he had so loved—whom he still loved beyond all expression—was gone from him. Nothing else mattered.

And days went by. The elder one went abroad among his newly acquired possessions, saying: "This is mine, now; and this; and this, also." And, because he was what he was, he forgot the dead man whose gift all these things had been.

But his brother, whose heart was heavy with grief, and who counted not the value of his portion, nor the lack, only longed to see his father's face once more.

Then the new moon came and looked down upon them both—the evil son, and the son who was good. And the moon grew to the full—lessened—and waxed old. And in the old of the moon the younger son journeyed to the mountain where his poor inheritance lay; to the miserable and barren land which was awaiting him.

His eyes looked with sadness upon it; not because of its barrenness, but that it was the last gift his father had bestowed upon him.

His heart swelled with sorrow; and tears which scorched and stung, flowed down his cheeks as he flung himself on the ground in his grief. He lay there long, so long a time he had lost all count of the hours, mourning as only they can mourn who are true of heart.

It was a great night, full of stars. A night when they burn like fire in the Heavens. A band—filmy and far—stretched across the arc like the ragged white smoke in the wake of a fast speeding steamer. Meteors shot through the infinite blue-black depth, and the vastness of space could be felt, like the presence of a thing alive, in the vitalized atmosphere.

Though he did not raise his head, he was aware that something most strange had happened. Though hearing no sound, yet he felt near him a presence.

Then a voice spoke to him from out the Heavens; and its vibrations fell upon his ear like the multitudinous cadence of birds in song.

"Why weep you?" the voice asked, and he replied:

"Because I loved my father, and he is dead."

"Though he is gone hence, he loves you in measure

now as you have ever loved him,'' he heard the voice say; and it sounded like the ringing of silver bells. And now his heart bounded within him with a great thrill of joy that a father's love was at last his. Yet it was in fear and trembling that he asked, falteringly:

"Even as he loved my brother?"

"Even as he loved your brother once; but he loves not your brother, now," the voice of music answered him. "The evil bandage across his eyes has been removed, and the magic glass is broken. He now sees into his children's hearts with the penetrating eye which belongs to the dead, and he knows the truth at last. Weep no more; your father sees you—touches you—loves you. And because of your faithfulness and loyalty through all trials, your reward shall be great. Here, where only sterility has been, shall henceforth be bountiful yield. Never again will the earth here be dry and barren; for your tears have wetted the ground so that for a thousand times a thousand years a generous moisture shall keep the plant-roots healthily growing. The prayers you have breathed here for the dead shall ward off all evil from the living—from you and the family that will be yours. The warmth of your true heart, as it has lain beating and breaking here on the earth, shall call forth blossoms of unearthly beauty.

"Dig into the soil, O, most dutiful of dutiful sons, and tell me what it is that you find."

And in the starlight the young man began scraping with his fingers; and digging, he found an unknown bulb.

"What is it?" asked the voice.

"A strange, new kind of root," he answered; "I do not know its name," and he covered it over again with the earth and bits of broken rock. Then once more the voice of sweet music spoke:

"Out of the land from whence your father looks

down on you here these roots came, sent by him in his remorseful love; and the flower which grows from the root and stalk is called the Flower of Filial Affection. Go, and come again the third day at noon!''

Then the young man went away. And when, at noontide of the second day, he came again, he was amazed, for green shoots had sprung up from among the stones that were now wetted with water which oozed from the ground.

The voice he had heard before, spoke at his elbow.

''What see you?''

And he answered: ''I see the earth rich with plant-life where it was barren before.''

''Even as your father now sees the living evergreen truth of your soul, where once his blinded eyes saw but barrenness! Mourn no more; go, now, and come again tomorrow, which will be the third day, at early morning light when the sun first shines here on the mountain.''

At early morning of the third day he came, as he was bidden; and lo! the air was weighted heavy with delicious perfume. It seemed to drop down from the Heavens and fall, fold upon fold, on the earth in inexpressible, ineffable sweetness.

All about him green plants were in bloom. From the root came the plant, and the plant bore a beautiful flower. From filial love, rooted deep in the heart of a man, springs all that is noble and good; and the reward of virtues in a good son shall be made manifest. The whole earth seemed to be covered over with blossoms of waxen purity—wax-white blossoms were about him where he stood, like the flowers of Heaven that we dream we see under the full moon. All the world seemed snowed under by petals of fragrance; and as he gazed in awe at the wondrous beauty of the scene, he shook with the intensity of his emotions. Moved to helpless weakness by the spirituality of what he saw, he fell upon his knees in worship of the great Power that had caused such exquisite loveliness to grow, and bowed his forehead on the ground.

Then, out of the Heavenly surroundings, spoke the voice.

"My son," it said, tenderly, and oh! so sweetly; and now he recognized the loved accents, for it was his father's voice that was speaking—that had been speaking since the hour he had first come to mourn on the mountain—"Oh, my son—son beloved—once a burden you bore, bore it with uncomplaining lips. Life has set no greater task for a child than to be loyal and loving in the face of injustice and misunderstanding. So, for this, your reward shall be great. Because of your heart's loving loyalty these flowers shall henceforth be made sacred to your race, and shall grow only upon this land of yours, and in that way be only for your family. Nowhere else—East or West, North or South—shall they ever be made to grow in the earth to the perfection of blossoming; yet here on this tearbedewed land shall they forever thrive, on this spot made sacred by your faithfulness. Yours, shall they be only; yours, and your sons', and your sons' sons, through all coming generations.

"The bulbs shall grow for you and yours to sell—for others to buy; and riches past all counting shall be yours. Greater riches will be yours than can ever come to him who is your brother. And now I go. Even as I love you I bless you; going hence to await you in that land from whence these white blossoms came. Farewell, belovéd child; most honorable son, farewell!"

And the one who was prostrate on the ground raised himself and—though he had seen nothing—knew that

The Land of Purple Shadows

the presence had gone, and that he was alone. But in his heart was comfort and everlasting peace.

This was the tale brought out of legend-land by the Chinaman for my charmèd ear to hear.

And this, and the poetic gem of the great minister—both alike, refuted my earlier conceptions of the race.

I could say nothing. It was a time for silence; but I think he understood, and knew how the beauty of the legend had entered my heart. For some time it was very still in the dusky little dug-out, then the older Chinaman spoke.

"Chinaboy, he no b'lieve him stoly tlue. Jus' plitty stoly; tha's all. That pla' in China country where flow' glow b'long all time jus' one fam'ly—more one hun'ed year b'long one same fam'ly. Chinaboy, he say same fam'ly like talk 'bout stoly; 'cause flow' nebber glow aly pla' else."

Only a legend. Only a story made by the fairies for children and these simple minded folk, who saw its poetic charm as did I. Only a tale brought out of lily-land for those to hear who have the poet-hearts of little children.

I was still under the glamour of the beautiful legend, when looking window-ward I saw that the storm had long abated. A shaft of yellow sunlight pierced the window-pane, and fell upon the lilies. I saw a speck of gold gleaming in the bright light, from one of the broken bits of pure white quartz. I touched it lightly with my finger, looking questioningly at the story-teller of the cañon.

He glanced at the one who spoke no English, smiling as he did so; the other said something in Chinese. To me the younger man said:

"My cousin have few gold specimens that man gave

The Wonder of Sui Seen Fah

him from quartz claim up in the cañon, and that been very rich—show much free gold in every piece. He want put all that rich kind in dish here, 'cause he say he think that flower lonesome in this country and want to go to China again. So he give best kind rocks he can get for this flower to grow in, and then the flower maybe glad, 'cause it know Chinaboy do best he can for it.''

Did I once say these people had no poetic feeling? Never again would I think so.

My eyes, too, had been blinded with the bandage of an evil spirit; but the gentle spirit out of lilyland had torn it away, and I saw in the hearts of those little people a fineness of feeling which vied with the delicacy of the gold-hearted snowy blossoms growing in the bowl filled full of snow-white stones, each bearing a golden star.

As I rode away from the little, low cabin at the edge of the mountain-trail, I was thinking that, after all, there is a quality in all peoples which answers to our poetic thought—even in the blue-bloused, bequeued yellow men—though I had been sceptical before.

Down through the cañon I went; riding over growing, young grass glistening with wet, and through brush which was dripping diamonds. Away below me, in the valley, a twin rainbow—big and beautiful—arched over the flats and meadows, across which my road ran straight to the hills beyond.

ONE DAY AT PACHECO'S.

THE air was drowsy with afternoon warmth, and the hills of the Coast Range, showing but blurred outlines through the violet haze, melted into the misty skyline. The sky itself was dappled with fine white clouds. To the West, where the harbor usually glistened and glittered under the yellow California sun shining out of a cobalt sky, today there was but a great sheet of water unruffled by any breeze. It might rain tomorrow—it probably would; and the wind would come tearing in through the Golden Gate, churning the bay into foam and washing away the soft pastels of the hills. But today it was a world of dreams. That is, if you were a dreamer. Here, at the water's edge it was bustle and stir. Of dreams, or of rainy days to come, no one thought—or cared. It was the day of a great race.

The steam cars, the trolleys, machines, everything on wheels, poured their thousands into the race-track enclosure, to see the pick of California horseflesh run. Nothing else mattered.

There were two who might have been taken for father and son, who were seated by themselves; the younger full of excitement, and trying to interest the older man in what most interested himself—the beauty and breeding of the three-year-olds, famous the world over.

The young man was twenty-two, and looked thirty. The other had passed three score and ten, and looked thirty years younger. He had seen life; he had loved life; it had kept him young. This is true of most Forty-niners.

"You think, because I don't grow enthusiastic over this horserace today, that I don't know what it is to enjoy seeing a good horse run, and a good rider keep his seat? Why, my dear boy, I have seen riding and running which stirred a man's blood so that this sort of thing wasn't to be mentioned in the same day with it.

"You men of another generation miss what we old fellows remember.

"While we are waiting for the start, let me tell you of a day—one day at Pacheco's.

"The Major and I had been over to Antioch, and on our return accepted the old Don's invitation to turn aside at his rancho, and witness the sport of a California Spanish gala day. Casa Pacheco was one of those big, delightful old houses of the early Californians, standing on rising ground in the center of the Don's domain, where fine live oaks dotted the rancho as far as eye could see. But no house of old Spaniard, or newer gringo, was ever big enough to accommodate the crowd we found there that day in July. Men and women were there thick as bees swarming about the place in the honey-sweet air. Tall, handsome caballeros, and pretty, plump señoritas, niños laughing for joy, and healthy as only those children can be who breathe the salt air that comes in from Pacific seas; old men and women with the fire of life still shining in their bead-bright eyes, though their skin was withered and flesh was shrunken; young men and girls, laughing and gay, and in love. These, and the Indians—scores upon scores of them—and the horses (such as you never see now on the ranchos), these, I say, made up a mass of moving, glowing life that day at Pacheco's.

"In the corral were two or three hundred head of wild cattle; steers, stags, and old bulls. Hot—untamed—restless—they surged back and forth in their narrow confine, while a perpetual cloud of light dust hung over them in the heat of the Summer sun.

"There was movement, excitement, life everywhere! The attitude of your race-track habitués here today would be called apathetic in comparison with what those flesh and blood beings—the old Spaniards—showed, and felt. Ah, my boy, you missed a great deal not being born at least a quarter of a century earlier! And I, too, would have missed it all, had I not sailed in through the Golden Gate before the close of the 'Fifties.

"Well; the crowd at Pacheco's had flocked in at his bidding from the country for leagues and leagues around. From Ciprian's, and Moraga's, and Briones', and from San Ramon, and Alamo, and Castro Valley. From Livermore they came, and Romero Valley, too; and Martinez. From everywhere that day the people poured in to Pacheco's.

"Every vaquero rode a good horse. Why, men like José Moraga and Martinez wouldn't have taken a double handful of gold slugs for any one of their saddle horses, and they numbered them by the hundreds! You never saw such horses, my boy, as we used to have in California—in the old days, in the golden 'Fifties. Great, big, fine animals; every one of them a picture. Made of muscle and bone, and—more than all—mettle. That was the kind of a horse a man rode in the days when to be a Spaniard was to be a first-class vaquero.

There were no "cowboys" then; the word hadn't been invented. Why, sir, the horses you fellows use now would fall down under the weight of the old Spanish saddles—the kind we used to have in the 'Fifties. They were embroidered with silver and gold threads; made heavy with such embroidery, and worked with silks in beautiful colors. The tapaderos almost touching the ground; and the saddles made with great machillas that half covered a horse. All heavily mounted with silver. Conchas on the spurs that were big as saucers; and silver chains jangling from the bit, to make silvery music.

"In those days a horse seemed to possess more intelligence than your horses of the present day do; and when he got fitted out with the fixings the old Spaniards used to put on, why, by George, sir, he carried himself like those who are of the blood royal!

"Everyone used to ride in the old days, just as no one rides now. What's that? You? You ride? Nonsense! What do you know about riding, when the most you ever do is to throw your leg over some pretty, prancing saddler for a short canter out through the park and the Presidio, or along the beach in the sunshine of a Sunday afternoon. Get on a horse—on a horse, sir—and ride in a storm, or at night, as we old chaps used to do, time and again, fifty years ago, and you'll wake up to the delights of some new sensations.

"I can remember riding at night with the wind shrieking in my ears, and the slap of sleet in my face as I rode neck and neck with the storm. Forked lightning flashing in my eyes, and a flying road under my feet; fording a river, finding my way in the dark through a cañon, climbing a hill, then descending into a gully—on, and on, in the night! Riding, riding, riding! Wet to the skin, but aglow with excitement and the electric current that made myself and my horse a

part of the storm and the elements! Ah, but it makes
a man young again only to think of it!

One Day
at
Pacheco's

"But you fellows who go for a gallop over asphalt
roads on days when it is sunny and pleasant, and then
trot leisurely home again to tell what you know about
riding, you—— Bah, what do you know!

"Eh? Oh, about that day at Pacheco's? Why,
that's what I'm telling you about. The young Spaniards there, who were to ride (and there must have
been a full three score of them), had their horses
trimmed up so, that it was worth a day's journey just to
look at them where they were standing, to say nothing
of what it was when they were responding to the touch
of hand and heel. That was one of the finest sights
a man could ever imagine, and one such as you never
have seen.

"The riders who were to take part in the contest,
where each would try to excel in the display of fine
horsemanship, sat in their saddles forming two lines
on either side of the opening of the corral. Lean, lithe
fellows they were, wearing their picturesque clothes as
only a Spaniard can wear them. Girt 'round the waist
with silk sashes; most of them a vivid crimson, but
some wearing blue ones. And every face was shaded
by the stiff, broad-rimmed sombrero worn with a chin-
strap, and tilted down on the forehead.

"The horses pawed at the ground, tossing their
heads and rolling their bits under their tongues. Quivering with excitement, and twitching their sleek skins
in nervous expectancy, they were as eager to be off as
were their masters.

"Then the bars were let down. The corral itself
was built like most of the old-time corrals—stockade-
fashion, out of stout limbs cut from the live oaks, and
set deep in the ground; and lashed together with rawhide thongs. There was no gate to swing easily on

oiled hinges, but big bars were lifted in place after the cattle were corraled, and lashed tight and fast with the rawhides. It took time to open or shut the corral, but what matter? The people of the Pacific had time —plenty of it—in the old days; with Indians in plenty to do their bidding.

"The bars down, an old steer (big, broad-horned, his eyes red and ugly, and his mouth slavering), comes to the opening of the corral. He stops. Motionless he stands, eying the multitude outside for a minute. His hoofs paw at the ground, and he moves a few feet forward, shaking his head and lashing his tail. Again he stops, and putting his nose down, smells of the uncertain ground; smells and snorts, afraid to pass through.

"'Vaya! Vaya!' The shouts startle him into action. 'Vaya! vaya!' There is a quick rush forward, and he is out in the open. It is a dash for liberty; and he makes straight away for the bottom-land, down where the oaks are the thickest.

"Then there is a shout from the people—and another —and another; and out of the crowd of waiting vaqueros, two (one from each side of the line), clap spurs into the flanks of their horses, and are off, after the steer which is running with head up and tail stiffened, at a pace which only a good horse can equal.

"But, look! One of the men is gaining on him! More and more—closer and closer—almost up to him —only a length behind—now half a length—ah! he is closing the gap—he is there, now; running with the steer, close side by side. Then—

"There is a quick movement of his arm as he bends low from the saddle, and (just how it is done, you cannot see) he has caught the animal by the tail, and

One Day
at
Pacheco's

taken a turn with it around the horn of the saddle. Spurring his horse, which leaps forward at the touch, he whirls the steer's hind-quarters around as horse and rider rush past, and—releasing his hold at the precise instant—the animal is tripped and thrown to the ground, where it rolls over and over from the force of the impact.

"A burst of cheers sounds from the hilltop; wild hurrahs for the victor.

"But the steer has bounded to his feet, and is up and off again. Away go the pursuers after it. They have forgotten the danger; their blood is stirred by the daring. If—at the moment of releasing the turns which have been taken—the long, strong hair should catch on the horn, and hold, horse and rider would be hurled to the earth with the steer. But this fellow acts quickly; and he is as cautious as he is quick, though in his picturesque grace he seems never to hurry. The supple figure leans from the saddle; there is a dextrous turn of the wrist, and the steer is down once more. This time thrown by the other vaquero. Again the air is filled with loud cheering. The Major and I are cheering, too!

"Cuidado! Look out, there! The steer is up again; maddened, and eager to fight; ready to make a quick rush and gore man or beast that may stand in his way. But, suddenly turning, he is off and away, and they after him; and again he is thrown. He is getting bewildered and exhausted from the repeated quick falls. Sometimes he starts up the hillside, instead of on down to the bottoms. He is dizzy and dazed, scarce knowing which way to go. Tired and panting, and with tongue lolling while the glistening slaver parches under his hot breath, he has no strength left to run.

"So—at last—they let him trot slowly off, while they

slowly turn back to rest themselves and their horses, and then—later—to follow a fresh one.

"But ere the bridle reins are drawn across the necks of the blowing, sweating horses, another wild yell goes up to the heavens; and another steer passes out of the gap in the corral, followed by two fresh riders. The two coming up from the bottomland—swing out—one to the right, to the left, the other—to give a free sweep to those who are charging like a whirlwind after the steer which is running straight to the lowlands.

"The bars are let down, and steer after steer is turned out—steers, stags, and old toros. And each is made to run a hard race for the freedom which is his when once he reaches the oak trees.

"There is shouting, and cheering, and laughing; and the vaqueros race down, and ride back, and rest as they sit in the shade and eat watermelons. Those who fail in the throwing are good-naturedly derided and jeered at by those who rest under the trees, and smoke, and laugh, and are happy—these children of a Summerland.

"Shouts, and laughter, and song; and the simple joys of a happy people! Losing or winning, the hours are golden ones that day in the blue and gold of a California July. That was back in the 'Fifties!

"And the winners? They found their reward in dark eyes; in soft, melting glances which bore to each victor a promise. As the two pairs of eyes met, a message sped—ere the long lashes fell on cheeks that blushed red with the red blood of youth—and a promise was given; for each knight had his ladye. All day —all day long in the warm Summer sunshine—

"Eh? What's that you're saying? 'It's a go! They're off!' Have they started? Bless my soul! so

they have. There they go! A good start! 'Gad! but
it's a fine sight to see a good rider on a good mount;
and the finest sight in the world is to see them on a
dead run!

"How I wish, my dear boy, you could have seen them
—that day at Pacheco's."

One Day at Pacheco's

UNDER THE CAMPANERIO.

DID you ever know the little old graveyard under the eaves of the Mission Dolores? Travel a full day's journey away from the city that lies by the beautiful bay whichsoever way you would, yet nowhere could you find another spot more full of peaceful calm and inviting beauty than God's acre under the shadow of the old gray church. It was a place for rest, and solitude, and dreams. No sadness was there; only the silence that charms—the quiet that soothes. Although it lay almost within the heart of the big city of busy, bustling life, comparatively few ever came to stand before the portals of the old Mission after they were no longer opened for service, or to pass within the cemetery inclosure when the dead were no more permitted burial there. One might, perhaps, sometimes see a solitary tourist walking slowly among the mounds, or a poet or a painter in sympathy with the quiet corners of the great town, or some mourner (gray, and wrinkled, and old) who had come to pray at the grave of some dear one, long dead.

Even in those days there were few new graves— already they were laying away their dead elsewhere. You tried to decipher the lettering on some of the moldering stones, but the carving had been eaten into by the years, and lichens and moss dulled the lines you could no longer read. Of the newer ones, none had been carved within a double decade; and these were scattered, and so few you could have counted them on your two hands. Here it was, more than a hundred years ago, that they buried the early Mission Indians who died believers in the faith to which (ere ever the gringo came to crowd them out of the land of their birth) they had been guided by the gentle teachings of the holy father—good Father Palou. Padre Palou— the first priest of the gray-walled, tile-roofed Mission with its graceful columns, and beautiful campanile where they—priest and peon, and soldier heard the bells ring out when San Francisco was born.

Above, where swallows darted in and out of the open belfry arches, you saw hanging the bells that were brought over-sea from old Castile. Over there, the women of Spain (so the priest told you), had, ere the bells were cast, flung into the hot, molten metal their chalices and chains of silver and of gold; and so these went to the making of that melody which rang forth from the shadowed campanile as the people of the new world came to San Francisco's first temple to pray.

Do you remember the pealing of those bells? If you are one of those who ever heard their clanging as you passed under the archway of the door to the cool shadows within, and you saw the shafts of golden sunlight slanting down from high windows to rest upon the bowed heads of devotees beneath—if you saw the filmy blue strands of incense float upward from the swinging censer, while you listened to the monotone of Latin words in chanting invocation, or the softer Spanish coming from the lips of the dark young priest —if you ever heard the Gloria swell from the recesses of the choir, where tenor notes (clear and sweet as the singing of the angels) thrilled you to your heart's core

with their melody—if you ever knew any of these under
the old tiles and rafters in the days that were, then
surely you have not forgotten.

And you remember how a time came that the church
was found to be too small for the numbers who gathered there to worship; and you know how it was soon
flanked by a larger, finer, newer edifice of red brick,
and the little Mission was closed. No longer did priest
or penitent pass within to prayers. Save only on Sat-
urdays and Sundays, of mornings—when the doors
opened to visitors—might one enter. Finally (so few
there were who ever came) it was not opened at all.
Good Father Palou had lain for more than a century
dead; time had made the Mission old—and us a forgetting people.

And all the while the work-a-day city had kept
crowding up to its walls, clamoring for the ground on
which it stood. It pushed back the graves where had
been buried—first, the Indians; and then the soldiers
(Spanish and American side by side); and then all
those others who may lie in consecrated ground.

. . . .

Years afterward, on a clear Spring morning when
the air was fresh-washed by the rain of but a day and
a night before, and the blue sky still held in its infinite
vault the great cumulus clouds which the wind had not
yet found to blow away, I went to see once more the
spot that was, so soon, to be a thing of the past.

The city authorities had decided upon cutting a
street through; and the dead must move on.

As I closed the little picket gate behind me, all the
rude sounds of the city's traffic seemed to be shut without. The din of the great living ferment echoed faint
and far. How very still it was! A hush that fell like
a brooding peace upon the fret of one's days! I wandered at will and undisturbed through the neglected

shrubbery, where the yellow shine of the morning sun was drying the rain-wetted grass and weeds. I suddenly felt myself far—very far—away from the commercialism of the world that was but just outside; that outside world which was stopped from entering in, as though the sword of a guardian angel at the gate forbade it coming further, a disturbing element which had no place in the garden of those who sleep, and where the old Franciscan Fathers walked in the days when they were hewing a way for civilization to tread in their march to the Western sea. How we forget them when we of the West boast of our deeds and our progress; how little of gratitude we give to those who made the way possible and easy for our feet!

The wooden fencing about the graves was rotting and awry; the iron red with rust. On marble and granite, moss (kept green all the year around by the wet fogs that nightly came in over Twin Peaks from the sea) had long since obliterated names and dates. Headstones leaned slantwise, and the flagging underneath was cracked and scattered. The church walls (boarded over to guard against the vandal fingers of relic-hunting tourists) were still lying in morning-shadow; but elsewhere the sun was shining warmly down from between the wool-white clouds which hung motionless in the California sky. It was drying the outer leaves of thick woven masses of vines it could not penetrate—climbing roses, growing wild; and jasmine, yellow and white, and ivy which held them together in its strong clasp.

The old churchyard had long been untended by man; but Nature was lavish in her care, and there had grown a wealth of glossy-leafed plants which ran riot everywhere, hiding what time had touched with decay. Such a wreathing and twining of tombstones with myrtle and ivy! Such thick growths of wide-bladed grasses as there were! They choked the old gravelled walks, and hid the broken flagging. Castilian rose-bushes grew as their own sweet fancy dictated—untrimmed, untrained, and beautiful in their fragrant pinkness. White moss-roses nestled against the weather-beaten wood of railing and fallen posts.

And so—under tall, wide-branching pepper-trees and cypresses that grew as Nature willed all trees should grow—I went, walking knee-deep through the rank, lush growth, and tangle of shrubs and unrestrained vines; only now and then finding some path made by the feet that went their way to the later graves.

I scraped the moss away, and spelled thereon names that marked the epochs of California history; and other names that belonged to far away lands. I came to the tall shaft under the eaves—close to the church's side door—where lies California's first Mexican governor:

Aqui yacen los restos

del Capitan

DON LUIS

ANTONIO ARGUELLO

Primer Gobernador del Alta California

Bajo el Gobierno

Mejicano

Nació en San Francisco el 21 de Junio, 1774

y murió en el mismo lugar

el 27 de Marzo, 1830

Farther along was a brown stone monument—quite the most conspicuous there; it was adorned with fire-men's helmets and bugles in stone. The shadows of

the drooping pepper sprays moved across its face as
I read:

SACRED
to the
Memory of
JAMES P. CASEY
who
Departed this Life
May 23, 1856
Aged 27 Years

———

**May God forgive my
Persecutors**

———

Requiescat en pace

Casey who shot James King of William—Casey who
was hanged by the Vigilantes! The stone was placed
there by the members of the famous fire company to
which he had belonged. It recalled a strange, wild
chapter of California history, oddly out of keeping with
the hour and the place.

But a few feet away I came upon a baby's grave—a
babe of sixty years before. On the white marble clung
a butterfly—slowly opening and closing wings splotched
in lovely color. It was as though that emblem of im-
mortality were the innocent soul come forth from the
mold into the sunlight of the incomparable day, unafraid of the shadows past or to come.

And there lay one who came from lands across the
sea. A wayfarer among a strange people, he lay down
by the Pacific's shores; and there had slept in alien

earth for a double score of years.   'Twas the tomb of
the Chevalier:

ICI

repose

PIERRE ROMAIN de BOOM

Chevalier de l'ordre

DE LEOPOLD

NÉ EN LELGIQUE

decedé a San Francisco

le 3 Mars, 1857

Age de 44 ans.

The myrtle—a tangled mass of purple bloom and
green leaf—had grown until it filled the square wooden
enclosure, stacking it railing-high, hiding the mound
completely.

Out through the little gate I passed, and back to the
world.   Softly I latched it, and turned away from
those who "after life's fitful fever" slept well; and
whose rest would be undisturbed, though the traffic of
a great city should roll above them.

IN THE DAYS OF HANK MONK.

OH, the fine, free days—the old-time days of the Sierra Nevada mountains ere ever they knew tie or rail, or the discordant sound of whistle or bell! When the long, brown road had many a twist and turn, and it was a joy to follow it in its windings as the six-horse stage swung around the grades on the sides of the pine-clad mountains! The day was never too long, nor the way too far, when one went with wine in the blood and song in the heart, in those years when we and the world were young. Time has grown gray, and we have grown old, and nothing is ever the same. The world goes round and round, and the years go over and over; but the cycles of progress bring us little compensation for those precious things we lost—and loved—when the open road was before us.

What did we care for discomforts, or delays, or the things which, today, annoy, and worry, and wear? We were young, and the world was our own; we were ready for any experience—for the rough-and-tumble of life and adventure.

Back, through the years, my memory goes to a trip I made over the mountains in the 'Sixties.

We were to cross the Sierras to a mining camp on the farther side, starting from San Francisco.

It had been raining incessantly for days, and the city's gutters were running with water to the curbs. Men hurried along bending their umbrellas against the storm; few women were seen on the streets. Rain, and wind, and the dirge of fog whistles on the bay! Not a well-chosen time for a trip into the very home of the Storm King! But—with that fine disregard youth has for consequences—we went up the gang-plank on board the old Chrysopolis, and began the first stage of our journey. Out through the gray rain, over the gray waters, she churned her storm-tossed way up the harbor, and into the Sacramento river. We ate dinner on dishes which refused to maintain their equilibrium, as the old steamer rolled and pitched in the face of the wind; and all night long, as we lay in our berths, we hearkened to the lashing of the storm. The wind was a gale; the rainfall had become a deluge. Yet we were undismayed at what was in store for us when we should be set into the heart of the mountains. Verily the faith of youth in youth's own ability to meet obstacles is a good thing.

Morning found us at Freeport (I wonder if it is still on the map?) but we found no abatement of the storm. Far as we could see, the country seemed a vast gray ocean. And out into the dripping sheets of wind-blown rain we went, and transferred to the State's earliest railway—a little stretch of track which later became (so I am told) a part of the Placerville branch of the Southern Pacific. But that was in the days before the Southern Pacific had come into existence.

Through the leaky roofs of those primitive coaches the water dripped; it dripped into the laps of the women, and down the backs of the men. Tiny rivulets found their way under the passengers' feet, as streams of rain found their way inside. Middle-aged pessimists stared at each other in gloomy silence, for now it was impossible to see anything out through the rain-washed window-panes. Optimistic youth found interest in studying the effect of the situation on the different temperaments, and in speculating on the depth of the snow in the high Sierras—for snow was a joy and a delight to the native-born Californian who lived down by the bay.

In the
Days of
Hank
Monk

Conditions did not change until the train (rocking from side to side over the uncertain roadbed, and dragging itself slowly on) came to the terminus of its thirty-mile run to Latrobe—a town somewhere in Eldorado County. The name comes back to me after these many years, but of the place I can recall nothing but the blur of rain. Here it was that—wading through mud and water which was over our shoe-tops —we again transferred; this time to one of the three six-horse stages which, together with a fast-freight wagon, evolved themselves out of the worse than Scotch mist. In these days we complain if a light shower leaves a dozen raindrops on us as we pass from railway car to covered motor-car at a station. The moving years make us hypercritical of our luxuries.

Once within the stage, where we packed ourselves and our small luggage in close quarters (for every seat was taken) quick fingers—outside—fastened us in, buttoning down closely the leather curtains; leaving us in a dismal half-darkness that was wholly eerie, but a delight to the young mind that wove stories out of the mysterious gloom, peopling it with creatures quite as real as the passengers who sat with hat-brims turned down, and coat-collars turned up, listening to the pelting of the storm. It seemed as though all the heavens had united their rains into one vast cloudburst.

The stages lurched, and rocked, and rolled their way up toward the mountains. Overhead, rain—rain— rain; and mud, and endless mud beneath us. Condi-

The Land of Purple Shadows

tions were too depressing to even permit of the exchange of jokes, and telling of best stories, that comes to those who are shut up in close quarters on a long journey. Only a girl—a very young girl—found it diverting.

Up the rough road, on over the uplands, across mesas and low hills, and finally the horses splashed along the roadway leading into Placerville. In those days it was full of bustle and life that even the drizzle could not dampen; and an interesting crowd stood on the platform of Wells, Fargo & Company's office where the steaming horses stopped, and the drivers unloaded, and took on mail. An interested crowd they were, too, for they peered curiously into the stage where sat a woman brave enough to tempt Providence by crossing the mountains during a midwinter storm. They stared at the woman and the very young girl; and the latter as frankly returned the stare of those in mud-spattered oilskins which shed oceans of rainwatery tears whenever their wearers moved this way or that. For three long weeks, they told us, there had been no cessation of the rain; not one hour of clear skies had there been. Business men—called across the mountains—reaching Placerville, had become fearful of what they might encounter beyond, and had not dared to venture, so had gone back to their homes at "the Bay." No wonder it was that those there found an interest in seeing the mother and daughter bent on essaying what men had turned back from.

Afternoon found the stages encountering less mud, as the road—now leading up among the pine trees and granite boulders— reached higher altitudes. Then climbing the "slippery ford" which all the old-time teamsters knew only too well. Ford indeed! A slope of granite had here inclined against the mountain, which was well-night impossible to cross. Like a plane of polished glass it had been for any man or horse to attempt to find footing on, until, the Stage Company had blasted off the smooth surface and, by macadamizing it, had given animals a foothold there. Even so, it was the dreaded spot in the road, and teams and drivers alike drew a sigh of relief when once it was passed. Our horses plunged up the so-called ford in leaps which brought more than one down with skinned knees, to at last reach the top; then on to higher lands, where the rain turned to sleet, and the sleet to fine snow. A bitter wind was in our faces, and the leather curtains which we had rolled up when the rain ceased, now came down again; and we sat in semi-darkness for hours till the creaking of the stage stopped, and our driver unbuttoned the curtains, saying cheerily: "Yere's whur we git supper and stay all night! Git out."

Oh, how good was the hot supper we sat down to about the long table in the "Strawberry Valley Hotel!" How the pine-log blazed! How delightful was the sleep that came to us in the warm, soft beds after the day-long ride punctuated with jolts and bumps! How hard it was to awaken before dawn, when thumpings on the panel of the door aroused us from deep and pleasing dreams, and to realize that the "Passengers for the sta—age! Breakfast in thirty min—utes!" was meant for us. Why, we had but just nestled into the soft blankets and clean sheets a moment ago—how could it be morning? But morning it was, though not yet daylight; and we ate breakfast under the yellow shine of the swinging coal oil lamps suspended above the long table. Someone came in from the street, shaking the snow from his overcoat, and stamping his feet to warm the chilled blood. Outside, we could see as the door swung in, it was yet dark. But when breakfast was eaten, and our luggage and ourselves again made ready for resuming the journey, and we went forth to take our places in the stages drawn up to the door, we found the dawn there, and all about was a great snowy world. Only ourselves and those engaged in getting us off, moved in the white silence.

Where were the wheels of yesterday's stage? These had been replaced by coach bodies set upon runners; we were to go sleighing over the summit! So into our seats, with the fur robes tucked tightly around us to keep out the cold; then to give the drivers free rein on the road!

Oh!——

And now befell the wondrous thing that made that ride the most memorable of all the trips in those, my early days!

It will not seem so wonderful to you of a younger generation, who know nothing of the glamor that hung about the heroes of that far time; but to those who lived in the old days, and who knew the old "characters" that belonged to the unspoiled West, it explains itself when I tell you that our own stage was to be, driven by Hank Monk!

Hank Monk, the incomparable! The most daring—the most reckless of drivers; and the luckiest. The oddest, the drollest of all the whimsical characters who made Western staging famous the world over. Hank Monk, the hero of the thousand-time-told-story of the great record-run he made to get Horace Greeley "there on time" when the great editor was to lecture in a little mountain "city."

In my mind's eye I see him now—his clumsy, awkward movements—his slow and bungling way of gathering up the reins, or reaching for the long-lashed whip. But, oh! the magic of his touch, as the horses answered the drawling "Gid-dap!" of the man whose

master hand they instinctively gave their allegiance to.
His fingers on the reins—a message went down the
telegraph-line of leathers, unread by us, which every
horse understood as a wire operator understands the
Morse code. They leaped forward into the snowy road
in answer, while I drew a long breath of delight. I was
riding behind six strong and splendid young horses
that were driven by Hank Monk!

It was a dream come true! I am quite sure that had
anyone asked me which of the two I would rather see
—hear—speak to, Hank Monk or the President (and
that meant Abraham Lincoln), it would have been the
former I unhesitatingly would have chosen. Without
doubt, my youthful judgment was biased, but the fact
remains.

Oh, the joy of that ride! I wish there was to be
found anything now, in this year of grace one thousand
nine hundred and nine, that could give me the delight
I knew that day!

Fresh horses every twelve miles; and every horse
"driven for all he was worth!" With the sharp air
stinging our ears, and the big white flakes whirling into
our faces, we awoke to the exhilaration of being carried onward to the heights of pines and firs, while Hank
encouraged his galloping team with the most unique
and amazing language ever used for such purpose.
From the bundle of furs on the box came that unceasing flow of words—forceful, grotesque and amusing—
which kept the six horses at a pace that put the miles
of lower roads quickly behind us. Before, and above,
was the mountain, a seemingly illimitable mass of the
softest of deep snow. Snow everywhere; underfoot,
overhead. Tamaracks, and firs, and pines were so
heavily burdened that the branches were bent downward till their tips were buried in the snow-covering of
the ground. Where the snowfall of a few days before

had half-thawed, and then again frozen, it had encased the spines and leaves of every tree on the mountain in a glittering crystalline network of indescribable loveliness; and all the while soft, new flakes were falling and weighing down the branches more and more, until —grown into great unwieldy masses—they would of a sudden tumble off, and the boughs—released of their burden—would spring up again, bare and green, to their wonted places.

Telegraph wires hung heavy; so coated with the frozen particles that—large as a ship's cable—they sagged from the poles; the buried poles themselves seeming to be great daggers driven hilt-deep into the bosom of the virgin snow.

The bells jangling their riotous music, the sleighs dashed through half a mile of white fog—a huge fog-bank that but made the cloudland scene the lovelier; for while a fog from the sea always seems to hide something that is dark and unlovely, a mountain fog in Winter suggests a whole world of white and radiant objects. Through that enchanted fairyland, walled by the clouds and the snow, over the Summit; past dark Tahoe (frozen and cold), out of the land of the pines, and tamaracks and firs, on, and still on we dashed; and so down the other slope of the mountain that looked into the Carson Valley.

Twice had the other stages gained upon us—twice had they passed; only to be, in turn, repassed by Hank and his matchless six. The snapping of the long lash cutting through the still air sounded like firecrackers on a Chinese New Year. He was putting his big bays to the utmost test of their speed, and now we were racing in earnest. Down the eastern slope of the Sierras we flew as though flung by some giant force from the crest of the mountain. The galloping horses leaped madly down, urged to renewed efforts by the cut of the lash swung far out over the leaders' backs by the driver, as in and out of ravines and cañons, swinging around sharp curves, tearing along the edge of precipices, where the slightest miscalculation would have hurled us hundreds of feet below, and where every turn must be figured to a nicety, we raced, and raced wildly— the snow striking back from the horses' beating hoofs pelted us like snowballs, while the sharp wind cut our faces like a whip-lash.

Twice had horses been changed since the race began. We had passed the other stages with a wild hurrah, coupled with Hank's jeers of derision; and the big animals jumped their length each time they threw their feet forward, gaining, steadily gaining—at every spring. Still was he urging them on. The pace was terrific for any but the best of roads—which this one was not; here it was the maddest of reckless daring to attempt it. No one thought of that now; for the spirit that had possession of all—the gambler's chance to win (or lose) dominated each one of us. To win! To be first in at the finish! The disregard of life and limb— the taking chances with death—it was all forgotten.

We were going like the wind when, without warning, we (horses, sleigh, passengers, driver and all), were flung into a tangled heap at the edge of the road, by the breaking of the tongue. But, Heaven be praised! it was at the upper edge. Hank had shot head-first into the soft snow, never losing his grip for one instant on the reins; and before the floundering horses could make the mishap any worse, he had been dragged out by the passengers who had topped the heap and were unaffected by the spill, and—though dazed a bit for a few minutes—in a marvellously short time he had straightened out the tangle, and spliced the broken tongue with short bits of rope, which, however, looked none too strong for safety. We were not yet back in our places when the rival stages and the fast freight wagon (racing, too)—exulting in our mishap—went by with whoops that would put an Indian on the war-path to shame, and we felt that the race was lost. We did not greatly care; for the little accident had brought us back to a world of realities, and we noted how far it was down to the bottom of the cañon. Our blood was cooling, and with it our ardor for racing along grades. "Go slower, Hank!" all cautioned him.

He shook his old head. "Why, I broke that pole on a purpose, so I could fix a jint in the middle; it'll turn sharp corners quicker." Importunities were of no avail. And, like Gilpin, away we went again; the "jint" working much better than might be expected. Or, it might have been we were too much occupied in keeping our seats to note precisely how it worked.

Faster than ever, now, went the team down the slopes of the Sierra Nevadas; and Hank shouted, and whipped, and swore his six whirlwinds into a fury of speed. The stage lurched from side to side of the road, and we swung perilously near the outer edge of the grade as the jointed pole snapped us around the sharp turns; but he only redoubled his yells and let the long lash sting the flanks of the flying horses. Faster and faster. It seemed the speed was like that of a comet, as Hank coaxed and cursed his living comets into a pace that was killing. We waited for them to break their necks—and ours. They did not. And no doubt they enjoyed the mad run as well as their master. Hank was too good a horseman to force them to their injury. And as to his language—— Why, he cursed his team roundly, but always lovingly cursed them. His oaths were terms of endearment which they and he understood.

Past our rivals we dashed, as we came down into the valley; and—in spite of delay and the broken tongue (or perhaps because of it), with the great Hank Monk driving them as no other stage-driver ever did or could guide horses—the six big bays were first in at the finish when we drew up in front of the Carson City stage office.

Stories of Hank Monk's driving are many; and these have grown threadbare with the telling. Yet there is no one who ever rode with him as he sent his horses on a run with that unerring precision which was surely a gift of the gods, but that recalls the old golden days with a longing for their realization again, and all it once stood for. To once more know the old delight that was half-akin to fear, when he sent his team along under the singing of the lash, up and down the roads of the Sierras!

The old stages are rotting by the roadside; and the old ways, and old days are forever gone. And Hank —Hank Monk (peerless, incomparable) lies at the end of the run, in the graveyard at Carson City.

Now we make the trip across the mountains in a few hours, where in the 'Sixties, it took as many days. We gain in time saved; but when all is counted and we balance the column, do we find we are really the gainers?

UP-STREAM UNDER A SUMMER MOON.

LITTLE waves slapped against the piling, sent hitherward by the craft plowing the Bay. Ships of strange sails, and strange names; other ships home from long months on the sea, and bearing the scars made by rough weather, rose and fell as they strained at their chains in the channel. Ferry-boats coming into their slips bumped against the piling which creaked and swayed from the force of the impact; and the planks underfoot—soaked with salt fogs, and smelling of bilge-water—trembled and shuddered in unison. Under the edge of the wharf, long green moss, and slimy sea-grasses brought in by the tides, writhed and coiled on the swell of each wave about the worm-eaten timbers.

But away toward the Northeast—up the Bay, and beyond the tangle of shipping—pink clouds hovered over the hills that were fair and sweet in their Spring-time freshness. All along by the Coast Range the light was like mother-o'-pearl; and out on the water (away from the wharves) the waves—freshened by the wind blowing in from the ocean—sparkled in iridescence. There, where the haze was like a pastel in pink, and lavender, and azure, the river came out of the blur of mist, and passed onward and out through the Golden

Gate, to mingle its waters with the salt blue of the sea.

Out of the shell-tinted mists, which were so elusive in their delicate coloring that they seemed not at all of this earth, but rather something brought from a world made of dreams, came a squat craft flying a pennant of black streaks of smoke, dispelling the illusion of un-reality.

Then I remembered that once or twice each week a flat-bottomed, stern-wheeled steamboat went its leisurely way up and down the river between the Bay city and Sacramento. Time was, when there had been no other means of transportation between San Francisco and the Capital city than this; but with the building of the great railway, the old river-boats had fallen into disuse, except for carrying freight, and were—by most of us—quite forgotten. Now and then, some country folk—living beyond the sound of the locomotive-whistle —who could reach the outer world by no other means, used the water-way. Or, some painter seeking out the picturesque bits off where the plains are yellow with sunlight, and the cañons swim in violet mists; or a hunter off for a week's gunning where game was still plentiful; or someone who (like myself) loved vagrant by-ways leading to vague places—these only sought out the little weather-worn boat for a journey through a day of quiet hours.

In the days of California's auld lang syne I, too, with the rest had gone up and down the river when traveling between the two cities. How long had it been? How many were the years since I had gone back and forth otherwise than by the railway? I tried to remember the last time; and with memory dwelling on the past, a sudden inspiration came!

Why not put back the hands upon Time's clock? Why not once more go up the river in the old way—as in the old days?

What if I did have my transportation by the other route? What if my sleeping-car berth was secured? What if it would be paying two fares; and losing time in getting to my destination?

I did not want to save time; rather, I wanted to squander it. Of a sudden I felt rich; rich in the capacity to live and enjoy! Let the train pull out of the station which, like the head of a great snake lying in the water, rose at the Oakland side of the bay. I would none of it! I could take up my journey again on the cars from Sacramento. There was no need for me to go tearing through the valleys at steam-speed, through the dust and the smoke, as though life itself depended on haste. Let me go back to the old peaceful, leisurely ways, ere I had fallen in with the world's mob of mad people who hurry their days away. It was so easy to drop out of it all—if I would; and I wondered why I had never thought of it before.

So it came about that on the morrow, as the little, out-of-date steamer lay at the wharf, I went aboard as a passenger; and the venture was so new and so unique that I felt I was embarking on some long and mysterious voyage.

Unhampered by any luggage (for already it had been sent forward on the railway-train) I had nothing to burden myself with but the small handbag I carried.

How jolly it was! I felt like a truant schoolboy with a day's stolen delights ahead of him. The very fact of its unusualness gave to it the zest belonging to things delightful, because forbidden. I smiled as I recalled the perplexed amazement of friends to whom I had confided my intention of going up the valley by steamboat. "What ever induced me to do such a thing? Were no trains running? What had happened to the railroad?" No one could understand.

I went over to the rail, and looked down on those who

were following me onto the boat. Who were they— what were they like—these people who (like myself) chose these little-used water-ways?

If I were to be on board for three or four days (for I had been duly warned by my friends that the boats had a way of getting on sand-bars, where they remained indefinitely) I wanted to get a comprehensive view of my fellow-voyagers.

There were two or three ranchman (looking as though they might be transplanted Middle-West farmers) in the too-evident discomfort of their seldom-used "city clothes." Equally evident it was that they had been down to "the city" to sell their crops (what, I could not determine), and were now gladly—so gladly getting back to their homes. The work, and the wives, and the children were awaiting them. I fancied I could see the delight of the latter when they would be given leave to untie the strings and unwrap the packages the fathers were bringing. Each was so loaded down with packages, and parcels, and bundles, that he looked like a veritable Kris Kringle. Good fathers—good husbands—good neighbors, I was sure.

Following, came two others; but young men—clear-eyed and alert. Splendid fellows they seemed, and unmistakably of the cities. They were shod for long tramping, and both wore trousers of corduroy and brown canvas hunting-coats showing the stains which come from much service. Each carried a gun-case, and one led a beautiful liver-colored setter—her silky hair shining like polished copper in the noon-day sun; her body a-quiver and her eyes a-light with expectancy. What a glorious fortnight was ahead of them—for the dog, and her masters! The happy wag of her tail told of the hunting-dog's delight at getting out of the city —at the prospect of going far a-field at the heels of the

The Land of Purple Shadows

hunters! And her pleasure but echoed that of the office-man, off for his yearly vacation.

Good luck to you! and a happy, care-free two weeks, with a full game-bag at the end!

Up the gang-plank wobbled a Chinese huckster, staggering under the load which filled two huge baskets hung to the balance pole over his shoulders. He had been to the city to renew his supplies for working the acres he leased from some big land owner. He was through with the business—and the pleasure; now back to the valley! Doubtless he had smoked many pipes with his friends and his cousins; without doubt he had gambled. In my mind's eye I pictured his week in that part of the city given over to the immigrant people of China.

Yen-she, and the fan-tan game; and then back to his labors!

There was no mistaking the couple that came next. Bride and groom going home from the honeymoon! Home to the new house—to the new life. With the other things he carried (she was carrying half of the luggage), was a four-horse lash-whip, and two new, shining shovels. I looked at his hands. They were the hands of the man of the fields—broad, freckled, and hardened. His face was burned by the wind and the sun—all except where, under the edges of his short-cropped hair, about his ears and at the back of his neck, a narrow, white, untanned line marked the recent work of the barber. How pretty she was! and how young she was! I hope they were happy—that he always was kind to her.

Just as the gang-plank was to be drawn away, a father, with two little girls came hurrying on, and behind him trotted his panting wife, carrying a fat baby on one arm and leading a very small boy by the hand. Closely following were two older boys. The family with all their belongings seemed to fairly overflow one side of the deck. Such radiant, beaming faces! Such radiating joy! Later in the day, sitting near them, I was an involuntary listener to their unceasing reminiscences of an unclouded week of pleasure, together in "the city." How happy they were—these people who travel the by-ways!

One or two more hurried on board, and then I heard the churning of the wheel. Turning, I saw a strip of greenish water edged with froth and foam, where the plank had been. The up-river boat had started.

Out through the craft crowding the San Francisco shore; out, into the beautiful bay encircled with violet hills; out past Goat Island's rocky steeps and grassy hollows; past Angel Island's smooth green hills, lovely in the Summer sunshine, and where, beyond her outlines, we could see Alcatraz—the Sentinel—standing watch and ward over the Golden Gate! Past the other lesser islands, and the scattering ships that lay at anchor in the harbor!

As the boat moved slowly up the bay I gave myself up to the quietude which reigned—the peaceful delight of the idle hours.

When the day had grown into late afternoon, and we had passed sleepy-looking Benecia at the head of the bay, the wide sweep of the water narrowed until the little steamboat found herself between the banks of the Sacramento.

Golden California! Where in all the world is her like? There were pictures all around me. Here, Nature usually in her landscapes uses strong color, laying it on broadly with a full brush; but that day it was a gallery of pastels with which I was surrounded —soft blendings of delicate colors. From desert levels to the land's edge where the sun drops down into the sea, never could you find more exquisite coloring than that with which we were surrounded as the late day found us far up-stream.

We had answered the call to dinner—a savory meal, wholesome and appetizing—of the sort which one finds in country farmhouses; and when we returned to the deck it was to behold a magical transformation. A golden mist (perhaps it was the river-damp showing yellow in the light of the dying sun) rose all about us to glorify the atmosphere. We seemed to float through a gilded sky.

When twilight came, it turned to gray, to again be changed by the white full moon to a silver haze when she had taken her place in the heavens after the sun had melted into the rim of the Western sea.

Surely, never since the beginning of time—that fourth day of Creation, when there was made the "light to shine by night"—could there have been more ferfect hours of white splendor than were those when I saw the ordinarily prosaic Sacramento river under the full Summer moon! The silvery mist rose about us, far and wide—softening, but not hiding the landscape. Objects along the shore—long reaches of tule-land, a deserted house set at the water's edge, an old boat-landing—whatever they might be that went slipping silently by us as the splashing wheel pushed the little steamer up between the low banks of marsh-land meadow—all were transformed by the magic of the moon's white light, and through the filmy veil became part of that scene of unsurpassed glory, where even the willows fringing the banks showed with theatrical effect, like the tinselled trees of a Christmas play. At times, deceived by the distance which lay between the guard-rail and the faintly marked lines of the shore, we would smother a cry of alarm at what appeared a too-close approach to the banks, and the danger of collision. Crossing from side to side to avoid the strong down-sweep of the current, as the steamer zigzagged her way up the stream, we seemed to fairly brush these objects which so unexpectedly loomed up before us, where in the deceptive lights of the night-time they arose from the shore in exaggerated size.

Up Stream Under a Summer Moon

The air was full of the blended indescribable sounds of a Summer night; and through it all one could hear the croaking of frogs, the brave sound of a distant watch dog's bark at a farmhouse hidden behind some mystic grove of trees, or the splash of a great fish leaping high out of the water in sheer joy to greet the white Lady Moon. Once, as it passed just above me, I heard the squawk of a mallard flying low, and it seemed I could almost feel the eddy of air which was struck aside by the sweep of the strong, swift wings.

Now and again the boat swung in to the shore, to leave at some little landing, a passenger or a part of the cargo. Many of these places looked so deserted that one wondered if anyone would ever come to take away the freight; wondered where those who disembarked would go when they went out into the vague uncertainty of the distance beyond the shore.

The broad valley land about us seemed so peaceful and idyllic in the moonlight, so quiet in its remoteness from the fret and jar of the busy mercantile world, it was hard to realize how the morrow and daylight would show grain-fields reaching away to the mountains, with thrifty orchards scattered here and there. Morning light would reveal the homes of a hundred farmers, and green pastures where—under the spreading live oaks hung with their gray cobweb moss—fat cattle and finely bred horses would be feeding in the clover growing knee-deep. It was hard to believe it now as the boat glided up a river which glistened like a stream of running quicksilver.

Puck and Titania were there; Mustardseed and Peas-blossom, too. They had trooped down to throw over it the spell of enchantment, and transform it into a land for the fairies and the elves. Softly fanned by the sensuous night wind into a delicious languor, one wished with all one's tired soul that there might never be a return to the bustling world, but that this might go on forever.

Sometimes we approached the banks so closely that we caught the sweetness of the garden flowers as we passed on our way—mignonette, and old-fashioned roses, and candy-tuft borne to us in heavy fragrance on the night air. Just there, where shone the lamps in houses built close along the shore under tall eucalypti, we saw a woman bending over her work, her face all in shadow. Just as the picture was passing beyond our line of vision, she rose quickly, and as quickly went toward one who came in, taking her in his arms. And so the stories were repeated to us all along our night-journey up the Sacramento!

One by one my fellow-passengers were leaving me. Among those first to go were the father and mother, and the six hearty, happy youngsters. A smiling, sweet-faced girl all in pink, greeted them where they landed; her dress making a bit of color there like a wild rose in a hedge, as she stood in the glare of a great oil lamp swinging above her—a light which showed garish and out of place in the moon's chastened lustre.

At each landing we left them in pairs, or singly, until all were gone save myself, and the two men in corduroys.

For another hour I sat on the deck, watching the few passing steamers gay with lights—white, green, and red—that were taking their places in the lovely river picture. Going down to the harbor city, they were carrying to the markets the fruits and vegetables raised in the valley. One passed, with military prisoners being removed to Alcatraz. There was a glimpse of uniforms, and glintings of steel; then it, too, faded into the rainbow river-mists.

And the dream went on as the hours went by, but one never had their fill. Finally the Spirit of Sleep began softly pressing lids down on eyes that never grew tired. Reluctantly I went to my wee stateroom, to go from one dream into others. And though the last thing I was conscious of was hearing voices outside my stateroom window, where the canvas and corduroys still sat talking together, and I heard them tell of a wonderful catch of Dolly Varden trout in the McCloud river, and of a glorious month there among the California pines, and other incidents connected with a very material hunting and fishing trip of the previous year, yet when I fell asleep, it was to dream that a gold and jewelled spider spun a silver cobweb across the sky, and that Titania and the fairies danced upon its slender threads.

When I awoke in the morning and sleepily opened my eyes, the little stateroom was shining with the yellow light of an early Summer morning's sun, which filtered through the shutters in fine golden grains.

The steamer was lying quietly at the Sacramento City wharf, and as I lay with lazy eyelids, I heard far church-bells ringing for early Mass.

JACK BRUIN: THE GOATHERD.

AR up on the side of Cerro Colorado, where you may stand (if you can find a footing—so steep are its rocky slopes) and look away off into the lovely valley of the San Joaquin, lying down beneath you; far up above the snow line of Winter, among the California pines and manzanitas, there was living a little more than a score of years ago, Lewis Ford, solitary and alone, but for his flock of eight or nine hundred goats, his half dozen horses, and Jack.

Jack was a bear.

Eight years previous to the time I write of, Ford had found the little, shining, black cub—soft and round as a ball—and had gathered it up closely to his breast, carrying it to his lonely log-cabin as tenderly as though baby Bruin was the fairest foundling ever born under the perpetual blue of California skies.

Neighbors he had none. Visitors were creatures almost unknown up there where a wagon road was an impossibility, and where Ford's own stores had to be carried up on a pack-horse that picked its way carefully along the dizzy trails.

The real love of solitude is an acquired taste. Man is, generally speaking, a gregarious animal; and if he

"The bear was trained to herd the goats as the shepherd dogs had done."—Page 107

cannot mix with his own species in his own way, he will—instinctively—turn to the companionship of the four-footed creatures of mountain and plain. So, Ford —wifeless, childless, and alone—on the heights of Cerro Colorado, sixty miles away from Mount Diablo's snowy summit, took into his home the little wild waif of the mountain, and which, as the years wore on, won its way into the heart of the lonely man.

But opening the cabin door with a "Salve, Bruin!" was not all there was needful to be done in so serious a matter as adopting a very immature bear. Jack had to be provided with a foster-mother; so a frightened, trembling, bleating she-goat was brought to the house to take the place of the parent he so missed. It was only after much combined force and persuasion that "Lillie" could be induced to adopt as her own, the very un-kidlike orphan placed in her care. But finally the time came when foster-mother and foster-child were as happy and content in their relations to one another as if the sight of a nimble-footed, blue-haired "Nanny" suckling a clumsy black bear-cub was of the most ordinary condition of affairs.

Jack waxed fat on goat's milk; and a more docile, tractable beast never grew up under the guardianship of a humane and loving master.

In the earlier days of his adoption the baby was a baby in truth. He refused to be left alone. And it would have been a harder heart than Ford's that could have resisted the pitiful whimper of the little fellow whenever he thought that he was to be left alone in the cabin.

Had there been any to see it in those days, they would have witnessed a strange sight. The great, broad-shouldered man following his flock as they grazed on the bunch-grass—sometimes five or six miles from home—and as he walked the steep mountain-side where it was so almost perpendicular that it seemed only the goats themselves could gain a foothold on the rocks, he carried the cub in his arms. Those arms grew very tired many a time and oft; grew tired with the growing weight of the pet that was getting "muy gordo," but Ford would not leave the little one to mope and mourn at home, and perhaps be stolen by some straggling stranger in his absence. Sometimes a stray hunter came that way, and Ford would take no risks.

Ford was a worker, and he felt it was only right that his charge must learn to work, too. Bears without number are taught to dance and do all sorts of amusing tricks; but this was no city bear, to waltz to music and hold out a hat for a dime. He was not to be taught accomplishments, but how to put his efforts forth in acquiring useful knowledge to be applied to the daily duties at hand. So Jack's playdays were over. He had become a big boy, and must go to work, as other boys in the families of the poor. So farewell to the days when there had been nothing but play! For Jack, there had been playdays in plenty, and playmates; just as though he were a boy instead of a bear.

There had been times when Ford left his flock temporarily in care of a herder—Leandro, the Mexican, from the other side of the mountain, forty or fifty miles away—and then Jack and Jack's master went off on jaunts, when the master hunted with rifle or shotgun, and the bear chased rabbits and squirrels—digging into their holes till he captured them. Sometimes their way lay across the mountain to Leandro's own place, and there he would make friends with the children as if he himself was a child among them—romping with Carmelita, and Rosario, and Petronilla, and even playing with baby Ramona, without so much as a single rough stroke of the great clumsy paws. If—

tired out in play—they threw themselves down on the ground, he too would drop down, his huge body across their feet where they sat; and when sitting on the edge of a pond, one day, they shoved him from where he lay sprawled out on their dress-skirts, anchoring the children to the ground, and the push they gave sent him into the pond, he displayed no other evidence of anger than a little growl of rebuke as he shook the water off after he had climbed out. With the boys he would box and wrestle as two boys will when playing together. Sometimes it was the bear that was thrown —sometimes little Leandro.

All these things came to an end; and Jack was trained to herd the goats as the shepherd dogs had done. The dogs, in time, were given away—for Jack could never be made to feel that dogs were other than his avowed enemies; and fights—frequent and fierce— were the result of their associations.

The dogs went; and Jack stayed. But he was made to take their place.

It was wonderful the aptitude he displayed in learning to dispense the duties of his new position! True, there were times, when being initiated, that he played the truant; and was found away off among the manzanitas, breaking off great branches and eating their dark and shining berries. But that was in the first days of his responsibilities as assistant herder—before Ford had trusted him alone with the goats, and made him herder-in-chief. However, a time did come, after much patient teaching, when—true as a soldier to his trust —Jack was the faithful guardian of his master's flocks, and earned the title of ''Jack, the Goatherd of the Cerro Colorado.''

From sleeping in the cabin at his master's side, he came to sleeping in the gateway of the corral. An

Jack Bruin: The Goatherd

army could not have invaded the goats' stronghold with the black bear on guard.

Nor was the tending of goats his only duty. He carried all the firewood into the log cabin and laid it down by the stove. The halter ropes of two or three horses would be put between his teeth, and he would lead them to water, and back again to their mangers. Strange horses, like human strangers, were terribly afraid of him at first sight, but Ford's horses knew him as they knew Ford himself.

One day, when breaking a two-year-old colt, Ford was obliged to go into the cabin for something needed, and there being no post nearby which was handy to tie his horse to, he gave Jack the halter rope to hold. The horse was unused to the bear, and, after Ford left them, became thoroughly frightened, plunging and rearing about the yard. But—though the strain was severe—the iron jaws did not relax, albeit the little bear was dragged ruthlessly to and fro, valiantly tugging at the other end of the rope.

There were times when they would go on a hunting expedition, miles away from home; and Ford would leave his horse and saddle, and the raw meat for his luncheon (to be roasted over blazing cones, by and by) and numberless other things in Jack's care. The bear would as little think of touching that raw meat as he would of attacking Ford himself. And the horse would be found herded not twenty feet away from the exact spot where he had been left to graze, with Jack walking around him in a circle, that he might keep his charge well within the limit of his pasture.

If Ford must go down to the valley—to Livermore, fifty miles away—a goat would be killed and given to Jack for food, with instructions to look well after everything while he would be alone with the herd. Who shall say that the words Ford used were not as well understood by Jack Bruin as if the message had been given in the silent speech of bear with bear?

And is it a matter of any wonder that those two loved each other as man rarely loves his fellow-man? Does man find his fellow-man so faithful—so steadfast?

By and by a day came when Ford sold the goats. He sold the log-cabin, too, where—among the Pacific pines and manzanitas—for a double decade he had almost lived the life of a hermit.

He was growing old. A sister and a brother across a continent, and far beyond the ocean that laps its Eastern shore, were waiting for him to come home. So there came another day when Ford loped his horse slowly—lingeringly—down the lower slopes of Cerro Colorado, and the black bear came loping at his heels; loping for awhile and then stopping to rest, and lying out as flat as if he were stone dead—then getting up again, and going on to where Ford waited for him.

When they came into the town and the people heard that Ford was leaving the country never to return, a hundred offers were made to him for the bear that had never known muzzle, nor chain, nor collar.

"No," said he, "where I go, Jack goes. If, when I get to San Francisco, I find that I can't get a passage for him on the steamer with me to New York, and another one when I get there that will take him across the Atlantic, why we will both stay on this side."

That was more than twenty years ago. Since then, letters have come across the seas from Ford. And Jack is with him.

THE TRANSFORMATION OF CAMP McGARY.

UNJUST, because untrue, is the implication: "As dirty as an Indian!" How often ones hears this expression used by white Americans who travel in cars through Indian-land! Aye, and how often (although knowing better than to be such a sheep) have I, myself, made use of it! When you, or I, have said it, we referred to the bodily uncleanliness of our brothers, the First Americans. As to the dirt of the camp itself—the hogans, the wickiups, the teepees, are mostly, I grant you, dirty. It is dirt without any disguises; but wholesome and healthy in raising large families, if one is to base one's belief upon the living statement made by the fat, roly-poly bits of bronze that tumble about the place playing with the puppies, and emitting such gurgles of laughter that your own heart is set singing at the sound.

We who are chiseled out of white marble do not take kindly to the lack of perfect cleanliness we sometimes find in our brother who is cast in bronze; but as it is mostly the dirt which can be cleansed with a bucket of water, or removed by a broom, let us try to forgive him. It might easily be worse—but it isn't. As to himself, Lo keeps his own body clean by way of a bathtub as thorough in its methods as your own.

Come with me. Let me take you with me across valley and plain—riding long hours, with the wind in your face and the love of life in your heart—away and away o'er the open road, to the range of mountains where, by the edge of the lake with its lava rim, lies old Camp McGary. Incidentally, I will tell you of Indians and show you their bath houses. It may be that you will say (when I have done) that I have told you how Lo bathes, and have but casually mentioned the old fort which was abandoned by our soldiers years upon years ago. Whichever way it may seem to you is immaterial. At least, let me prove that Lo in general, and Paiute Lo in particular, is often traduced. Come, and I will show you a beautiful bathing-place (and there are hundreds more that are to be found like it) where the folk of Caracalla's time, or any other luxury-loving old fellow of those other old times— though having more luxuriously appointed bath-houses —could never have been made cleaner.

Away up near the top of a volcanic mountain (which is all blended blues and violets till you reach it, and all greenish-gray with sage, and mottled with mountain mahogany when you do) lies a lake, long and narrow, cold and clear. Soundings have never found bottom. It lies on the shoulder of the mountain—almost, but not quite, at the top. By the white people it is called "Summit Lake," but the Paiutes have a very much better name. It is the lake best beloved by the Paiutes; not because of its trout (yet where else are their like to be found?) but because the white man considers the place as one too remote for him to think it worth his while to encroach on his brown brother's domain. Also it is cool—deliciously cool there all through the hot arid Summer. I have known fresh snow to whiten the peaks in August. All the year the creek runs bank full, and cold as ice water; for the snows, melting, send a stream—such a stream of beauty and song—down through the cañon to fling itself joyously into the arms of the waiting lake.

All up and down the high slopes are antelope and deer—not scattering ones, but large herds. Still higher, where the rocks are, live the big horn—the Paiute's favorite game.

If you go there by the creek when the morning sun first finds it, you will hear the rush of wings—the partridge-like whirr which, if you are a sportsman, makes your trigger finger itch for the touch of a shotgun—and dropping down by dozens and scores come sage-chickens gray as the sagebrush that here grows tall as the willows, and wild gooseberry and rosebushes that border the banks.

This was a favorite haunt of the brown man long ago. He lived here and found it good in the days when his name was a terror to the emigrant whose wagon crept down the valley beyond. This is the place his great-grandchildren seek today, loving it no less than did their grandsires.

A little less than half a hundred years ago, men wearing the old-time soldier blue, marched here and, at the creek's edge, built around three sides of a hollow square the substantial stone and adobe buildings that made their shelter in the days when they went a-fighting the bronze men of the mountains. When they came, the brown man drew back and away— farther and farther, till there was no more need of soldiers to protect the scattered settlers, or the emigrant down below, winding his way Westward. When the bronze man melted away—like a campfire smoke blown by the wind—the man in blue went also. There was no further need of him. Only the houses he had builded, remained. Afterward—a very, very long time afterward—the bronze man came creeping back.

Quieter now, and wiser. What use was it to take up arms against a foe that could not be counted, so great were the numbers? Back came the brown man, and to the empty and deserted buildings of the fort.

Would you see it today? The walls shows the wear and war of the years and the elements, but the name of the old fort survives—Camp McGary. Still are the buildings inhabited; but those who go in and out of the officers' quarters, or greet you at the door of the guard-house, or whom you meet on the parade ground, do not wear the soldier-blue. The Indian brother has sole possession of the walls which were upreared against his arrows, and by those who strived for his undoing.

It is here the Paiute today is happiest when he hunts and fishes; here he lives, and loves, and—yes, bathes!

Down by the creek-edge, fragrant with the breath of sweetbriar and mint and plum-bushes a-bloom, is something that attracts your unaccustomed eye. Bent willows, stripped of their branches and leaves, have been thrust—each end—arch-like into the ground, forming the framework of a tiny dome-shaped structure whose uses you are yet to learn. Willow bands hold it together—tied at their crossings with the willow hoops with thongs of buckskin or bits of bright cloth. This one is perhaps four feet in diameter; not more than two-and-a-half high. In one side there has been left an opening—large enough for a grown person to crawl through. The floor is smooth and clean, and beaten hard. At one side is a deep hollow in the ground—bowl-shaped, and plastered with a sort of cement. There are four or five large stones lying near—smooth and clean. Such is Lo's bathtub. His bathroom is the wide sapphire sky, the sage-scented hills below, and the cedar-sweet heights above, the rim of the silver lake at one side, the rippling stream at the other.

Hark! Hear the songs of larks and linnets!

It might be worse.

And now Lo, himself, comes down to the place that of old knew the bugle call; that today is echoing to child-laughter—the laughter of Indian children. When Lo reaches the framework that the white man has named for him "a sweat-house" he unwraps the blanket from his body, and winds it about the small willow hut, fastening it down tightly everywhere that no cold air may pass through, except at the very small doorway.

Then he proceeds to build a fire of the half-dead roots of a sagebush near by. Soon he has a great bed of red coals, and into them he rolls the big smooth stones that were lying near the sweat-house. While they are heating, he sits on his heels, and looks away off into the valley and meditates—sits silent and as motionless as—well, an Indian. Once in a while he arouses himself and rises to add more fuel to the campfire; to again squat on his heels and—with folded arms—look long and steadily toward the great white plains. You might easily take him for a figure cast in bronze, he is so still. He has not forgotten, though he sits so quiet you begin to think he no longer remembers what he came down to the edge of the lovely bloom-bordered creek for. By and by he rises, and fills the bowl-shaped hollow in the floor of the sweat-house with water which he brings from the creek—fetching it in a basket marvellously woven of willows by some woman of his camp.

Then, at last, when the stones are as hot as the fire may make them, they are rolled into the earth-bowl which he has filled with water. There is a hiss of rising steam—Lo's raiment drops from him as by the touch of a magic wand, and he stands bronze-brown and naked as when God made him. He stoops—crouches—and now has slipped under the curtained doorway, which he tightly fastens, and—Lo is taking his bath. Bathing himself in the fashion known to all nations as the most thorough and cleansing.

Lo stays there longer than his white brother could endure those clouds of uprising hot vapor. So long does he stay that you fall to wondering if after all he may not have succumbed to the suffocating heat.

But no; after a long—a very long time, there is a movement of the blanketed doorway, and a bronze statue emerges therefrom—a statue glistening like polished copper. Lo comes forth shining with the perspiration which has cleansed every pore. There is a rush to the creek's edge—a plunge into its deepest pool (ice-cold from the melting snows which have gone to its filling), and when Lo comes forth, his body is all aglow from the quickened blood which now courses through his veins; and he is made fresh-skinned and clean by a bath which knows no betters.

"Dirty as an Indian?" Lo, I beg your pardon!

OLD CAMPFIRE DAYS.

ERE, in Roseland—in this land of the sun, this land by the sea—where each night as I fall asleep I am fanned by flower-sweet breezes; where (growing close to the head of my bed) a white La Marque clambers to the wide eaves; where orange and lemon trees in bloom brush the pillars of the veranda on one side of the patio, making the air heavy with their over-sweet perfume, there come to me recollections of other nights—nights spent by the campfires, and under the stars of the desert.

Do you care to listen—to let me tell you of those nights—and their days? Will you let me tell you of one ride, in particular, that memory now brings back to me?

Ah! such a glorious dawn it had been—that day when we began our journeying. All purple and blue with the morning mists was the valley, turning golden as the sun climbed higher. Out through the gate we rode, and away from the ranch; and on—up the wide valley. Across brush-covered mesas, through a narrow pass in a low-lying range of hills—hills that were pink and gray, with never a sign of verdure; falling in with a "cattle outfit"—cowboys driving beef-cattle to the railroad, the railroad that was miles and miles away.

We kept pace behind the lowing herds, on the long drive to water; but at nightfall we reached an inviting cañada, where a beautiful stream tumbled and shouted down its rocky way; and there we spread our camp-outfit and built our fires. After the stock had been watered (we had seen to it that they had their suppers ere we had our own); and when we had eaten our fill of the roast ribs, hot and juicy, sent over from the cowboys' camp, we foregathered about a huge brush-fire and listened to frontier stories, while the low-hanging stars came out in a sky all purple with dark. In the creek we could hear the ripple of water, and the twitterings of sleepy birds disturbed by the fire-glow; but farther off, the cattle made no sound—tired, lying down after the long drive. Only the man on guard, whistling "Kathleen Mavourneen," and the crunching of the brush under his horse's hoofs, came to us out of the shadows.

Back we went to our camp; and to sleep under a thin thread of a moon.

Morning! Saddle—mount, and away! Up where the air was clear, and cooled by the wind blowing from the snow-heights, under an azure sky where hung clouds like battle smoke. Away down on the plains we could see the dusty banner unfurled by the slow-moving cattle on their way to the stockyards! And further down the bleached levels—we watched a herd of antelope drift away, looking like balls of thistledown carried along by the wind. We watched a wild stallion lead his little harem warily up and down hills over a well-worn trail to the springs we had but just left; and we saw him (as he scented our recent presence there) take fright, and—without waiting to drink—

go racing off and away with his little band at his heels. Off to his grazing place, and to—safety!

Crossing the range, we descended into a long cañon filled with groves of cottonwoods where the leaves fell upon us as we passed beneath, and where the quaking aspens shivered and shuddered in the chill autumn wind that swept down from the snow-heights, bringing tidings of approaching storms to levels down below. The trees were arrayed in every imaginable shade of crimson, and russet, and brown. Nature was announcing her "Fall Opening," and every leaf was dressed for the season's occasion. Some wore small spots of red, others great splotches of the vivid color; streaks and stripes of yellow and of brown dappled the leaves. None went unadorned. Only the junipers, up near the snow-line, were attired in conventional green—quite unconcerned at the frivolous ones gone mad in a riot of gaudy color. The scarlet and yellow of the buffalo berries shone through the greens growing along the creeks. Bunch-grass, blown by the wind that was scattering its seeds, grew on the slopes; and from it our ponies snatched mouthfuls as we passed.

Leaving the cool heights, we went down to the hot, dry valley and joined our slow-moving team which, in our morning hours up aloft, we had almost forgotten.

All the rest of the day—surrounded by wavering mirages—across dry lakes and their shores of drifted sand, we rode. Over the bleached alkali plains, toward the ever receding foothills which we must reach before the violet shadows should grow gray, and gray shadows turn to black.

As we rode we tapped our heels against the horses' dusty sides at every step, urging them toward the distant spot where the steam from the hot springs at the cañon's mouth beckoned us on, the long streamer of misty white floating like a magic veil—blowing lightly to the Southward. It waved and beckoned; but at sunset we seemed no nearer to it than we had been at noon; and twilight found us yet many miles away. Not until the purpled shadows of the night closed in upon us, and faint stars began to shine, did we find ourselves there.

We who were in the saddle had been riding far in advance of our commissariat, so—while waiting the arrival of the wagon with its supplies for our hungry horses, and ourselves—in the dim starlight we went on a voyage of discovery through the labyrinth of wickedly boiling springs (of all sizes, and apparently without number) that in the darkness seemed an array of frightful monsters with yawning jaws, ready to draw us down with them into the black depths. It was weird—uncanny, to go about cautiously pushing a foot along to feel our way lest we step into a too-near caldron. In the faint light we could discern half a dozen ramshackle buildings of unpainted wood. They were grouped irregularly about a half-hundred of the evil-smelling holes where sulphur-waters boiled and bubbled, and steamed and gurgled incessantly. A dense vapor hung over the place; and soon our clothing was damp from its touch—as though we were under a fine rain. The earth for half a mile around (as morning showed us) was crusted with a greenish deposit from the overflow. No spear of grass, not a tree, nor shrub other than the stunted greasewood and sparse sagebrush, grew on the tableland over which the boiling waters spread.

So—striking matches (which the desert wind as quickly put out!) we made our timorous way from spring to spring. From a rusty tin we drank of its healing waters—each spring yielding a yet more nauseous draught than its predecessor; and we left them, and groped our way through the steam and murkiness (fearful lest we slip into some of the treacherous vent holes), on toward the shacks which loomed up unnaturally tall in the world of mist, waiting us in unfriendly silence.

Up and down the length of the porch of the one-time "Hotel" we went; our feet clattering noisily on the loosely laid boards. There had been a time, now long in the past, when the springs had enjoyed something of a reputation as a health resort; but now—it would seem—they were quite deserted. However, we would try to rouse some one, if human beings were there. We rapped; we stamped; we holloaed—to hear our voices come back to us in mocking echoes. Echoes answered echoes through the empty rooms. Again—louder, as we struck with doubled fists on the loosely hung doors. Silence—absolute silence, save for the hoot of an owl above the springs. On the cracked panes of the curtainless windows our knuckles made a vigorous tattoo, but only the scurrying of rats and mice within answered us. It was evident that no other human beings than ourselves were within many and many a mile; the place was empty—abandoned. And an empty house—in the desert and at night—seems the loneliest thing in the world.

The rattle of nearing wheels was answered by quick whinnyings from our horses, and we turned from our eerie surroundings to meet the camp-wagon, and make ready our supper. Soon, in the clearing near the weather-worn shacks, we had a cheery campfire roaring.

What a good thing life is, to be sure, when one is young, and healthy, and hungry, and the feet are eager to go their way on the far-reaching, long, brown trail!

Over and over, we turned the spit on which we had skewered tender and juicy slabs of yearling beef-ribs, while we shaded our eyes from the heat and the fire-glow, with bent arms held across our foreheads, and watched the meat grow brown and crisp as the fat dripped into the blaze, and the appetite was whetted as it never is at the table that is spread under a roof. Oh! the savory smells that rise from the meal that is cooked on a bed of glowing coals! How hungry we were—how light-hearted we were! How good it seemed to be there, where we circled the fire like gypsies; how glad we were just to live and laugh, and find content in the hour!

Old
Campfire
Days

By and by, we watched the fire die down to a bed of red embers; watched them dull, and then darken, and then become a white ash. And with the smoke from the blackened log, was blended that of the "Golden Scepter" as it floated up from the men's briarwoods. The talk died down with the fire, and we dreamed the time away, as all who watch a dying fire always do dream. In fancy, one goes riding away to that land where all our dearest dreams come true.

Then a coyote yelped from a near-by hill, startling us with his staccato cry; and once more we were roused to a consciousness of the time and place. To bed! A night of deep sleep—sleep under the blurred stars; to be ready for the morrow! So the camp beds were unrolled and spread out on the mineral-whitened earth, and we lay down (still amid the fine clouds of warm and sulphurous steam) and fell asleep to the rumblings and mutterings of half a hundred springs, and the mournful wail of the lone, lean coyote.

We awakened to a golden day! We had slept late (tired from our long afternoon across sand-hills and alkali flats) and the sun was in our faces. We opened our eyes to a transfiguration! No longer were the vapors gray and ghostly. Changed by the magic of the morning sun, rainbow-colored wreaths of mist

Old
Campfire
Days

floated lightly everywhere about us. The early sky
was amethyst; the hills were burnished gold. Up and
away! The day was glorious; and—today—the world
was ours. Breakfast; break camp; mount; and onward!

Before us were the mountains. The road went up,
and higher. It is good to climb the heights when the
blood is young.

"Sing, riding's a joy! For me, I ride." Away
with wheels! Give me the bridle-rein. To drive, is
to be a slave—to shackle attention to the team and
the road; for the road may be filled with badger-holes
and boulders, scarcely passed over by man once in
five years. But in the saddle! Ah! there one's horse
is given his head, and one's thoughts and eyes have
freedom—free to roam as they will; to go a-seeking
out the little things which otherwise would surely be
missed.

To know the desert well (to be close friends with it,
and then finally to be taken into its confidence) one
must of necessity either travel on foot or ride in the
saddle. If the distance one would journey be far, then
into the saddle! But to drive— Why, one misses
most of the pleasures, and all of the little discoveries.

We left our team—that followed the road which ran
along by the foothills—while up and down deep cañons
we went, and where there was never a sign of road, or
track, or trail. Riding in sunlighted shallows, where
high walls, close at hand, still lay in their deep morning-shadow. Quail ran swiftly up the slopes; and
sage-chickens—that the horses flushed where they
scrambled through the slate-strewn uplands—rose with
a whirr and rush of strong wings, as they flew in great
flocks to hillsides beyond. The loaded shotguns lay in
our laps, and we shot from the saddle; and riding

along the steep slopes we picked up our game without dismounting.

Less than a mile away, three deer calmly looked down on us as we laboriously climbed upward; but when we stopped, taking fright they went like a wave over the hills and melted into the distance. Up and down another ridge; and we came upon a Shoshone village tucked so out of sight that it was startling to discover our brown brothers living there. Far from the railroad and the towns that so soon teach them the white man's ways, they were almost aboriginal in dress, and seemed a different clan from any we had known. Theirs was the dress of those who lived in the land when the white invader first found his way there. Still they were eating dried seeds and the things eaten by their forebears before them; still they lived in huts wattled with rabbit-brush and willows. None spoke any English, though some of them knew what we said. So, giving to one of their number—an old, old man crooked of limb, and weather-furrowed of face— cigarette papers and a sack of tobacco, we turned our reins again across the horses' necks, and were off once more on the long trail.

We found an abandoned mining-claim—scarcely more than a prospect—yet there had been enough work done to show us that some one—some time—had hoped, and worked, and failed, and lost heart, as so many had before him. The broken rock was red-rusted with age and the storms; an elderberry tree had grown up, barring the doorway of the cabin. How strong he must have been when climbing the mountains in the beginning! How wearily his feet must have dragged when he turned and went down, and away! And then; was the itch for the pick-handle in his palm again—and did he go to other mountains, to meet other failures? It is the old, old story of the old prospector.

The Land of Purple Shadows

We shot at a coyote, and—missed him; and could not find it in our hearts to be sorry. We sat by a spring a full hour, watching an "ant-lion" that lay in wait for unwary ants, which trapping, he dragged mercilessly down to his dungeon. We found a place where bees had hidden their stores; and became their robbers. Arrowheads, we found; fashioned by the untamed Red Man in the days when he made war on his white brother. We saw a mother-coyote carry a jack-rabbit home to her young ones; and we left her at peace in her den.

No mountain sheep had we seen, though finding their tracks; and in one of the water-trails made by wild creatures we saw the pad of a mountain lion.

We reined in our horses on the high ridge of a bald mountain, where the wild winds buffetted our clothing, and we held to our hats with both hands; while we sat there among trees that grew slantwise—trees which from long bowing their heads to the storms, now leaned to the ground like old and bowed men.

We faced the four winds; they seemed all blowing at once. We looked at the world beneath and about us. Our eyes sought still other mountains far away, yet hemming us in, lying fold upon fold; gray here, and blue in the distance, the highest peaks hooded with the first snowfall of the year.

At our left—blue in the sunshine, in the shadows shading to lilac—lay Table Mountain. Vertical rocks rose from its top, walling its uttermost rim—close-walled with granite and porphyry rising from one to three hundred feet high, and through which but three or four breaks gave entrance to the level, grass-covered plateau there. To that haven, hundreds of wild horses came daily to graze, till deep snows drove them into the valley.

Tales have been told of how cowboys riding hard after a fast-running herd of wild horses, have caught an instant's glimpse of rare little black foxes that live in the rocks.

In a ravine beyond the mountain, is the wonder of all that range. Unnamed by any, almost unknown by any except the stockman who rides the ranges, is the Cañon of the Titans. At least, that is the name we gave it.

Immense, imposing, the symmetrical rocks rose in huge masses from the point of a sage-covered hill projecting, like a promontory, into the wide cañon. Surely they must have been sawn in some mill of the gods, for no haphazard chance could make them so true. From eighteen inches in thickness to those that were more than two feet through, the dark, reddish-brown monoliths seemed to have been squared, and sawed, and planed as though by a giant master-workman. Thirty feet high they stood, some standing higher; some not over ten. Side by side, like posts, standing on end, they covered acres innumerable.

Here, they stood in perpendicular masses, like timbers suddenly turned to stone; over there, hundreds were lying horizontally as though piled in that way by giants who had placed them there for building their castles. As before the Giant's Causeway, and the Devil's Post Pile, and others of Nature's similar fanciful vagaries, one stands and wonders, overwhelmed and silent. We climbed to the divide at the farther side of the cañon and gazed down on them from that height. We went up the cañon to get a long vista. We drew deep breaths of wonderment, and regretfully turned away.

We were in the saddle many days, going whither our fancy willed. It was late October, and the air was like wine. Long distances were covered without either tiring our horses or ourselves. The spicy smell of the junipers; the bitter-sweet of the sage; the mingled odors of many weeds that the horses trampled under foot—all these come to me now and here; and I close my eyes and am back again on the wild-horse trails over the Kennedy mountain! The memory of it all is so fresh that it comes close to me—is here. Again I journey through the desert-dried seas; once more I cross plains of shifting sand, with their leprous spots of alkali. I remember how we lost our trail one day —and were ourselves lost, and spent long hours straying hither and thither trying to find an old road. Then, when night suddenly fell, we were forced to halt at that pool of stygian blackness—"The Mud-Hole" —and under the clouded sky make our camp. No supper had we, nor could we drink of the inky waters of that mysterious spring. Under the sunlighted sky they might have seemed less eerie, but we came in the dusk and left before the sun had found us out. On the badger-bored, dust-harried clearing about the pool, we spread out our blankets, and laid down to sleep. But no, we slept not. Whirlwinds of black dust, and the troops of wild horses that came down to drink, were not of those things that encourage sweet slumber; and in the gray dawn we harnessed, saddled, and rode out to meet the brightening day. Even the mishap that made us enforced campers at the "Mud-Hole" had not spoiled the day, or our joy; there had been so many more things that were delightful, that this was only as a passing event on a long and happy journey.

It seems but a day since I rode those heights with a good horse under me, and all the great blue arch of the desert-sky overhead. Yet, it is all the world away! Sighing, I look down at my wrists, almost fancying I will see shackles which have been snapped thereon. A prisoner! For call ourselves free agents as we may, yet are we slaves to the work-world, and always—always necessity somewhere tugs.

Sometimes in the night, when I lie down to sleep here among the roses of the Southland of the West, I hear the querulous barking of a little coyote that comes down the arroyo—perhaps to make raids on the chickens of my neighbors across the way. I have a very friendly feeling for the little fellow, even so be he does come with malice prepense; for the sounds of the sharp young barks are reminders of those I have heard under the desert stars, and I grow homesick for the old life of the alkali plains, and sorry for the little gray waif that has the courage to come so close to the fringe of the big city. I hope that no one will kill him—that he will not get caught in a trap; poor, little, vagrant coyotito!

One cloudy day's end we halted beside a stream flowing out of a cañon, which was part of a ranch where we found a quartette of Mexicans. The old house was falling to pieces, but such as it was, they offered us the shelter it afforded. For a dust storm was blowing up the mesa. We declined their proffered courtesy, preferring to spread our blankets on the sweet, fresh-cut hay stacked in the barn. But gladly did we gather with them when they brought from the little lean-to kitchen (which smelt of onions, and garlic; and had "jerky" and strings of red chiles hanging on the wall) the things so tempting and savory. The carne, and corn and frijoles, and many and various other dishes of Mexican cookery. Ripe, red tomatoes, lettuce fresh from the garden, bread white and sweet, and just out of the oven; coffee, hot, strong, and without milk; fresh meat taken from the glowing coals; fruit that was but now picked from the trees! What would you better, or more?

Then—when supper was over, and the table cleared of its dishes—resting on a couch of furs arranged for my comfort (for what Mexican is ever unmindful of the courtesy due a woman?) I listened to songs, and to stories. Songs which have never been written, learned from the lips of another. Songs that are fast disappearing—crowded out by the new education.

Now—years after—the lilt of the music comes back and I hear again, in fancy, the voices of those dark-skinned men singing to us, away off there in the dilapidated old ranch-house, at the foot of the gray, grim mountains. All around was the desert's night-silence; and within, the songs and the stories. Stories of wild days back in rough districts; of deeds of daring, coupled with bits of outlawry; of reckless, dare-devil riding, and raiding. Tales told in broken English, mixed with the soft, sibilant language of Spain.

The evening winds came up from the sage-scented lowlands, across the alfalfa-fields, and the orchard, and in at the open windows of the smoke-blackened room, blowing the flickering candle-light alternately into brightness, and then semi-oblivion. The candle, thrust into the neck of an empty bottle for support, stood on the bare boards of the rough table around which, or in shadowy corners, were scattered the men whose dark-skinned faces showed dimly in the glow of the fickle flame. The wind-blown candlelight in its vagaries made strange, grotesque expressions to come and go on the half-hidden faces of Mateo, and black-bearded Manuel, and little Vitoriano, and the big Basilio— Basilio of the sweet tenor voice, singing to us the simpatica songs of Spain. The smoke from the cigarettos made blue streamers float toward the ceiling in lazy undulations. Our eyelids, by and by, grew heavy; and lulled by the melody of the singer, we listened dreamily, and so went drifting—drifting—

Then some one sprang up to say that the hour was late, and there was mucho trabajo to be done on the morrow; so—with a hearty "buenas noches!" all around—we left them and went down to our beds in the barn-loft, on the fresh-stacked alfalfa, where we dreamed of the Alhambra, and the dark eyes of Spain, and those things they have lent to the New World since the far days of Cortez. So we drifted into sleep in our clover-sweet beds, with the horses in the stalls beneath steadily grinding their hay.

We rode; and rode the days away! And on one of those last days we came to an open cañon that, once given up to Chinese placer miners, is (other Chinamen will tell you) now given over to two little moon-eyed ghosts. It is such a pretty, pleasant hollow in the hills that one is prone to doubt the truth of their story; but they will tell you that once upon a time gold-dust was found in the gravel in the bottom of the little rosebush-edged stream, and that because of it the creek banks were soon lined with Chinese dug-outs and tents made of old sacking. The gold mining prospered, and the little men planted gardens where they raised the vegetables that they used; and one of their number molded bricks of mud—the sun-baked abodes—and he built him a good house, and started a store. In it, on the shelves, were Oriental supplies; and under the counters were stored the things gotten from the "white devils"; and a portion of the largest room was set apart for Joss, where they could worship before his image, and so propitiate him. The smoke from the tapers ascended and mingled with the odors from the "yen-she" pipes; and there the little blue-bloused men sat together of evenings, and gossiped, and gambled, and were happy.

But one day an unseen evil Spirit came among them, and in a black hour stood at the ear of one, saying: "Do murder! Do it! Do it now!" And listening to the persuasive voice of the evil one, and seeing a shining and sharp knife lying on his palm, he yielded—for he had not prayed to Joss nor burned as many tapers as formerly, and the god was angry, and he was left unprotected—and in that hour a foul murder was done. So, lessened by one was the number of yellow-skinned miners who kept on digging in the creek-bed for gold.

There followed a trial, by white men; and then the conviction; and then a hanging in the jail-yard off at the County-seat. But the little yellow-skinned men dug daily in the creek, seeking gold; and their number was lessened by two.

But those who were left working day after day in the placers, began telling strange tales soon—telling how shovels, and buckets, and picks which they laid down when quitting work with the sun, were taken up by mysterious hands, and used every night.

In the dark some one stood at the windlass—turning and turning—hoisting up the gravel from the shaft; while another, down in the bottom, filled the buckets all the night long. In the dark, every night, these two came; came back from the Nowhere. Then the little miners, affrighted, fled as stampeded sheep scatter; and so the place became deserted.

Here, one night, we camped near the store where still (it is said) little yellow ghosts sell goods over the counters all covered with dust, to others who come out of ghostland; and by the shaft where the creaking windlass (they say) still turns and turns in the night-time.

Just at twilight, when the day's violet shadows were turning to gray, we halted our horses, and there in the gravel-dump at the shaft—when I washed out a bit of the diggings—I found a nugget. A very, very small one it is true, but it was gold. So the story of gold being there is true. That being true, may not the story of the little blue-bloused ghosts be true, also? I, for one, shall not dispute it.

It was Hallow-e'en when we camped there. Perhaps that fact may have had something to do with strengthening my belief.

On the creek-bank, among the wild sweet-brier and brook-mint, we spread our beds. And there, that last night of October, by our campfire of blazing juniper-boughs, we told stories of past Hallow-e'ens. With the warm fire-glow on our faces we sat in the lonely cañon many and many a mile from other creatures of our kind. Deer were in the hills, and down below bands of antelope swept along the plain. Remembering they were there, we did not feel lonely.

We had dragged huge branches of the green juniper to camp, and we built a great fire; it lighted a wide circle where—at the edge—the dug-outs and the old adobe stood in the shadows. Into the fire we threw great boughs of the resinous greens, and each would blaze up in a magnificent illumination—a veritable Christmas-tree with every branch and twig a-glitter with tinsel and gilt. And each of us hung wish-gifts there for the dear ones who were not with us—for who ever looks into the heart of a campfire whose own heart does not go out to some unnamed ausente?

With outward-turned palms shading our faces from the heat of the roaring, crackling green limbs, while golden sparks went flying upward toward the silver stars, we watched the green boughs burn to pink, looking like branches of pale rose-coral from far Hawaii.

And we grew silent with the dying fire, and we saw ghosts—ghosts in the coals where wavering shadows danced and flickered; but they were only memory's spirit forms, and those that were well beloved. The two little Orientals who (it is told) haunt the cañon, came not; or, if they did, came while we slept, and—moving ever so softly—made no sound at the windlass, and our sleep was undisturbed.

After the day dawned, yet before the sun broke the morning twilight of the cañon, with my face pressed close to the pane, I peered through the dusty windows of the old adobe. My curiosity whetted, I was not satisfied in seeing no more—I must pass within. So finally I effected an entrance. Spiders stretched nets across dusky corners for unwary flies, and mice scurried away into the rubbish which littered the place. On the counters—built in "Melican-man" fashion, and which made me wonder why—lay dust an inch deep; and as I moved (instinctively stepping as lightly as I could, lest someone—something be disturbed) the empty house echoed loudly my tread. Save in the larger of the three rooms, nothing remained bearing witness to any former occupancy. A gallery high up at one end of the store held a small temple erected to Joss—the Joss that had not been great enough, after all, to ward off evil spirits; and now deserted by those who had placed him in the midst of a shrine greatly bedizened and betinselled, and decked with gaudy rice-paper flowers, and many-hued tassels of silk. About him grinned, and grimaced, and stared an imposing array of small gods; all arranged in the long shelf-like gallery from which depended dozens of paper strips, vividly crimson, and inscribed with big, black Chinese characters. These fluttered and rustled in the morning breeze blowing in through the open door—the only movement in the empty house.

Much incense had been burned, if one was to judge by the many half-consumed tapers still there. One god—hideous and gnome-like—seemed to have been especially chosen for the supplicating prayers. Was it the "god who sends money?" Doubtless the weather-beaten coolies, washing the creek for gold, prayed oftenest to the gold-god. It is to be feared, however, that the supplications miscarried, and the little yellow men with the tip-tilted eyes lighted the punks in vain. Ah, well! we whose eyes are set at a less oblique angle, sometimes find the money-god is deaf to our prayers, in spite of the punks we also burn. In this fact may be found a tie of kinship between the little men of the Orient and their Occidental brothers.

I came out of the shadows that lurked in the old house which the little yellow man had built out of the sun-dried bricks he molded in the long-ago. I turned from the shadows and the silence, and met the morning sun coming in across the threshold. The years had been many since his rays had trailed across the bare floor; it was not for me to bid him enter. I closed the door tightly behind me, forcing the sunlight back— back! Again the house was left to the ghosts and the gods, and the squirrels and mice, and the little black crickets in the walls, that shrilled to the silence.

Up from the cañon depths we went. Up and away to the heights of purer, sweeter air.

And here ends " The Land of Purple
Shadows," as written by Idah Meacham
Strobridge, with illustrations made by
Maynard Dixon, and printed on the R. Y.
McBride Press, and Published by the
Artemisia Bindery, which is in Los Angeles,
California; and completed on the First
day of December, One thousand, nine
hundred and nine.

THE ARTEMISIA BINDERY

Books by

IDAH MEACHAM STROBRIDGE

Published by, and for sale at The Artemisia Bindery, 231 East Avenue Forty-one, Los Angeles, California.
Home phone C 1235.

"In Miners' Mirage-Land"
"The Loom of the Desert"
"The Land of Purple Shadows"

8vo., autographed and numbered. Heavy paper $1.75—(except "In Miners' Mirage-Land," which in this style is out of print.) Extra bound in three-quarter morocco, with illuminated chapter-heads, $6.75. Full morocco, $10.00. The hand-bound volumes executed by Mrs. Strobridge. Highest award (silver medal) California State Fair, 1908; Gold medal, Alaska-Yukon-Pacific Fair, 1909.

What the Critics have said about
MRS. STROBRIDGE'S WRITINGS:

"Idah Meacham Strobridge has given to the world one of the best and most characteristic collections of Western desert sketches ever written, and the volume possesses distinctive and peculiar charm quite its own. . . . She has shown us the great gray desert in an entirely new phase, a phase that attracts us and lures us on, enticed by the very magnetism of her sympathy and understanding. . . . As a study of human nature the book is valuable. . . . Aside from its value as a study of physical geography and a bit of early history is the value of the word pictures which are so vividly and so strongly drawn. There is a picturesqueness of simile and metaphor, a preference for personification that adds to its distinctive style."—**Pasadena News.**

"Mrs. Strobridge is a clever writer, and she writes of the things she knows as well or better than anyone who has yet written on the same subject. . . . She binds us to her chariot, and we follow her in the chase of the golden will-o'-the-wisp. . . . There are many readers who 'never can understand,' but there is a pathos in 'In Miners' Mirage-Land' and a wealth of descriptive power that will appeal to anyone that is a lover of Nature."—**Paul N. Boeringer in Overland Monthly.**

"The writer of these tales has the gift of presenting vivid and graphic impressions."—**Boston Transcript.**

"Dramatic stories . . . full of force and vivacity that make telling appeal to the emotions."—**Chicago Record-Herald.**

"This collection of stories should take a high place in the literature of the desert as actual transcripts of life and strong in their realism. Nothing better of their kind has been done, nothing with such a palpitating atmosphere of the plains, or so saturated with the spirit of the scene. The incidents themselves are invariably dramatic, generally grim and gray, while their treatment has a spontaneous art that fascinates and holds."—**San Francisco Argonaut.**

"On the subject of the desert Mrs. Strobridge writes with authority. . . . Mrs. Strobridge's pictures of the changing phantoms of the mirage and of the equally elusive phantoms of lost mines and buried treasure, stamp her as, at her best, a writer of power."—**Los Angeles Times.**

"Every chapter of this little volume is more than interesting. It is fascinating. Read a page and you read on."—**Los Angeles Examiner.**

"The generation that is now gray-haired studied geography in books that showed on the map of our country a great stippled region marked 'Great American Desert.' The greater part of that region has proved to be anything but a desert—a very fairyland of hidden riches—and Mrs. Strobridge has found or made within it many bits of unique romance." —**Criterion, New York.**

"Not often do we commend books for our friends' consideration. Right gladly do we make exception for 'The Loom of the Desert.' "— **Reno, Nevada, Gazette.**

" 'The Loom of the Desert' . . . strong stories of the Western desert life."—**Riverside Press.**

THE ARTEMISIA BINDERY (*The Patio*)

"A study of the American desert that has quite as much atmosphere as Mrs. Austin's 'Land of Little Rain,' and that even seems to get closer to the strange heart of the matter. . . . The stories have a strength and directness of style that make them very real."—**The Dial, Chicago.**

"Stories that are intense in interest and action. . . . In each there is consumate art in the telling. 'Greater Love Hath no Man' and 'Where the Burros Browsed' are remarkable tales in their insight into human character. Perhaps no stronger recital of the inevitable operation of the law of compensation can be found than in 'Where the Burros Browsed.' 'The Vengeance of Lucas' tells the story of primitive hate and revenge with a master hand. Mrs. Strobridge has reason to be proud of these stories; she has established herself as the one western writer who can tell western stories that have the real flavor."—**René de Quellin in Los Angeles Graphic.**

" 'In Miners' Mirage-Land' is a literary work of the highest rank. Mrs. Strobridge has given to the world a little classic that will ever be treasured by those who appreciate what is best in the realm of books."—**Los Angeles Herald.**

"Very realistic and exciting sketches. . . . An interesting addition to the list of books that successfully depict the characteristic types of various sections of our country."—**The Lamp.**

"Human studies, now vivid, now sombre, but always intense."—**Pacific Outlook.**

THE ARTEMISIA BINDERY (*The Front Corridor—South*)

"The author knows what she is writing about, and that in this day of cheap literary superficiality is something so rare, and rich, and strange, that one is bound to feel a keen sense of elation and keen appreciation as one turns the pages. . . . If anyone . . has more clearly laid bare the secrets of the desert, I do not know of it; and I have been reading all I could get hold of on this subject. . . . 'In Miners' Mirage-Land' has a practical as well as an artistic value, and those who go forth to seek fortune in the desert ought to read it to know something of the true nature of the land into which they are to adventure."—**Bailey Millard, in San Francisco Examiner.**

"The book as a whole is fascinating."—**H. W. Boynton, in Atlantic Monthly.**

"An important addition to the literature of the West. . . . Deserves a wide reading for its historical as well as its literary value. . . . Written in a crisp, original style that compels attention. The individuality of the author is stamped on every page, and the power of her pen is best shown in the vivid word pictures that reveal the very heart-beats of the desert and the hills. . . . The closing section of the book is as powerful as anything that has ever been written about the waste lands. . . . The make-up is very artistic."—**Leavenworth Macnab, in Sunset Magazine.**

"Her manner of telling is dramatic; the narratives themselves are intensely interesting. . . . One of the most entertaining books that have been written in the West this year."—**Robt. W. Ritchie, in San Francisco Call.**

THE ARTEMISIA BINDERY (In the Patio—West Corridor)

"Clever short stories. . . . The bite of the sand and the burn of the wind have not been lost. They are delightful to read, not only because they are well constructed, but also because they tell of the desert life we people of green valleys know nothing of. . . . The author has struck a note of human interest in all these stories that will make them live when countless other stories of today are dead. With the almost faultless art that characterized 'In Miners' Mirage-Land,' Mrs. Strobridge has penned these unusual stories that breathe of the desert and the desert people."—**Gilbert Weigle in San Franciso Examiner.**

"Stories, each with a point, all told artistically, and in excellent English; and all describing Western Life with the proper restraint." —**New York Sun.**

"If Idah Meacham Strobridge's book, 'In Miners' Mirage-Land,' contained only the one story of 'Old Man Berry,' it would be worth the price. . . . She speaks as one having authority of desert folk and their ways."—**San Francisco Argonaut.**

"Rare, thrilling and beautiful stories of the grim old desert and its people. . . . Mrs. Strobridge is a most delightful writer."—**Los Angeles Express.**

" 'In Miners' Mirage-Land' by Idah Meacham Strobridge is certainly a well written book, and will be read with keen interest."—**Chilton's Guide, Manchester, England.**

THE ARTEMISIA BINDERY (*The Shop*)

"Into her stories Mrs. Strobridge has put much of the feeling which the strainers after the artistic are wont to call atmosphere. A better word for it is the simple emotion that charges words with a strange potency and makes them move the sympathetic reader like a strain of fine music—haunting the memory long after the sound has died upon the ear. . . . To those whose senses have not been blunted and whose mind is open to the sweet influences of the stars and the great silences, these sketches will appeal with unusual force. . . . May be warmly commended to anyone who is fond of the desert and its literature. It is unique in its contents as it is in printing and binding and illustration. In a word, it is a genuine book and a real contribution to our knowledge of the desert."—**George Hamlin Fitch in San Francisco Chronicle.**

"Those who love stories that quiver with life—that are intense in interest and action, will find the want satisfied in these tales."—**Los Angeles Herald.**

"Told by the author with an intensity of poetical description. . . . The glory of the desert rises above its terrors in the exquisite chapter that closes the book, and the sunset she has painted there seems almost a reality. . . . She tells the story as no other has yet."—**Charles F. Allen, in Sports Afield.**

"What Mary Austin has done for the California desert, in 'The Land of Little Rain,' Mrs. Strobridge has done for the desert lands of Nevada."—**Los Angeles Record.**

" 'In Miners' Mirage-Land,' by Idah Meacham Strobridge, is a simple book, in so far as construction and the plain straightforward manner of presenting the stories is concerned. But if—as who can doubt—the clear re-construction of the reader, of the scene and atmosphere dominant in the mind of the writer means literary success, then is 'In Miners' Mirage-Land' decidedly successful from the literary point of view. The Great Desert, inexorable, majestic, monotonous, wonderful, indescribable; its marvels, its mystery, its charm, its horror, its beauty, its despair, its spell of ever-changing but ever-potent fascination, its dread cruelty, its glory—all these are made real to the reader. . . . In no inconsiderable degree has Mrs. Strobridge the gift of verbal reproduction, and only an artist, surely, could write of and call up, such alluring visions of rare color as does she."—**Record-Herald, Chicago.**

"A score of tales which have all the charm and fascination which comes to those who have an intimate knowledge of the desert, with its allurements. . . . All handled in splendid style. . . . This interesting book is out in a very pretty form."—**Truth, Kansas City.**

"It is not the West of cowboys and Indians she writes about, but the mysterious deserts with their tawny hills, and their long gray stretches of alkali and fables of lost treasure. . . . The story is told in a way which convinces the reader that she has caught the spirit of the desert admirably."—**Register, Mobile, Alabama.**

"Mrs. Strobridge has touched the book with her own unique personality."—**Los Angeles Record.**

"Full of dramatic touches, and no one can read them without feeling the reality of this strange land."—**San Francisco Chronicle.**

"The best book in the world of fiction from any Western press since the publication of 'In Miners' Mirage-Land' " . . .—**Everyman.**

"Well written and full of character . . . there is an air of reality about the stories."—**Montreal, Canada, Witness.**

"Pictures of the desert that are full of charm."—**Sunset Magazine.**

"From every standpoint the book may be regarded as a success. . . . Mrs. Strobridge has caught the true spirit of the desert, and reflects it with the fidelity of a mirror. . . . 'The Loom of the Desert' is a valuable contribution to real literature of the better kind, and exploits a vein of descriptive writing hitherto scarcely touched."—**Petaluma Courier.**

"Into the stories the author has put the gray of the desert and its atmosphere of strange monotony. She has a keen sympathy and an appreciation for its inhabitants, which her readers cannot help but have also."—**White and Gold (Mills College.)**

"A vivid style, an atmosphere of verity. . . . Idah Macham Strobridge has done capital work in her stories of the desert."—**Los Angeles News.**

"Much historical and practical knowledge is to be gained from all of the stories. . . . Mrs. Strobridge's style is dramatic, yet the language is simple and picturesque."—**Stockton Evening Record.**

"A score of interesting tales of life in the desert country, under the alluring caption, 'The Loom of the Desert.' . . . The book is full of fascination."—**Pasadena Evening News.**

"Mrs. Strobridge writes as one having authority. She knows the matters of which she tells, feels them perhaps still more, and puts down in straight away manner the history of these happenings. Her stories are strong with the strength of the silent West, sombre-hued with the gray of the desert. They have what literary people call 'atmosphere'—that power born of emotion in the writer to make the reader understand things which are not written. . . . 'The Loom of the Desert' is work of high rank. . . . Mrs. Strobridge's ability to refrain from anything hysterical mark the book as an unusual contribution to the literature of the West."—**Los Angeles Times.**

"These tales of what Mrs. Strobridge calls 'the land set apart for Silence, and Space, and the Great Winds,' are full of dramatic touches, and no one can read them without feeling the reality of that strange land."—**Field and Farm, Denver, Colorado.**

" 'The Loom of the Desert' is a fascinating book of tales of the desert. The author knows the people, and subtly represents the silent, grim atmosphere of the plains."—**Reed Moyer in Mobile, Alabama, Register.**

"The author has the power of drawing a character in a few strong strokes, and she has the real dramatic quality that is so rare in the ordinary short story."—**F. Marion Gallagher in Overland Monthly.**

" 'The Loom of the Desert' should by all means be in the collection of all who travel in thought close to Nature."—**South Pasadenan.**

The author has knowledge of this desert country."—**The Bookman.**

"In her choice of subject Mrs. Strobridge has a comparatively new field; only Mary Austin and John Van Dyke have as yet brought us into contact with the very heart of the desert, and from their work it differs in that it gives us the magic of the desert, the lure of that infinite sweep of 'gray waste of sand and sagebrush lying in pitiful loneliness under a gray sky.' . . . The work is remarkable in that it gives to us not only the charm and beauty of the desert, but the sense of the facts of the lives lived out there in almost brutal reality. . . . From the moment one takes the book in the hand the emotion that the desert inspires in the author is communicated to one."—**White and Gold, (Mills College.)**

"There is material for a dozen novels in these pages; and—better still—hints and visions of rich old dreams that have lured men for almost three centuries away from the haunts of men into the mysterious and prodigal West. . . . Full of fascination to one who, loving literature, yet loves the West still more."—**Elia W. Peattie, in Chicago Tribune.**

"There is no author today who can write of the great stretch of cacti-studded, dull sand as Mrs. Strobridge, who takes her readers into an atmosphere of actuality, as she does, and make them forget. It is a gift for anyone to transport a reader to the scenes which are being depicted. . . To have achieved this, is something which few writers have accomplished, and those who have, possess a peculiar talent."—**Kansas City Post.**

"These stories are all intensely interesting—the style is dramatic and convincing. . . . There is something so human about them that one perforce believes."—**Una H. H. Cool in San Francisco Call.**